The Green Fuse

Our deep connection
with the power of plants

Hilary Miflin

Matador
9 Priory Business Park,
Wistow Road, Kibworth Beauchamp,
Leicestershire. LE8 0RX
Tel: 0116 279 2299
Email: books@troubador.co.uk
Web: www.troubador.co.uk/matador
Twitter: @matadorbooks

ISBN 978 1800461 819

British Library Cataloguing in Publication Data.
A catalogue record for this book is available from the British Library.

Printed and bound by CPI Group (UK) Ltd, Croydon, CR0 4YY
Typeset in 11pt Adobe Jenson Pro by Troubador Publishing Ltd, Leicester, UK

Matador is an imprint of Troubador Publishing Ltd

For Ben
for my daughters Gail, Clare & Johanna
for my grandchildren Soledad, Luca, Raphael, Nathan and Dylan
and for the plants in my beautiful Chevenoz garden

Contents

Notes   ix

Acknowledgements   xi

Credits & Permissions   xv

Introduction   xvii

Chapter outlines   xxi

I	The early years	1
II	Cancer: the turning point?	23
III	The London years	43
IV	Plants as medicines	63
V	The separations: from traditional medicine to the development of modern pharmaceuticals	73
VI	Creating the herb garden	89
VII	Ideas and influences: the theories and the practice	111
VIII	A place to work	135
IX	Herbes de Chevenoz: the products	155
X	Essences for body and psyche	173
XI	Evolving life in the garden… and in the meadows beyond	185
XII	Creativity, Spirit and Subtle Energy	203
XIII	Plant profiles	231
XIV	The Breuss Diet revisited	257

Epilogue	In the midst of the Covid-19 pandemic, Spring 2020	277
Appendix I		281
Appendix II		333
Appendix III		335
Appendix IV		338
Appendix V		341
Bibliography		348
Contacts		354

Notes

1. Use of capitals: according to convention, I have used a capital letter for words in Chinese medicine where the word does not correspond exactly with its English use e.g. for the organs Heart, Stomach, Kidneys etc. and also for the Seasons. This also applies to the mediaeval terms Humours and Elements.

    In specific instances I have chosen to capitalise certain words e.g. Spirit, Soul, Ego, Will, Consciousness, Journey, Nature and Earth to show reverence (and in shamanic terms, Power).

    Common English names for plants are in lower case and their Latin names with a capital letter for the genus and lower case letter for the species name. This does not apply when for instance I have referred to Spirit of Lavender.

2. Use of italic font: Latin names of plants, foreign language quotes and references are in italics.

Acknowledgements

This book has been many years in writing and during that time I have been inspired, supported and guided by some very significant people. I would like to offer them my deepest thanks. In particular I'd like to mention:

Jeanne Vernaz-Michiaz who gardened with heart as her mother had done before her, Stéphane Paccard who loved his cows and tended his meadows and Roger Bel, *'charpente extra-ordinaire'*. These three inhabitants of the *commune* of Chevenoz understood Nature with their bones and were generous in their capacity to share.

Dr Wolfgang Gattlen whose persistence most probably saved my life, Professor Tondelli, surgeon of Claraspital Basel and Frau Dr. Peters who gave me a precious gift: 'six months off to find my happiness' all set me on a new path.

Joe Nasr of Avicenna Ltd who welcomed my oils into his range of beautiful herbal products and whose Damask Rose Water, distilled by him from his roses grown on the high mountains of Lebanon, is sublime; Charles and Jan Wells of Essentially Oils whose professionalism and enthusiasm for my products and in what they were doing was totally infectious; Antoine Pouget, a herbalist who healed with his meticulous blending of Chinese and Western herbs; Jeremy Cherfas who sold high quality seeds and encouraged us all to eat unusual vegetables.

Especially Nicholas Spicer who guided me to the edge and showed me that there were worlds within and beyond worlds. He was a deeply wise and cultured man and to have met and worked with him for so long was an intense experience and great privilege.

Sue Minter who invited me into the Chelsea Physic Garden, and also Fiona Crumley, the Head Gardener whose calm presence set the tone of the place, Jane Knowles who understood seeds and taught me to handle them, the gentle gardeners – Sean O'Gaithlin, Christopher Leach, Simon Vyle and Alice Oswald and the librarian Ruth Stungo.

David Lorimer of the Scientific and Medical Network with his extraordinary breadth of knowledge, prodigious appetite for reading and his generosity in passing on ideas.

Jonathan Horwitz who has taught me that Shamanism is a beautiful, accessible and powerful spiritual practice and as relevant today as it has ever been. Zara Waldebäck for her deep spirituality, her clarity and her rigour, Annette Høst for bringing Shamanic practices closer to home. Their teachings pulled so many of the ideas in this book together giving an understanding of our age-old connections with the Earth.

John Caddy who taught me to feel Qi with my hands and as a scientist, realized the gulf between objective and subjective knowledge.

Gabriel Mojay who introduced me to essential oils and generously gave permissions for the many quotes from his course.

The Wellcome Foundation for their wonderful library.

Julian Franklin and Tim Denny who helped me design my still.

The Rudolf Steiner Michael Hall Markets in Forest Row with all their customers who understood and loved my products, my other loyal customers who returned again and again for oils, floral waters and balms.

My Shamanic friends in Seaford and beyond, especially Robin Shell whose creativity and innate spirituality has been an inspiration.

My massage partner and friend Ayako Iwata who understood Qi from her grandmother and balanced it with her strong and delicate hands.

My childhood friend Clare Pollak who generously introduced me to Nicholas and to Charles Wells.

Carlos Tejada, who with Clare designed and rebuilt our beautiful barn.

Clare Miflin & Soledad Tejada who supported me with interest, enthusiasm and valuable editing and design advice.

My eldest grandson Luca Tejada who used his eye for design and colour to produce the diagrams in this book.

Catherine Stewart whose encouragement, attention to detail and critical editing skills helped me along the way. She also widened my brief to include Drugs & Sex & Rock & Roll.

Kevin Liffey who suggested the William Blake inspired title and also used his professional editorial skills on the texts.

Peter Warne for the generous and arduous proof reading of this very long text.

The Matador team who led me through this publishing process with cheerfulness, efficiency and courtesy – in these difficult COVID-19 times.

And then my grandchildren: granddaughter Soledad who helped me make Rose Water so long ago; my grandsons Luca, Raphael, Nathan and Dylan who have slept with lavender oil on their pillows and could feel Qi with their hands.

My beloved daughters: Gail – the 'blood doctor' with a big heart, whose efforts affect every patient in England who needs a transfusion or a transplant. She knows in her heart that I am deeply grateful to her work and Western Medicine and see my efforts as complementary to hers. Clare – the architect and environmentalist who loves and is working to protect our beautiful planet Earth and who journeys with the drums. Johanna – the BBC studio manager whose innate sensitivity and spirituality was ahead of the game from the beginning and who has music in her veins and her heart. I thank them for supporting and encouraging me throughout this transition.

And lastly, my beloved husband Ben. He is a countryman and deep within him is a closeness to Nature. His creativity lies in photography of landscapes and plants – many of his beautiful photographs grace these pages; in his wonderful vegetable garden which enlivens and nourishes us daily and in carpentry. He is a conscientious and committed scientist, a logical man, a humanist. He has watched on, incredulously, over the years but has never ceased to help, to support, to argue rigorously and to be my sounding board. And this has been invaluable in bringing the two worldviews together. I thank him from the bottom of my heart.

Credits & Permissions

Permission to reproduce the following materials has been obtained from:

Gabriel Mojay, Director ITHMA, for the basic diagram layout of the correspondences in Chinese medicine; for details of essential oil analyses and therapeutic actions of herbs (as cited in text).

Floris Books for the tables in Appendix III: Maria Thun's 'Regularities which become apparent from plant trials and weather observations' and 'Correspondences between the planets, the Elements and the constellations'.

La Pharmacopée française for the illustration of the snake and the palm tree: frontispiece (PF 1937).

Ben Miflin for photographs of the Chevenoz garden and artefacts.

Luca Tejada for the design of the diagrams: a simple alembic; the Chevenoz still; the correspondences in mediaeval herbalism; the correspondences of herbs in the Breuss Diet; the correspondences in Chinese medicine; the sense of smell.

Ann Morden for permission to use the gas chromatography trace of lavender essential oil (from the late William Morden's estate).

Evelyn Roe for permission to reproduce her four stages of Goethean enquiry.

A Green Man carved on ancient pear wood from a fallen tree in Chevenoz orchard.
A copy of the Green Man in Norwich Cathedral from 'Green Man: The Archetype
of Our Oneness with the Earth' by William Anderson and Clive Hicks[1]

Introduction

This book

… is about plants, about connections, about health, and ultimately about our relationship with the Earth. It is a tribute to a beautiful garden of healing plants that I created over a period of more than twenty years in the French Alps, and it describes the garden, the plants I chose to grow in it and the medicines made from these plants. Alongside this account, it charts the development of my understanding of plant connections and the healing nature of plants. The story alternates between periods of intense activity working with the plants in that beautiful landscape and long Alpine winter 'down time'. This is a gardener's life, giving the time to rest, research, read, contemplate… and write.

Over the course of this study, I have had time to consider many different aspects of plant healing, drawing from scientific research, from traditional knowledge, and my own experiences. The holistic nature of plant healing requires a broad treatment to give adequate explanation, so in this account I play the part of a generalist, working close to the edge, travelling to boundaries and looking beyond for connections. And since my study is about connections – ours with plants and plants' with their environment – this approach serves me well. But it also means that in most areas that I touch on, there are specialists who describe the topics in much more detail, and can be referred to for a deeper understanding.

This is my attempt to describe the process and influences by which I take the long and seemingly unconscious path back to my roots, in such a way that I can now hold two worlds together: from my viewpoint as a biologist, I also wholeheartedly embrace the age-old human connection to Nature, our beautiful planet Earth and the plants of her exquisite green mantle.

And the author

All my life I have loved plants. My earliest memories of my childhood garden are of forms, colours and scents, with numinous experiences of sunbeams, sensual depths of flowers, luxuriant textures and colours, wafting scents, emerging greenness. Nothing had a name and everything was somehow connected. These are deep and lasting memories – a child's view of Nature.

Life in post-war rural Essex had its benefits. I didn't start my formal education until I was seven years old, and in my earlier years filled my days in the company of a home tutor. Mornings were spent studying the Three Rs and in occasional art and knitting lessons. In the afternoons we had glorious freedom, roaming the fields, lanes, woods and hedgerows. We called it 'Nature Study'. Out in all weathers under wide Essex skies, two inquisitive and like-minded individuals followed the seasons, and alongside the familiarity and appreciation came the naming. This education was precious and deeply formative. The curiosity and ability to observe closely, learned in the company of my beloved 'Min', have stayed with me throughout my life.

As for many girls at that time, my formal education was academic, with highest status given to the sciences and medicine, maths and the Classics. Art and creativity were considered to be 'pastimes'. I followed my enthusiasms and aptitudes and eventually studied botany at university. But here, soon the plants I knew and loved were seemingly irrelevant. This was a world of separations – classification, anatomy, cells, sub-cellular particles, biochemistry and genetics. We studied smaller and smaller particles until the plant was reduced to a molecular structure or an isolated chemical reaction – an inanimate object. Undoubtedly I found much of this study fascinating, but I came to understand that the scientific and objective study of botany was a world apart from my subjective and deep attachment to plants and to Nature.

Over the years, I have come to realise that this gulf between an objective and a subjective approach to plants is not peculiar to me. Many people's experience extends beyond a purely scientific worldview, and this has huge implications for our attitudes to plants, to health and to the environment. I have written this book to draw together my experiences, practices and research to give my life a coherence, but I have published it, above all, to elevate and enrich the status of plants within our society and to show our historical, deep and necessary connection with them.

This is my personal and current view. I am neither messiah nor preacher.

Hilary Miflin
Chevenoz, 2020

Note:

1. *Anderson, William and Hicks, Clive. Green Man – the Archetype of our Oneness with the Earth. 1990. Harper Collins. ISBN 0-00-599255*

Chapter outlines

I The early years: *Chevenoz ma Belle!*
The urge to leave and the journey; searching for somewhere to call 'home'; finding Chevenoz on a May morning; La Vallée d'Abondance and its history and culture; the house; developing the garden – artefacts and relics of a bygone era.

II Cancer: the turning point?
The initial diagnosis and treatment; six months off 'to find my happiness'; the Breuss Diet – 'The Cancer Cure'; the extraordinary power of herbs; aspects of the regime: the isolation, the long days, facing up to things, looking inwards, the power and sense of wellbeing; diary excerpts; Jung's book that initiated the breakthrough; herbalism: what was its power?; finding a way forward.

III The London years: making connections and grasping opportunities
Settling in; the 'Bash Street Kid to love' – adopting the Chelsea Physic Garden; the Jungian in Kew Gardens; research at the Wellcome Library – the British Pharmacopoeias; shamanic practices I; dispensing for the French herbalist in Holborn; meeting like-minded people: The Scientific and Medical Network; reductionist versus holistic ideas – parting company with the School of Phytotherapy; Gabriel Mojay and the Herbal Study tour in La Drome, France; completing the Diploma in Traditional Herbal Medicine and Aromatherapy; preparation for *'Le Grand Oeuvre'* in Chevenoz.

IV Plants as medicines: so much study… how DO plants heal?
World healing systems – a survey of healing systems the world over: traditional European herbalism, Ayurvedic medicine, Chinese medicine, shamanic healing, traditional knowledge from indigenous cultures; the correspondences in

mediaeval herbalism; the correspondences in Chinese medicine; the connections in shamanic practices; the Rod of Asclepius and the Hippocratic Oath.

V The separations: from traditional medicine to the development of modern pharmaceuticals

From the apothecaries to the spicers and grocers; the Medical Act of 1858, leading to the publishing of the British Pharmacopoeias; analysis of the Pharmacopoeias showing the systematic deletions of plant formulations; the roots of modern herbal medicine – the National Institute of Medical Herbalists and the British Herbal Medicine Association; how herbs work; the rise of Complementary and Alternative Medicine – the holistic therapies; another separation – food from medicine; the development of synthetic vitamins; new ideas of health and disease – Third Era Medicine.

VI Creating the herb garden

The model for the garden: grass of Parnassus – a plant with connections of history, culture and place; the first venture: the nut garden; sourcing the plant base; ploughing up the meadow: preparing the plots for planting; the plots; rose plantings; garden practices: organic cultivation, minimum intervention, rotation of crops, composting; cosmic influences on planet Earth.

VII Ideas and influences: the theories and the practice

Winter work: Theories from the polymaths (those who have learned much): Edward Bach – Flower Remedies; Johann Wolfgang von Goethe – holistic science; Rudolf Steiner – human extensions: the Etheric and Astral bodies; Alexander von Humboldt – the man who saw connections…

And the Practice: Maria Thun, Johanna Paungger and Thomas Poppe Moon Calendars; biodynamic principles; *L'Almanach Savoyard* and *Le Calendrier Lunaire*; gardening with the Spirits of Nature; networking with the Network; the concept of Qi; auras and power; shamanic practices II.

VIII A place to work

Spring time and back to the garden: the glasshouse/*la serre*; the cold frame; the *Cave* for the still and laboratory; drying racks; research and design of the still; the prototype – school chemistry revisited; an Australian field still model; the Chevenoz still!

IX *Herbes de Chevenoz*: the products
Tinctures; dried herbs and tisanes; infused oils; balms and salves; Bach Flower Remedies; floral waters; essential oils; incenses.

X Essences for the body and psyche
Aromatherapy in history; the modern aromatherapy movement; the holistic nature of essential oils; aromatherapy and our sense of smell; a detour back into history.

XI Evolving life in the garden… and in the meadows beyond
Evolving community life; the gardening year – month by month; local home pharmacies – Savoyard medicinal herbs; …and further afield: a study of herbalism in the Vercors; the rituals of the year's cycle.

XII Creativity, Spirit and Subtle Energy
Dream: this morning on waking; more dreams and Journeys; creativity and Spirit; creative pursuits; a modern idea of creativity; shamanic practices III and plant spirit work; vitalism – an ancient idea and traditional knowledge.

XIII Plant profiles
In-depth descriptions of cultural uses and the healing properties of lavender, juniper and rose.

XIV The Breuss Diet revisited
Years later, doing the diet a second time, and a more holistic appraisal of how the herbs work.

Epilogue
Bringing the threads together.

Appendix I
Ch IV British Pharmacopoeia research tables I–VIII and British Pharmacopoeia 1864 plant entries

Appendix II
Ch VI Plant provenances; Chevenoz roses

Appendix III
Ch VII Synopsis: Maria Thun biodynamic cultivation – the Correspondences

Appendix IV
Ch VIII Distillation records

Appendix V
Ch IX The products and infused oil records

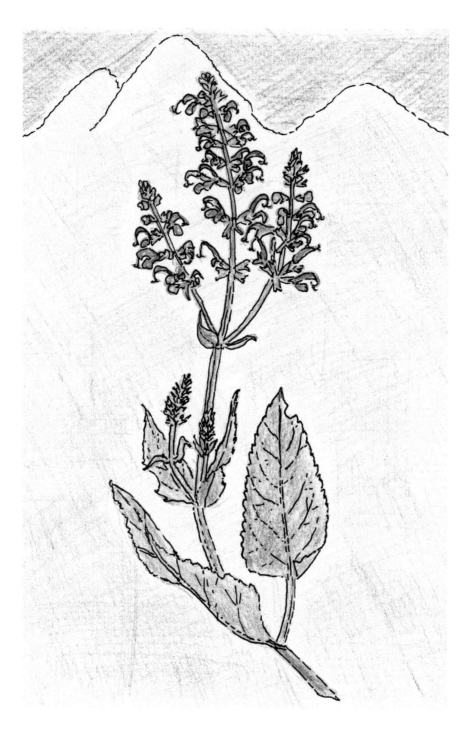

Meadow sage (Salvia pratensis) from the meadow below the house with the mountain silhouette of L'Aiguillette. This ancient herb has been an inspiration throughout this project.

I

The early years

'Whatever you can do or dream you can, begin it.
Boldness has genius, power, and magic in it.'
JOHANN WOLFGANG VON GOETHE

Chevenoz ma Belle!

It was the first of May when we saw the house. This day, beloved in the French Savoyard calendar, is dedicated to the Blessed Virgin Mary – queen of all flowers and blossoms. By tradition, on this day the Savoyards give each other posies of lily-of-the-valley (*muguets*), which grow wild in the beech woods and are cultivated with care in secret and sheltered parts of vegetable gardens.

Our journey here was a long one. Some families stay rooted in one place all their lives and others have the urge to move on. We belonged to the second category. After travelling around the world while our children were young, we had established ourselves in a small town in the south of England and, over twelve years, had forged two successful careers and cared for three daughters. Besides our connections with jobs and schools, we all had friends, acquaintances and many social activities.

But my husband Ben and I were restless. We looked at our colleagues leading materially comfortable suburban existences, and realised that we could continue to do that for the rest of our working lives – and beyond. We were ready once again to 'move on' and search for something 'Other'. One or two ideas came up but never reached fruition – and then, in 1986, an opportunity arose. Ben was offered an excellent job in Switzerland in Continental Europe, with possibilities of a new life and new experiences. With so much to consider and five lives, two careers, three educations, family responsibilities, smooth exits and new lives to arrange, we had to try to make some good decisions in a short period of time.

We decided that our best strategy was for Ben to establish himself in his new job while I made a slower transition and sorted out the girls' educational needs and schedules and my own career change. In Basel, Ben rented an apartment that we thought could temporarily serve our needs on our visits. At that time, prices and residence requirements prevented us from purchasing a property in Switzerland, so France or Germany seemed the obvious locations. Our enthusiasm for the European Union (of which Switzerland was not a member but was closely affiliated to) also encouraged us in this direction.

Basel sits on the bend of the River Rhine where Switzerland, Germany and France border each other. So a house in either France or Germany would have been very accessible. Although linguistically, Germany would have been the sensible choice, the way of life in France was much closer to our hearts. We spent weekends looking around the Alsace and the Jura mountains, but the darkness of the lakes and the steep conifer-clad mountains didn't really appeal. Also, the French/German struggles and the later reconciliations somehow pained me in a way I didn't then understand. The next nearest French border was in the Alps, to the south.

The summer before I left the UK, I had a contract with the Open University to audit a Roche Pharmaceuticals' management training course on 'Decision Making'. I decided to use the technique practised in the course to assess what we all hoped for as a family – in the short- and in the long-term. Having designed the parameters, we all evaluated our needs and our wants for our new family home. Our desires were almost unanimous: freedom, space, togetherness, sunny climate, French language, the chance to ski, swim, sail and walk in the mountains and (for me especially) to tend a garden. So the Alps had it. A short trip to the region of Haute-Savoie with our daughters Gail and Jo led us to the Abondance valley and the village of La Chapelle d'Abondance. The name 'Vallée d'Abondance' had overwhelming appeal. At that transition time especially, we needed its generosity and bountifulness. This valley fulfilled the requirement of being within a three-hour car journey from Basel and could be entered either by the top of the valley from Switzerland and the Rhone Valley at Monthey, or from the French base of the valley at Evian, on Lake Geneva – depending where in the valley we found a house.

We knew in essence what we were searching for. Both Ben and I grew up in barn-like old houses – spacious, draughty, charming, but in no way luxurious. We knew deeply that freedom for us meant having both inside and outside space; we knew how to snuggle down in eiderdowns and blankets to avoid the frost that would paint fern fronds on the inside of bedroom windows; and we knew how to be untidy… to expand with body and Soul into the available space.

It was before the days of internet research, so we started an estate agent trawl within the valley – looking for an old farmhouse to renovate, with land and view, near the mountains and the lake. We ploughed through the responses, pored over maps, and made long- and shortlists of houses to view. The variations in price surprised us, as did the condition of some of these properties. We then arranged a complex itinerary for three days of viewings around the May 1 holiday. A lovely Alpine-style chalet hotel outside Bernex – 'Le Bois Joli' – was our base for the trip.

At our first breakfast, we were given the most valuable piece of information. *Madame La Patronne* told us to be careful to check that the house was in sunshine throughout the year. Coming from flat Hertfordshire, and even flatter Essex before that, it never occurred to me how much the height of the sun in the sky would influence which parts of the valley received sunshine in the long winter months. She pointed out to us the difference between the south-facing slope, where we were basking in glorious winter sunshine, and the opposite side of the village, where houses were in dark and cold shadow – 'for months at a time', as she said.

We started our visits with a young, enthusiastic Frenchman – an Anglophile and an anthropologist. He showed us a beautiful old chalet that had belonged to a very old man who had recently died. The place had been left all the previous winter with water in pipes and tanks. Everything had frozen and burst, resulting in cracked toilets, basins and pipes. Walls and ceilings had been soaked through. Oh, the joys of Alpine winters! He then showed us an old farmhouse much further down the valley. It was traditional, completely unconverted, with pigs in an outhouse and sullen, uncommunicative tenants sitting in a huddle round the fire in the kitchen. The negotiations with owner and tenants and the work that needed to be done were daunting. But we realised that we didn't know where in that 26km-long valley we wanted to live.

Our second guide was a small, Gallic-looking Frenchman, whom we nicknamed Napoleon. With military precision, he concentrated on the middle part of the valley. Among other places, he showed us a new chalet with superb views over the valley (we later found it was directly under the planned cable car route of the new ski station, La Pantiaz).

The following day, on the beautiful May Day morning, we were shown around by a charming, very experienced and cultured estate agent from Evian. He knew the region and its traditions well, and was interested in us and our needs –things that suggested a successful outcome for us all. He explained that May 1 was a national holiday and he wanted to be finished by noon as he planned to follow tradition and take his wife to the woods to gather lily-of-the-valley. His first choice for us was an oddly constructed old house in the centre of Bernex. It was owned by a maker of marionette puppets for a Paris theatre and every room was full of puppets, completed, in construction or un-assembled. Fabulous artefacts and fabrics covered every surface – including carpet on the washing machine. It was late in the visit that I realised we hadn't seen a bathroom, but one was quickly brought into being by whisking open a curtain behind the bar. The toilet was hidden in a closet some distance away.

The next house was a huge old '*fruiterie*' (milk depot for the *commune*) that had also been used as a '*colonie de vacances*' hosting holiday camps for children from Paris, Lyon and the region. Then there was a lovely old farmhouse that had been partially renovated but had no land – and lacked winter sunshine. Finally, the estate agent said he had something a little different to show us. He led us to nearby Chevenoz, down a narrow drive to a strange, squat, single-storey modern house on what seemed to be a building site. We drove into the yard and walked round to the front. I told him not to bother to open the shutters – it wasn't the kind of house we were looking for at all. Experienced estate agent that he was, he coaxed us to take a look inside. He did open some of the shutters, and we noted that the view from the large windows was magnificent. He then ushered us out and rushed off to his next engagement – the woods and the '*muguets sauvages*'.

In a strange sort of way, we were tempted. The next couple of days we scoured agency windows for more properties, revisited places we had seen and measured them against the criteria from the decision-making course, and then, following hearts more than heads, returned to Chevenoz. The house was empty, so we lingered outside, looked at the old barn alongside, and then strolled down past the orchard to the meadow. This place had lots of land! The view opened up before us – down into the valley, upwards to the mountains the other side. We were cradled in a perfect feng shui living space. The fruit trees were in full blossom with clouds of pink, cream and white petals gently floating in the breeze, and the meadow was bright yellow and green with cowslips, dandelions and buttercups. Lying in the grass on that south-facing slope, looking up at the sky with its fluffy white cumulus clouds, the light was magnificent, the sun was warm on our faces, the insects were buzzing all around us, and the air was pure and soft. Hearts had won. This little part of paradise could be our French home and we would do what we could with the house in the course of time.

Just over a month later, on June 5, 1987, we bought the house. Ben, our daughter Clare and I met up at the solicitor's office in Thonon to complete the formalities. The owners were there, and the estate agent. After much hand-shaking and greetings, we all sat down in a crowded little office and the process began. We tried to understand the legalese read out by the solicitor, trusting that our estate agent would protect us from agreeing to anything we might regret. At one stage, the solicitor left the room – the cue for us to hand over a cash sum, untaxed, for the 'contents' of the house. Those contents were sparse at best, and the vendors were mightily pleased.

The solicitor returned to the room, papers were signed and initialled *ad infinitum,* and more shaking of hands and jubilation ensued. Madame Morel, the Portuguese wife of the vendor laid on a splendid spread for us in her family's apartment in Thonon. And then we drove up the valley to our new home. This was the beginning of our wonderful adventure – our life in the French mountains.

The Vallée d'Abondance and its history and culture

Haute-Savoie is a ruggedly beautiful mountainous region in southeast France on the northern slopes of the Alps. It stretches from Lake Geneva on the Swiss border to Mont Blanc. Within this region is the Vallée d'Abondance – a glacial valley in which flows the river Dranse. There are six *communes* along the length of the Dranse, which flows down from Châtel to Thonon-les-Bains on Lake Geneva.

The valley was so named by the Augustinian monks who arrived there at the beginning of the twelfth century. From Châtel, the Dranse runs through a fertile plain that the monks cultivated, where they built a church – the Chapelle d'Abondance. They continued down the valley to Abondance itself, where they built their abbey. Abondance is surrounded and protected by high mountains. Because of the abbey, and the fact it is the regional centre, where taxes are paid and justice is done, it has a coldness and aloofness about it. Further downstream, the valley widens out, letting in the sky, and the mountains cast less shadow. The next *commune* is Vacheresse, with beautiful pastureland and wooded slopes, which give it prosperity. And then, about halfway down the valley, comes Chevenoz, with its small hamlets either side of the river. The centre of the *commune*, the '*chef lieu*', is on the gentle south-facing slope, at 900m altitude and 16km directly south of Evian.

Below Chevenoz, the river enters a deep ravine and plunges down to the market town of Thonon-les-Bains on Lake Geneva. Snowmelt in spring and abundant rainfall at all other times make the Dranse a fast flowing and vibrant river, carrying its cold and clear waters over dark granite rocks from mountain to lake. Over a distance of 26km, the river falls 1,100m.

Because of the strong presence of both church and state, the history of Chevenoz and the valley is well documented – in church records since the 13th century and in state records from 1860s onwards. In recent years, local Savoyards have researched and written two definitive volumes of history and culture of the region[1] – the first describing the three *communes* at the top of the valley and the second describing Bonnevaux, Vacheresse and Chevenoz. This geographically isolated valley has been deeply influenced by the monks that settled here and the church has been used to mark rites of passage, baptism, marriage and death. But for all this, the population is not overly religious.

The *commune* of Chevenoz

Le Plan de Chevenoz is the fertile plain within the *commune* and is the site of the old church and the priest's house. Originally the church had been surrounded by large farmhouses of traditional style. They were one-storey dwellings built of local stone, with high wooden barns built on top, and slate-tiled roofs. This was the traditional way of life where man and beast lived close to each other and shared the same roof and warmth. Farming was on a subsistence level with each farm keeping a small number of cows, perhaps a pig, and hens. The land was used to produce hay for animal feed during the long winters and grain for flour and bread. It had a large potato patch and a traditional kitchen garden (*potager*) with savoy cabbages, leeks and salad lettuces. The inheritance laws resulted in land being divided up between successive generations, and smaller and smaller parcels belonging to each family member. By tradition, families were large and the male members stayed put within the *communes*. It was the wives who travelled to neighbouring villages, moving in with their husbands' families. Church and state records since the 1400s show that the same families have lived in Chevenoz to this day – as farmers of smallholdings or as artisans passing skills on from generation to generation. With this history comes a lot of tradition and pride in 'Le Patrimoine'. The difficulty of traversing and developing the narrow gorge always deterred fast and heavy traffic in the valley. From Chevenoz, the 16km journey down to Thonon with livestock on market day was considered a day-long trip only one generation ago – and still in living memory.

Chevenoz was never as prosperous as other *communes* in the valley, because its geography meant it had relatively few of the *alpages* or mountain meadows where cattle were grazed in summer before being brought down to overwinter in the barns, or of the forests that provided fuel. Chevenoz's main *alpages*, at Darbon, were valuable assets, shared by family members who lived there simply and traditionally all summer long.

When we arrived in Chevenoz, Le Plan de Chevenoz was a traditional Savoyard farming community. In essence, it was a peasant community of large intermarrying families. The Mercier, Charles, Paccard, Dumont, Lausenaz, Galley and Vernaz families had lived there for generations. This gave them a deep connection to their land, the *commune* and the local climate and geography, as well as the flora and fauna of the region. Just as more secular France loves *La Marianne*, the symbol of the Republic, here the Virgin Mary was worshipped, and bouquets of wild flowers were left at grottoes in rock faces alongside mountain paths. The Earth, family life and mothers were much loved and respected. People here lived very close to Nature.

Except for our Swiss neighbours from Geneva, we were the only foreigners in our part of the *commune*. Nobody spoke English – not even the children. We arrived from Basel each weekend and slowly started to make connections. The local shop was the meeting point where much greeting, kissing and exchanging of news went on, alongside the purchase of bread and a limited selection of fresh and canned provisions. The shop was owned and run by the Mercier family. Father August was a former mayor of Chevenoz, later relegated to burning packaging and boxes behind the shop. His sister, aunt to the family, held court and sold cheese from the counter in the middle of the shop. Maurice, an elder son, was buyer and manager. He married a savvy wife from outside the *commune* who led them on to expand and eventually build the region's largest *hypermarché*. A daughter, Monique, a classical guitarist and professional cyclist, worked the till;

brother Jeannot was baker *extraordinaire*, famous for the enormous holes in his bread and his intricate plaited Sunday loaves, called '*Kinnouï*' in the local patois. Another brother, Michel, was training in Thonon to become a pastry chef, and already *tartes aux myrtilles* (bilberries) and *tartes aux fruits* – with apricots, pears or apples – were being sold on Sunday mornings. This was the highpoint of Chevenoz life: Sunday Mass for the women of the parish and a visit to the shop and the bar across the road, run by Jeannot's wife, for the men. By 11.40 a.m., the church had emptied and the great doors were shut and bolted, husbands and provisions were collected, '*au revoirs*' were said and people clambered into cars with sackfuls of baguettes and large tarts in boxes. At 11.50 a.m., the church bell chimed out the Angelus over the land – three times three peals followed by long, repeating chimes, during which anyone who was still in earshot stood still and prayed:

'*L'ange du Seigneur est apparu à Marie et elle a été conçue par le Saint-Esprit…*'

'The Angel of the Lord appeared unto Mary, and she was conceived of the Holy Ghost…'

This prayer marked the phases of the day, first at 6.50 a.m., to call people to work in the fields, then at noon to tell them to down tools and return home to eat, and lastly at around 6 p.m., to signal the end of the working day and time to rest. Somehow it connected the fruit of the Mother of God to the bounty of Mother Earth, pouring down grace on them both.

Le Plan is undoubtedly a blessed spot – a flat piece of land where an ancient 'onion-bulb' church had stood surrounded by its graveyard with large, slate gravestones. It is situated on the south-facing slope of the valley, where the land falls gently down to the deep ravine of the Dranse. On the other side of the river, the north-facing wooded slope rises up steeply to a sharp peak – L'Aiguillette (the Little Needle). To the west side of this lies the col of Tréchauffé, and behind that the dramatic and beautiful summit of Mont Billiat. To the east of our plot, the skyline is mountainous – Mont Baron slightly behind the house, a high Alpine grazing plateau with the Chalets de Sémy, then the more distant mountains around Darbon. To the southeast, there is a high rocky outcrop – the Pointe d'Autigny. Below this mountain, the Dranse arrives in a deep gorge from Abondance. It appears that the rock face is continuous with the mountain range to the south. The southwest and west aspect is less steep but wooded with a mixture of deciduous trees and conifers, and rises slowly to the neighbouring *commune* of Vinzier. Behind us is the steep wooded slope of Le Crêt, hiding the road out of the *commune*. Thus Le Plan is cradled within the landscape formed by the glacial drift that is now the bed of the river Dranse. This geography gives protection from the extremes of weather, and the verdant mantle of Alpine meadows and mixed deciduous and conifer forests provide an extraordinary energy and sense of wellbeing – as our Swiss neighbour called it, 'a bowl of oxygen'.

The shallow but fast-running river brings energy and music to the valley, especially at night, when its rushing can be heard clearly from the house, permeating our sleep and our dreams. Within our contained sky we observe summer and winter sunrises and sunsets – the variation between the solstice positions being around 60 degrees. The trajectories of the moon from its low points (apogees) to its high points (perigees) are also clearly visible from the front of the house. We had been well advised by Madame at *Le Bois Joli*. Here at Le Plan, even at the winter solstice, the sun's rays clear the Pointe de L'Aiguillette and bathe the houses in sunshine from sunrise to sunset.

When we arrived, Chevenoz was a traditional pre-Alpine rural community of around 250 inhabitants. This had marked effects on the flora and fauna of the valley. At this altitude and this latitude, the winters were long and cold – sometimes snow-covered but always with frozen ground. The summers were warm and sunny with adequate rainfall – this was towards the upper limit of the catchment area for two famous mineral waters – Evian and Thonon. The growing season was between early May and late October. Once the earth had warmed up – and on a south-facing slope this happened quickly – germination of seeds and growth of plants occurred at an astounding rate, by English standards. As the meadows greened and the buds broke on the beech trees, I used to say I could 'hear' the plants grow. After a dormant April, the orchard suddenly bursting into blossom was a magnificent spectacle from the overlooking balcony. The contrast between the creamy pear, the pink-tinged apple and delicate wild cherry blossoms was glory to behold. The trees on the facing slope slowly turned from winter black to spring purple as the carpels on the beech trees swelled. Then as the buds opened, the dark conifers were interspersed with a vivid lime green of emerging beech leaves and the early yellow flowers of small clumps of field maples. The meadows came alive within days – a spectacle of yellows and greens. *Le voilà!* Spring was with us.

The meadowland had been untilled for centuries. It supported grazing cattle and wild animals during part of the year and hay was made from the copious growth during the summer months, when the cattle went up to the high *alpages* above the *commune*. The ancient practice of transhumance was still a way of life for both man and beast. In late May, the heifers and bullocks went up, along with donkeys to keep them calm, to the *alpages* at Darbon for the summer. The milking cows and cows in calf stayed at Le Plan. Haymaking was done in late June/early July, after the longest day, and then, if growth was sufficient during the later summer months, again in September. This hay was needed to feed the animals during the long winters. The cows that went up to the *alpages* in late May returned in early October with celebration and ritual – their necks and horns decorated with the last of the Alpine flowers. This tradition had a profound effect on the diverse flora of the meadows – supporting those many plants whose life cycles of seed production, dispersal and germination could survive the grazing and haymaking schedules. At this time, life was designed to be sustainable for these subsistence farmers, who would balance the number of cattle with the amount of grazing land at their disposal. Besides the cattle, the meadows were the food source for rabbits, hares, badgers, foxes, wild boar, deer, black squirrels, moles, mice, shrews and a diverse population of birds.

In the early years, while I was developing the garden, farming methods were very traditional. Our neighbouring farmer Stéphane had studied farming practices at a local college and was very knowledgeable, but nevertheless followed the old methods. At that time, EU subsidies were useful, but not sufficient for him to expand his activities. He had around twenty cows, which he looked after mostly by himself. He milked twice a day, starting at 5 a.m. and often finishing around nine in the evening. His dedication to his beloved cows created a contented and healthy herd. The cows were kept in the barn all winter (which resulted in a lot of 'mucking out') and were set free in the meadows in early April to graze in the now-lush green grass. At this time their joy was tangible. Although quite a lot of fencing-off and staking-out of grazing land occurred, for a short period of time the cows were given free range to graze where they fancied.

Haymaking was a frantic and exciting time, with the few tractors available working from dawn to dusk, cutting, raking, winnowing and finally baling the hay. Raking up and baling was a noisy, communal affair, and scythes were often used at the same time to cut nettles and thistles and clear the verges on invading scrubland. In a good year, this was all done in a few days. This strategy sustained a beautiful and varied pre-alpine flora. Many of these plants found their way by whatever means of dispersal into my eventual garden.

The fauna of Le Plan had been very much influenced by our orchard. In bygone days, each smallholding had its own fruit trees. The varieties of apples and pears were very typical of the region. They had to tolerate the cold nights due to the altitude, the possible spring frosts during the period of the *Saints de Glace* (the days of the Ice Saints) in early May and the *lune rousse* (russet moon), which froze the emerging leaves and turned them red. By tradition, apples were either dessert varieties used for tarts or eaten raw, and pears were rock hard and stored to make rissoles at Christmas or, more likely, to produce cider, which was distilled to make *eau de vie*. Plums were dried as prunes for winter consumption. At this altitude, grapes could scarcely produce enough sugars for wine making, and cider was the local beverage. Traditional Savoyard cuisine was based on cider, butter, cheese, ham, potatoes and lettuce salad.

The intensity of this environment was something very new to me. Here, the sun was strong and the position of the house and plot meant we got lots of it – from dawn till dusk – with beautiful sunrises and sunsets. We learned that bad weather came from Vinzier. Rain came down in sheets, causing the emergence of slime moulds and armies of Roman snails on the paths and drive; storms rocked the house and cut off the electricity. Lightning at night was so bright that you could see colour. Rainbows were magnificent. Like my neighbours, I got to learn the movements of the winds up and down the valley according to the time of day: upriver in the morning, often carrying mists from the Dranse, and then down at dawn, bringing cold mountain air from the east. There was a time in early evening when everything was still.

And then there were the birds. I had never known so many in one place – the buzzards swirling on the thermals, the crows calling to each other across the valley, the screech owls in the woods at night, the barn owls hooting from Stéphane's barn, the magical herons gliding across the sky and alighting near neighbour Thierry's trout ponds, the cuckoos, the magpies, the woodpeckers – green and black… And the smaller birds – the nuthatches, the pied wagtails, the salmon-breasted bullfinches, the flashes of gold from the groups of fast-moving goldfinches, the yellowhammers, blue tits, long-tailed tits, the coal tits. Lastly, there were the migrants: swallows, house martins and swifts; fieldfares and thrushes; the winter-visiting alpine choughs, the summer's golden orioles. They were such a presence in the valley, their calls the music in the peace.

The meadows of Le Plan were my first introduction to the succession of pre-Alpine flowers – in such abundance and variety, it was breathtaking. The season started late, since the earth needed to warm up and growth took its time to recommence after the long winter dormancy under deep frost and snow. But then the yellow carpets of primroses emerged, followed by cowslips, dandelions and buttercups, then the gauze of lacy white cow parsley and lime-green grass inflorescences, and even later the profusion of purple, pink, red and blue summer flowers – the geraniums, salad burnet, yellow rattle, sainfoin, sanicle, chicory, bird's foot trefoil, vetches, peas. The season finished with a glorious display of autumn crocuses. And how things grew! The monks perceived this long ago and honoured the land with its name. Our joy at having found this blessed place was immense. It sustained and comforted us, and we enjoyed the mountains, the lake, and the 'Frenchness' of it all.

It was our dear neighbour Jeanne who introduced us to Chevenoz society and explained the traditions and customs of Savoyard life. We thought we knew France quite well, but here was a rural part of France with its own patois, or dialect, Sardinian connections and mountain character. In fact, we hardly knew it at all. Jeanne was a fiercely independent woman in her sixties with one son, whom she had had when she was seventeen. She lived in the large Savoyard farmhouse that she had inherited according to the complex laws of French family life. She kept the large house and barn spotless and cultivated a large, south-facing vegetable garden in front of the house. In typical French tradition, this was a delightful mixture of fruits, vegetables and herbs interspersed with rose bushes, African marigold flowers and spurges – companion planting at its best. In the easternmost corner behind the gate, she had planted a large clump of *muguets*, Christmas hellebores and a large yucca plant. Down the valley beyond this garden was her orchard, with ancient apple, pear, walnut and cherry trees. In summer, her Alpine geraniums bloomed in pots along the balcony, down the stairs, and around her front door. The swallows returned to nest under her eaves year after year. Here was a woman living with her son in the house where she had been born, in a way that felt natural to her. It was a life she understood and could cope with well. Jeanne was an inspiration to me and taught me a lot – about the climate; how and when to do things in the garden; when the soil was warm enough after winter to plant seeds; how the weather would change. She recognised cloud patterns, knew the winds, knew when bad weather was about to arrive from Vinzier. She was a woman who was attuned to her environment and lived in a very sustainable way. It was several years later, when I started to buy lunar calendars, that I realised she followed so much of the routine that they set out intuitively or by tradition – ways that she had learned from her beloved mother. Over the years, as we developed the gardens, Jeanne became a cherished friend. Her competition with Ben to grow the largest tomatoes, the earliest heritage potatoes, the tastiest strawberries and courgettes, or the best succession of lettuces, amused us all. Her appreciation of the beauty of my garden and the variety of plants I introduced her to always delighted and encouraged me. She gave me a lot and in return I did some things for her for which she was eternally grateful.

One beautiful summer morning, Jeanne and I set off together to climb Mont Billiat. Jeanne was in her seventies at that time. It was a Sunday voting day in the *commune* and we needed to stop at the *Mairie* for her to cast her vote. Afterwards she bade the mayor good morning and told him where we were heading. He was shocked. How dangerous was that? He had never in his life considered doing such a thing. Jeanne had prepared a traditional Savoyard picnic – cheese, *jambon fumé*, hard-boiled eggs, lettuce, bread – and a bottle of red wine and two glasses carefully wrapped in a red-and-white checked tea towel. We set off for the 20km drive to get behind the mountain and approach it from a far easier and less steep route. I had done it a couple of times previously and knew it was well within our capabilities on such a beautiful day. It was about a three-hour climb along existing tracks, with only one part where we needed to use chains set into the rock as handholds. When we got to the top, we sat in glorious sunshine with a 360-degree panorama of Mont Blanc, the Dents du Midi, Lake Geneva, the Jura mountains, and Geneva itself. And with my binoculars, we could look down to Le Plan de Chevenoz and our homes! Jeanne had looked at that peak nearly every day of her life, and was now sitting on it, gazing down at her home. Her joy was immense. News travelled fast through the *commune* and word had already got around by the time we returned. For lack of experience, most of Chevenoz's inhabitants considered Mont Billiat dangerous, and only a few younger men boasted of having conquered this summit – Chevenoz's answer to the Eiger's North Face!

And this showed me just how containing mountains could be. How life in a valley is separate from life in the neighbouring one. How, within a couple of generations, boundaries would be brought down – because travel became possible, and with it, new experiences. Within one generation, so many of the traditions of this agrarian lifestyle would change, and so would the names in France Telecom's telephone directory, the *Pages Blanches*. Although by departmental decree all houses now have numbers and street names, for decades our house had no name or number. Nor did the other houses around. Everyone knew where everyone else lived, so there was no need. The postman knew we had bought the house from *Famille Morel*, and the mayor's secretary had us on his roll of taxpayers, so that was enough.

What constitutes a 'home'?

Our desires for our home in this beautiful region were simple. It was to be rustic, even primitive, but with certain comforts. In such a setting, it was also to be aesthetically pleasing. We wanted space for family and friends of all ages to enjoy, and above all it needed to be 'easy-care'. For the house, our first priorities were to strip all walls of paint and Portuguese-influenced wallpapers and friezes, and to cover the flaws with neutral-coloured textured plaster, or *crépi*. Carpet was lifted and sisal matting was put in its place, and the more orange than terracotta-coloured Portuguese tiling left *in situ*. This was something we later regretted.

We visited second-hand shops in Thonon and bought a table and chairs in various states of repair, and a beautiful dresser. Older local furniture was often made of walnut and so were our purchases – beautiful golden-brown silky wood, with a fine grain and sheen. A job lot of foam for mattresses from a trip to Annecy for the August 1 firework celebrations on Lake Annecy completed our elementary purchases. These were transported on the top of Ben's whim purchase – a long-wheelbase, ancient, entirely power-UNassisted Land Rover that had recently crossed the Sahara Desert.

Now we had our French home, and we were delighted with it. Somehow, the house itself was unimportant – its huge windows facing east, south and west from the upstairs living area led your eye outwards. It was a 'looking out' house – constantly inviting you to experience the delights of the Vallée d'Abondance and all it had to offer. That first summer, Gail and Clare spent their long vacation decorating the house and then extending their efforts outside. From our conversations with neighbours, we came to realise that our strangely constructed house was the result of a fire that had destroyed the ancient farmhouse on the site (and endangered neighbouring properties as well). Alongside the house on one side were stone-built ruins of the old farmhouse, which we decided to adapt to a walled terrace garden.

Our first summer in Chevenoz was idyllic. We lived outside and thus close to the Nature of our childhoods. We enjoyed French food bought from Thonon market, from the little village shop (excellent home-baked bread and croissants, and Abondance cheese), from huge shopping trips to the 'ant heap' hypermarket in Evian, or from visits to the butcher in St Paul. We drank wine and our own 'Evian' water – from the nearby spring. Milk came straight from Stéphane's cows, warm and frothy. We enjoyed eating in the orchard from a table made of planks, lying on the old quilt that we had inherited from the previous owners, and getting to know the Vallée d'Abondance and its landscape and culture.

This was a happy existence. But as we knew to expect, in winter it was different. With only basic electric heaters, the house was cold. When we arrived from Basel on Friday nights, the temperature was often little above freezing. The floor tiles were so cold that our cat, Mog, jumped from one piece of furniture to the next to cross a room. We used to light the enormous log fire, turn on the electric heaters full-blast and air the bedding – usually sleeping in front of the fire that first night. Eventually, we dared to turn on the water! We realised that we needed a quicker way of making the house habitable.

By our second year, we had made connections with tradespeople within the community, and we started improving the house. The French apprenticeship system meant that people had very specialised skills, often guarded within family businesses. If you wanted work done, there was a series of contacts to be made within the community and then the conveyor belt would clunk into action – first Monsieur Busquet for excavations, pipework and foundations; M. Charles Noël for building walls; his brother for plastering; floors and tiling by M. Delieutraz; carpentry by M. Bel Roger; ironwork and welding by M. Lollioz. It was a closed shop and workers from outside the *commune* were vehemently excluded.

Our first ventures were to develop the downstairs area, create a staircase and hallway, rearrange internal upstairs walls and build a balcony. These things were accomplished in our absence during the week. Acquaintances were made and our French improved, with highly specialised vocabulary. Saturday mornings were busy with visits from workers needing to be paid and wanting to discuss future jobs. Our visits to the shop on Sunday mornings became social affairs. As one of the very few foreign families in the village, we were gaining acceptance in this closed, traditional and very proud Alpine community.

For all our renovations, our intention was to keep life simple in Chevenoz, in contrast to our more manicured life in Basel. Over the next few years, we effectively doubled the size of the house. We also opened up the east-facing wall with a large door onto the terrace area and east-facing windows in the two upstairs bedrooms. Most importantly, we created a continuous south- and a west-facing balcony along the length of the south and west walls, and also a small east-facing balcony from the new French window in our bedroom. These balconies had a profound effect on life in the house, giving access to the outside at the level of the orchard blossom, and superb views in three directions. The main balcony also became the viewing platform from which to observe the life and events of the valley. Jeanne often impressed on me that we were very lucky that we could 'see so much' from our house. At first, I interpreted that as the ability to see so many 'goings-on' in the life of the *commune*. Later, it was here that I understood her better and really learned to live the rhythms and orbits of the sun, the moon and the planets – from east to west, from month to month, an uninterrupted view of events against the backcloth of a huge open sky. Sitting on my ottoman cushion (which became my favourite place in all this world), I could also survey the natural events of this region: the birds, the clouds, the changing colours of the forest, the meadows, the animals of the valley, the sunrises and sunsets. This was where I learned to 'be' in Nature.

Another significant change was to lighten the stain of the window frames and external shutters from dark to light oak, which improved the light intensity indoors and made the view more continuous with the interior. Unlike our neighbours, I needed to install curtains rather than be surrounded by pinewood shutters at night. My luxury was to buy beautiful Liberty fabrics for curtains. This was all in the time before Liberty changed owners and marketing strategies. On trips to one January sale, I came away with metres of 'Ianthe' curtain fabric based on a design by the French Art Nouveau designer René Beauclair from around 1900 (*Ianthe* is Greek for purple or violet flowers); metres more of 'Lilien' – a fine window netting for our long bedroom windows, which we later saw running the full length of a gallery in the Charlottenburg Art Deco museum in Berlin; and finally, at full price, Archibald Knox-designed cotton curtain material woven in Gloucestershire for Liberty and the Manx Museum. These beautiful fabrics have lasted and are an essential part of the style of the house – in fact, they are its style. All are Art Nouveau plant-based designs honouring the beauty of plants and the creativity of artists who loved them. It was considerably later that we attended to basic comforts such as central heating, and replacing the orange glazed tiling with warmer oak flooring.

We then turned our attention to the garden. Initially we were very content to live in a meadow and orchard. But building the balconies necessitated excavations for support columns, and produced piles of excavated boulders. The land in front of the house was dug up to install the new sanitation pipes for the downstairs bathroom and laundry room. A new and larger septic tank needed to be installed. All this called for a major clearance and landscaping of the terrace as well as the orchard and meadow. We thus started the grand task of working on the garden.

Developing the garden

At this stage we had no grand plan. Our lives now were full – with distant family connections and commitments, two busy jobs and a new life in Basel to forge. It was the space and the landscape that we needed and loved. But I had been deeply attached to my childhood garden – in many ways, it was my mother. And we had always developed the gardens of our previous family homes in England, planting vegetables and fruit. I have always needed a hands-on connection with plants.

The plot here was irregular in shape, with a barbed wire fence a few metres away from the front of the house. Our meadowland and orchard stretched down the valley on the east side of the house. The southern boundary of that plot was again fenced with barbed wire on aged posts. Along it stood a row of assorted rogue plum and wild cherry saplings. In the middle of the plot stood an ugly corrugated iron hut with 'Salvadori ANNEMASSE' painted on the door. This had been a workman's hut beside the railway lines at nearby Annemasse station. It had been brought to Chevenoz by the previous owner's Portuguese cousin, to house tools or even as shelter. It was constructed with railway sleepers as the floor, and proved to be very difficult to move. At the other side of the plot was a large old plum tree. Directly in front of the house stood another ancient orchard belonging to a former Chevenoz resident. Alongside the house on the west side was a traditional wooden barn and a kitchen garden. This was completely overgrown, but on investigation we discovered numerous strawberry plants, which yielded a small but delicious crop that first summer.

So in effect, when we bought the house, apart from the overgrown *potager*, there was no cultivated garden on the plot. I recall a walnut sapling about one metre tall behind *Salvadori ANNEMASSE* (perhaps coming from a walnut from a neighbouring tree buried by a forgetful squirrel); a mass of rosebay willowherb growing amid the ruined stone walls from the old farmhouse; masses of vervain flowers that glowed in the summer evening light; and the wonderful succession of flowers in the meadow – primroses, cowslips, violets, lady's smock, dandelions; and then the glorious summer mixtures of scabious, geraniums and

17

cranesbills, yellow rattle, vetches and trefoils, buttercups, globeflowers, meadow sage, sainfoin, harebells, orchids, campions, ragged robin and many species of grasses, both fine and coarse – sweet vernal grass, bromes, foxtails, fescues, meadow grasses, quaking grass. This was a wonderful and diverse pre-Alpine flora conserved by sustainable farming practices over the centuries.

But gradually we followed our urge to develop the garden and we did it in spurts – starting with the terrace area. Our strenuous efforts eventually created a south-facing stone-paved terrace enclosure with overhanging vines, beautiful ancient species of French rambling roses (*Zéphirine Drouhin, Fantin Latour, Albertine*), honeysuckle and white jasmine. It was a sheltered, scented paradise. Lying in the ruins we found a handsome moulded iron pillar, about 2.5m tall. We used this to hold up an arbour with a vine, giving us green dappled shade for our table. Only later were we told what the pillar had meant to the *commune*. It was one of the eight columns in the nave of the old church at Le Plan that had been deconsecrated and demolished in 1895, and would have been prized by any of the old Chevenoz families. Although there were still claims to it, we had installed it securely, and the result was appreciated as a fit use for such a column.

Beyond the terrace, there was little to do in the meadow. In our first June, a farmer from across the valley arrived with his mowing machine and announced that he had always cut the hay for *Famille Morel* – and would we like him to continue to do so? I think some cheese was exchanged for the hay. After a negotiation failed to have *Salvadori ANNEMASSE* dragged over some meadows to a dammed stream where a neighbour was breeding trout, Stéphane helped us drag the hut to the edge of the plot. The walnut sapling was exposed and staked – the beginning of our tree planting exploits.

In 1989, we were informed that the owner of the orchard in front of the house had moved across the lake to Switzerland and would be willing to sell to us. Since it was agricultural land, the price was very low. We had already exchanged small pieces of land on our northern perimeter fence with neighbours, and now knew the legal ropes. We visited Madame Bovey and her husband at their home near Lausanne, agreed a price, and the deal was done swiftly and amicably. We now also owned the beautiful but rather unproductive ancient orchard directly in front of the house. One apple tree bore beautiful red dessert apples, but the rest were inedible and almost un-cookable. But the plums were excellent – for eating raw, for compotes, for jam, and also to dry as prunes. We could now take down the barbed wire fence, landscape in front of the house with drive and lawn, cut down decaying trees and interplant with new ones. This was a huge and very exciting project. The orchard had a wonderful atmosphere and provided dappled shade on the lush grass that grew under the trees. The bank was riddled with springs – all draining down the valley into the Dranse. Consequently, the beautiful earth of the whole garden was always humid and, as Jeanne said, there was never a need to irrigate. Some of the trees had twisted trunks, which an old carpenter told me was because they were growing on a water course. I tried dowsing later to verify this and the ley lines were strong. Interestingly, it is the preferred place for cows to give birth. Over the years, many calves have been born there.

The trees in the orchard and their roots attracted animals in summer and winter from the surrounding woods. In summer, badgers came up from the ravine to forage for fallen cherries and plums. One year they constructed their latrines along the perimeter fence, showing that the quantity of fruit eaten was significant, as measured by the number of evacuated cherry pits. Deer grazed fruit from branches, and stripped off bark from the trees in winter. Wild boar sows and their piglets rooted around for fallen fruit, walnuts and hazelnuts – often buried by smaller animals. Squirrels, mice, magpies and woodpeckers enjoyed the nuts. Foxes and badgers searched for roots in the earth that had been churned up by the wild boar. Fallen and rotting fruit sustained deer, foxes, voles and many birds well into the winter. There was always activity in the orchard, which was one of the few remaining on this sunny, south-facing bank. The trees were being consumed by mistletoe and, despite rigorous pruning, some were beyond saving. For that reason, as soon as we bought the orchard, we decided to restore it and replant where possible. During the early years, trees were being lost rapidly. One enormous pear tree was cleft in half by lightning, which also struck the house. A nearby apple tree fell in a storm one night. We took advice and cleared debris and replanted with more varied and useful fruit trees: Morello and eating cherries, French and English varieties of apples – *Reine de Reinette*, Cox's Orange Pippin, Bramley, Blenheim, Worcester Pearmain – Comice pear, *Quetsch* plum, and local damson and greengage plums. And then, optimistically, an apricot tree and a fig, which we planted against the stone wall of the terrace. All French varieties were sourced from a reputable nursery further down the valley. The English trees were brought either by car or in airline baggage when possible. We felt the varieties chosen assured us of success. Alas, within a few years – and it takes a few years to realise mistakes in these matters – we saw that the old varieties were the ones that could survive these Alpine conditions and the endemic maladies. The cherries did well, as also did the Bramley – which, because of the altitude and hours of sunshine, produced huge and beautiful rose-blushed apples. The other new varieties suffered from multiple diseases – leaf scabs, viruses, aphids, weevils. The apple fruits were small and often pitted. The pear leaves were severely rusted. And the old trees radiated good health and bore bumper crops of fruit that we didn't much enjoy. Some of the older residents of Chevenoz did, however. At that time, there was still a travelling distillation team with a mobile still and other equipment. Certain families had kept their status of being permitted to distil a fixed quantity of *eau de vie*. Jeanne's family was one of the last to have a permit as the government tried to combat the effects of alcoholism within the rural population. When the still arrived in the *commune*, large barrels of fermented fruit were brought on the backs of carts, trucks and all manner of vehicles, and poured in. The volumes of permitted alcohol were approximately noted in the record book, and the surrounding air was near its flash point. The populace was stocked up for the winter months around the fire.

Since we now had a plot of land of considerable size and an understandable shape, we decided to integrate the various parts of the garden and to start tree planting on the whole plot. Slowly, over a period of years, we have planted a lot of trees. I had the idea that each family member should be represented by a tree in the garden. We started by dedicating the walnut tree, which was growing apace, to Ben. Since I have always loved lime trees, my childhood home was called Lindens, and I also fancied my own supply of *tilleul* tea, we planted a lime tree. This was followed by three silver birches planted close together in a copse – our three daughters. Then, with the birth of each grandchild and in memory of friends and family, we have planted a quince (Soledad), hazelnuts (Nathan and my father), yew, four mountain ash trees (Nicholas and Dylan), may trees, maples, sumachs, a beautiful golden *Robinia* (Raffy), larch (Luca), a copper beech that was a leaving gift from Ben's place of work, and two hornbeams. We also introduced bushes and shrubs – wisterias, roses and clematises around the house; honeysuckles and white jasmines on the terrace; and tree peonies, *Philadephus*, beech and scented *Eleagnus* hedging around the plot.

We decided to landscape with broad brush strokes – to plant trees and to make steps and pathways down to a 'lawn' area. In our excavations, we also discovered large slate blocks for steps and seats. These were lying either partially buried or exposed around the ruins of the farmhouse. On one occasion, I was trying to dig a hole to plant a bush behind the house in what we later discovered was the old farmyard when my spade hit a stone. This was not an unusual thing to happen. I moved along and tried again, with the same result. This happened over a space of three or four metres. Excavation revealed an enormous slab of local slate that had been the entrance threshold to the old barn. Later, with the aid of a tractor and the trusted Land Rover, this was dragged around to the front of the house and installed on huge concrete foundations and legs filled with cement and iron rods. It makes a beautiful table of grand proportions, on which we have eaten memorable meals ever since.

Chapter notes

1. Chatelaine, Claude and Baud, George: Habundantia: *La vie au Val d'Abondance à travers le temps.* 1983. Sopizet. ASIN: B0014MWQE6

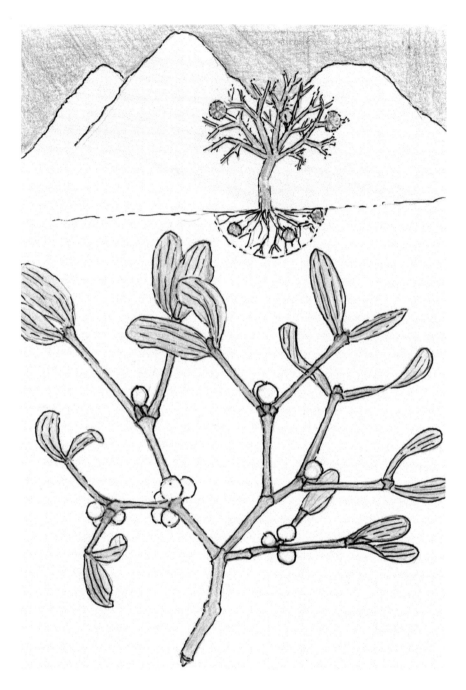

Mistletoe (Viscum album) and apple tree from the orchard in Chevenoz. According to the mediaeval Doctrine of Signatures, mistletoe resembles both in its form and its habit the disease that it can cure.

II

Cancer: the turning point?

'The years when I was pursuing my inner images were the
most important in my life – in them everything essential
was decided.'

C.G. JUNG, 'MEMORIES, DREAMS, REFLECTIONS'[1]

In the early years of transforming the house *something changed*. The girls were with us for a holiday and we were enjoying our time together. We spent our days walking in the mountains, swimming in the lake with the surfboard, playing tennis and enjoying life. One evening in the bathroom, naked, I remember raising my arm to take something off a shelf and noticing a 'dimple' under my right breast where my breast joined my ribcage. I examined it and wondered what could have caused it – did I hit myself with a ski pole? A spade? It never occurred to me what else it could be. As I recall I then put the incident out of my mind. I believe that evening we went down to the lake and restaurant and had a lovely meal. The holiday came to an end and we all parted and picked up our various lives.

We had bought a flat in Islington and it needed re-arrangements for the girls to have a London base, so I went to London in October of that year and worked really hard setting up the flat. As I said goodbye to Clare, I gave her a big hug and said to her, 'Now I'm going to look after myself'. I don't recall that I was aware of any deep meaning behind this statement. Ben was in the United States for two weeks and I returned to Basel on the Sunday evening. I went into work the next morning and was sitting at my desk in my office. Suddenly I felt very strange and sweat started pouring out of the palms of my hands. I sat there for some time wondering what was happening and whom to turn to. At last I got up and went down the corridor to a colleague's office. I told him I felt ill. As I didn't have a doctor in Basel, he suggested that he took me to the polyclinic nearby. He rang, made me an appointment, and took me down there in his car. A doctor examined me, arranged for me to have an extensive range of tests – heart, blood pressure, blood – all of which were performed with Swiss efficiency. I waited for the results. He could find nothing wrong with me. I seemed to be in good health. However, he thought I should also see a gynaecologist and recommended one. By then I was feeling better and wanted to wait until Ben returned before doing any more investigations.

The following week I went to see Herr Dr Gattlen. After a long interview and then examination, he declared he was satisfied that everything was in order. He was rushing off to take his daughter and family to the *Herbstmarkt* – a Basel autumn celebration. As I was getting dressed, I suddenly raised my arm and asked him, 'What's this?' He took one look and was visibly shocked. I needed another appointment because this needed investigating by biopsy. I still didn't take in the seriousness of the situation. I had had two manual examinations and neither doctor had found anything untoward. What was wrong? How fast things went then. I had the biopsy the following week and the results were negative. But still Dr Gattlen wasn't satisfied. He wanted a second opinion so we went together early one morning to another clinic for a second biopsy. Results of this were also negative but by now an appointment had been made for an initial visit to a surgeon at the Klaraspital hospital.

Around six weeks after my strange experience in my office, I met Professor Tondelli. He was a small, grey-haired, wiry and energetic Swiss. Although initially it had been a very dubious diagnosis, he took one look at my dimple and breast (by now swollen from biopsies), and declared *'Typisch Krebs'* – there was no doubt at all in his mind that this was cancer. Again with Swiss efficiency, plans were set in motion for hospitalisation and surgery. I was booked in for as much intervention as they offered. Numbly, I accepted.

On that cold, grey Saturday morning, I left his clinic and Ben and I drove to Chevenoz for the weekend. We were both shocked and frightened, and I was angry. Tears flowed and my mother's cancer and death invaded me. Lying on the old red leather couch in front of the fire that evening, fear wracked my body and I felt that the decline that cancer brings had already started in me. I offered no resistance – my confidence in my body and my health shattered instantly. I felt drained and empty.

Three days later I went to the Klaraspital with my bag, awaiting admission. Ben and some dear friends were with me to keep me company. We waited a long time and eventually someone came to say that my operation for the next day was postponed for a day. I could go home if I liked. I preferred not to – having come so far down this path, and asked to be admitted and to be knocked out/made mindless for the next day. This was done. It was later that I realised why Prof. Tondelli couldn't be there that Wednesday. His mother had died. On the Thursday morning I was woken early and prepared for surgery. Prof. Tondelli had told me that he still wasn't sure of the extent of the cancer spread or even of its malignancy, so he might need to excise lymph nodes. That would be a lengthy procedure. My last recollection before going into the operating theatre is of having my legs strapped to the bed. I begged them not to – and then oblivion.

Much later I awoke to a hazy, muffled world. A woman was calling 'Hilary'. My immediate reaction was to put my left hand to my right armpit. Yes, he had operated there. He had extracted lymph nodes. It was malignant. I had cancer. I wanted to return to that anaesthetised void.

I was in hospital for eleven days – sharing a room with a lovely Swiss woman. She was very sick having fought cancer for several years, and was now losing the battle. For me, I was now finding some fighting spirit, looking for incremental improvements to my strength and mobility and the progress of post-operative treatment – dressings changed, reduction in the number of drainage bottles attached to me like anchors. I lay in my bed by the window looking at the winter branches and listening to my Walkman – a tape of Bizet's 'Carmen' – over and over again. It took me out of my mind to somewhere else, to the mountains, which is where I wanted to be. During this time I had visitors: Ben, then Gail visited straight after my surgery before leaving for South America, friends, work colleagues eventually, and then Jo arrived to be with me. These visits from my daughters made me realise that their very existence was a reason to fight for survival – it was about mother love. This was a very different emotion from the way I felt for Ben. In hindsight, the separation I had felt when I went to Basel, leaving the family life that my daughters and I had shared in England, was a major contributing factor to my cancer.

Christmas was approaching and I was told that if my drainage bottles were sufficiently empty, they would remove the tubes and I could go home. In that protected little environment with its 'hands-on' nursing care I was 'doing well'. But I was bored, restless and angry and wanted to get out. And on Christmas Eve they said I could. I returned to our Basel apartment but we couldn't go to Chevenoz as I needed to be in contact with the hospital over the holiday period in case of any emergency. Fear suddenly overwhelmed me again. I went to bed and my only memories are of Jo and Ben being beside me and comforting me. Of what happened in the next few days and weeks I have little recollection. I went into my shell, dumbfounded, bewildered, shocked beyond bounds and not knowing where to turn.

To this day I am surprised by the instant shattering of my image of good health brought about by this crisis. I had always perceived myself to be strong, resilient and in very good health. This was the state I had been in for my entire life. My hospitalisations had all been concerned with childbirth and related matters. But gradually some drive did return. In the New Year I went back to England with Jo as Ben was going to the United States (again) for a couple of weeks. I stayed for some of the time with my sister Monica and her husband, Douglas, who showed me great kindness. They took me to see another sister, Jan, and I realised my humour was coming back. I had been with Monica and Douglas for a few days and was beginning to feel very listless. I thought it was a result of my illness. Jan prepared me a cup of coffee – fresh and aromatic. I drank it gladly and had an immediate and powerful response. I mentioned this to Monica who explained that we had been drinking de-caffeinated tea and coffee at their house. So that was it! Not due to my illness at all.

My Ego wanted to show people that I was coping, was doing well, and would be back to normal and work again soon. While in London I determined to go to the Liberty's sale and buy more curtain material for Chevenoz, and Liberty Lawn handkerchief material. One morning I travelled from Highbury to Oxford Circus and came out of the underground. I was walking along Regent Street and then something very strange happened. The base of my spine 'froze' and I had to put huge effort into putting a leg forward in a stride. I came to a halt. It had a dreamlike quality and I couldn't walk. I leaned against a shop window and wondered what to do. I was so fearful that I could hardly breathe. I waited for I don't know how long and eventually found it had passed. I could walk again and with determination, I went slowly to Liberty's and bought my beautiful material. Whether it was caused by something physical, I don't know. But I can recall it now as if it happened yesterday – so clear and so powerful and unusual. It stopped me in my tracks. In retrospect, I'm sure my Spirit was depleted and I was being driven by Will and Ego.

My return to Basel in early January was the beginning of a new era. I had survived surgery, my stitches had come out, and now it was time for the relentless radiation – five days a week, lasting two minutes a day. I found the experience deeply disturbing. After my visits to Kantonsspital, I returned to the apartment, lay on the settee and fell into a dry, resentful and dreamless sleep. Alongside this treatment there were check-ups with doctors, visits to the physiotherapist for shoulder mobility and lymph drainage in my right arm, and then psychiatric treatment. In the home of Jung, self-help groups and psychotherapy were unheard of, but Dr Gattlen offered me the possibility of treatment at the Frauenspital with a gynaecologist/psychiatrist – with the proviso to be careful. I wouldn't want to be labelled! But I really needed to talk about these events and my feelings. So started my conversations with Frau Dr Hollenstein.

All these activities took place during the week and then on Friday evenings we left Basel for Chevenoz, transported to another land, another world even. That summer we had the front drive and croquet lawn landscaped and the house began to sit more comfortably in its surroundings. We now had a house with a beautiful balcony, a new kitchen and spacious accommodation downstairs. We also planted the structural plants round the balcony pillars, the perpetual flowering borders of Rush roses and many trees.

Meanwhile in Basel, appointments, treatments and check-ups continued relentlessly. My conversations with Frau Hollenstein were useful. We studied all the New England Journals of Medicine looking at statistics of cancer survival. My cancer was of low grade and I had been given a 95% chance of survival (for five years). In answer to my question 'should I say I *had* cancer or I *have* cancer?' she firmly recommended the latter. But I wanted to know where I was in these statistical curves and distributions.

At work I threw myself into interesting projects: making videos and slideshows, writing articles and arranging workshops on the benefits and risks of pesticides. This was work to keep me busy and help me move on. But something inside me told me that this was curing my cancer but not healing me. I had a huge 'hole' inside of me. In September 1991 I went to Brussels to meet people from the D.G. XII (the Environment Directorate) to discuss pesticide residues in ground water. Since it was my birthday, Ben arranged to come to meet me and spend an evening together. Career-wise, I was at the top of my game, but my heart wasn't in all this and I wanted out. At Basel airport I needed to ring Klaus (my boss) and left my appointments diary in the telephone booth. A destructive force was at work! Or was it? Talking with Ben, we discussed how to begin the plan to leave Basel – he was willing to go as well.

Back in Basel, Frau Hollenstein was pregnant and left and was replaced by Frau Dr Peters. She was a lifestyle coach interested in Well Woman clinics. I had little rapport with her and called her my 'occupational therapist'. After about six months she told me she was leaving. We had looked at all the scientific evidence and I was not satisfied, so her suggestion was to try a non-scientific approach. She presented me with a small book written in formal German. It was a 'Krebskur' (Cancer Cure) written by Rudolf Breuss[2]. With it she offered me 'six months off to find my happiness' and attempt the regime if I wanted to. My immediate response was to say no – I had a lot of work to do and in any case, I feared for my job security if I was absent for so long. At that moment her beep went off and she had to leave me. In the silence of her empty office I suddenly heard a voice: 'Why not?' When she returned I accepted her offer and she wrote me a sick note for six months on full pay and gave me the book as a gift.

That evening I tried to make sense of it. By all accounts this Austrian engineer, naturopath and healer had cured himself of stomach cancer by adhering to a regime of beetroot and other root juices and herbal teas. Instead of statistics, the little book was full of empirical accounts – thanking him for successes and full of hope. I searched for some sort of rationale in it all and accepted the idea of starving metastatic cells with different needs and growth patterns to the normal cells in organs. The teas sounded strange but beautiful, made of familiar plants: lady's mantle, white dead nettle, *Melissa*, sage, herb robert, nettles, horsetail. These were supplemented by beetroot juice, onion soup and grapefruit juice. That was it! So many of the herbs grew in Chevenoz. My mind was made up. I made an appointment with my boss, told him I had a sick note on full pay for six months and proposed that I would organise the forthcoming workshop in Cambridge – 'Dialogue on the Benefits and Risks of Pesticides' – and would then take the proceedings to Chevenoz with me. During my leave I would write it up as a manual for the group companies and would also produce a script for a video to be made of all the material we would record during the workshop. He agreed.

I then went to the marvellous *Reformhaus* (Health Food shop) in Basel Marktplatz and bought the requisite number of bottles of beetroot juice. The assistant weighed out the herbal teas, carefully selecting the relevant wooden boxes of beautiful aromatic dried preparations, mixing them together, bagging them up and labelling them. In my heart I knew this was the right thing for me to be doing. It transported me to a time so long ago – to one of my earliest childhood memories when I was going into the local chemist shop with my father. We had just left the doctor's surgery, where I had waited in the waiting room for him to see the doctor, and hand in hand we had walked across the road to the chemist shop. It was a sunny morning, the shop was empty and the bell tinkled as we opened the door. Inside was an amazing sight. There were rows of beautiful blue and white Delft pots and jars on shelves, all with undecipherable labels. Sunlight shone through blue glass bottles in the window, diffusing the light in the shop. I was transfixed. Suddenly a tall and handsome young woman had appeared from behind the shop. She had long blonde plaits arranged and pinned around her head – like Gretel in the fairy story – and she greeted us with a big smile. She was the daughter of Mr Baugh, the pharmacist, and was his dispenser. She took my father's prescription, read it, and started to mix aromatic substances from bottles into a large stone mortar. She ground them together with a large pestle and tapped the resulting yellow/brown powder into pill moulds and compressed them. She then carefully counted out the correct number of pills into a small brown bag, sealed it and put a label on. Hey presto! She had made pills that were going to make my father better. How wonderful was that? As we left the shop in that brilliant light that makes moments 'other-worldly', I told my father I wanted to be a dispenser.

A week after the Cambridge workshop, I set off for Chevenoz with our cat, the juices and the herbs. The next day I started the regime. I decided to do forty days instead of the prescribed forty-two because I liked the biblical symbolism of a forty-day fast and it fitted in better with family arrangements. And so began this experiment – by myself in Chevenoz with cat for company, looking inwards.

The Breuss Diet – Chevenoz style

How very long those first days were. I arranged the kitchen for tisane preparation and cleared all traces of food away. I hadn't considered how much of a normal day is taken up with thinking about, buying, preparing, enjoying, eating and then clearing up food. The routine of preparing the teas and drinking them in the right order didn't take long and later turned into a ritual. I drank the beetroot juice from a wineglass – sipping it slowly during the morning. If anyone could have seen me they might have thought I was a wino. The hunger in the first few days was intense and I really doubted I would be able to continue. But I had reached the stage where I wanted to contribute to my own healing. I had been treated in so many ways by others and now it was my turn to work on myself.

I spent my time listening to music, skiing, walking the 5km circuitous route round the *commune*, working on the video clips and script, and reading in front of the fire. Other than the ritual tisane drinking, my life was without structure or companionship. I had found Lyall Watson's book 'Lifetide'[3] in Jo's room and decided to re-read it. I had read it so long ago as a student and remembered having concentrated on the biology and skipping the other parts. This time I was stirred by the quotes from C.G. Jung's 'Memories, Dreams, Reflections' at the beginning of each chapter. I was so moved by them that I knew I had to read that book. The weather had turned very bad – dense, freezing February fog and icy roads – and I wondered if I could possibly drive down to Evian to see if they had it in the bookshop. I was worried by the fog and the thought of driving down the slalom bends of the valley road with my low blood sugars, so wandered round the house during my deliberations. I went into Gail and Clare's room and stood by the window, vacantly surveying the swirling mists. On looking up at the little wall bookcase, there, flashing like a beacon, was 'Memories, Dreams, Reflections'. Clare had had it there unbeknown to me for ages. What a find!

That day I sat and read it through. This was a defining moment in my life. Whatever my future, my goal from then on was to find a deeper 'meaning' to my life.

With this support I then continued the regime. Over the period of forty days I lost a total of 11kg but was struck by the *extraordinary* energy that I had. My scientific ideas of diet, calories and energy didn't hold here. I became used to the lack of food and exercised in the middle of the day by skiing at nearby Bernex, and it was only towards the end of the diet that I started to feel cold at night. But at the time, I didn't understand what was going on and was intrigued by the herbs and wanted to know what they were really doing for me – especially the reason for the ongoing feeling of supreme wellbeing. I felt so alive, so comfortable in my skin, somehow 'bright'. True, many facets of this regime were excellent – a beautiful location, bright sunny weather in winter, comforts, no stress, and peace. But to live alone and follow such a rigorous diet was a huge demand. However, as shown by my diary excerpts, I reported (mostly) consistent wellbeing and happiness.

Day 2

'Finding my happiness and having a nice time are not the same thing.'
'I need to make some decisions of how I want to lead my life, however long or short it will be.'
'I need a religion – meaning a sense of belonging, of connection.'
'For Jung, religion was really *religare* – the binding back to the roots of one's self'. Quote from 'The Wisdom of the Dream: the world of C.G.

Jung' by Segaller and Berger[4].

'At times I am really feeling healthy – beyond what I have felt for a long time.'

'For all this hunger, I am beginning to enjoy the rituals of preparing the teas and the wonderful smells – of sage oil, for instance, which I inhale as it boils away, and the meadow smells as the herbs reach the water.'

Day 6

'I have plenty of energy and feel so healthy, skiing in the sunshine. Onion soup – so beneficial and tasty. Certainly my sense of smell and taste are heightened. No cooking smells, no fridge smells. When I get a whiff of something I am like a fox – chasing it with my nose until I find it.'

Day 7

'When I can put my hunger aside – and a lot of it is in my mind, I'm sure – I really feel that this place and this situation are helping me to heal.'

Day 8

'I'm wondering if this cure will 'work'? I really enjoy the sage tea. So doubts are still here but I'm finding some comfort.'

Day 13

'I've settled into the regime now.'

'I'm beginning to be convinced that this cure is working.'

'I find this sense of wellbeing really surprising. It is not just that I have energy to use in physical activity. I have a sense of elation and light-heartedness.'

Day 18

'Today I re-read the scientific cancer papers without fear and then I burned them! They don't concern me anymore. I watched the flames go up the chimney! I'm very happy with my own company and projects. I've found 'God' in my meditations and also a fierce independence.'

Day 20

'What a wonderful cure! I feel so good and so happy. Somehow death is no longer the appalling fear that it was. I have a tremendous longing to go on living and being.'

'But sleeplessness at night… Often I am wide awake! Perhaps this is a result of my high spirits?'

Day 21

'What do I really believe about this cure? Rationally I think it is plausible. Perhaps most importantly, I'm looking for strength within my own body – and in a way that strength is coming from abstinence. I'm also finding a strength in my Spirit – a happiness, a determination and a trust in myself.'

Here, I was over halfway through the regime. I was emotionally elated but my energy levels for physical effort ebbed and flowed…

Day 24

'I get cold and am awake sometimes at night. As instructed, I stopped taking the diuretic tea so now my weight loss is getting less.'

Day 25

'I walked the circuit at noon today but felt so weak that I panicked that perhaps I wouldn't be able to complete the fast, or even the walk!'

I realised that I would have to take things more gently physically and keep myself warm.

Day 26

'I can't really keep my body warm but otherwise my energy is good. I'm impressed by my inner self-preservation.'

But then things improved:

Day 27

'I've worked calmly and well today. This afternoon I walked the circuit and could feel my inner physical and emotional strength. I feel that my body and Soul are striving in unison now. This will help me through the next fifteen days.'

Day 29

'I've had a peaceful day – working, playing the piano, juggling, sewing. It's funny – my temperature regulation is OK now. I've hardly lost weight for nine days (no more diuretic tea) and I don't get tired, or rather, last night I slept long and deeply. I feel I need to plot out what I want to achieve in the next eleven days.'

Day 31

'I return to Basel to go into work and for hospital check-ups – but for the latter I have no fear. Work clothes fall off me…! I realise that meeting people again requires huge energy – they can easily drain me.'

Day 33

'Medical check-ups today – all OK. Met Dr Peters and we both agreed the cure suited me well. I realised during my trip to Basel and by talking to people just how good this cure has been for me. I really do feel that I have found my happiness – which was the reason for doing it! The aim is now to keep it.'

Day 35

'I'm re-reading Jung's 'Memories, Dreams, Reflections' and am very inspired by it. It makes me think that this year I'm going to do a lot of reading, for myself and not for a Ph.D. or for my job. I have found a dimension that I want to grow into and I feel that this sort of reading, plus meditation and doing gentle things like planning the garden, could be very 'happiness building.'

Day 37

'This afternoon I meditated on the balcony in the sunshine and felt so well and happy and high-spirited. I've come a long, long way during this cure. I really feel it has been a deeply healing time. I realise there is an urgent need in me to expand into another dimension.'

Day 39

'This has been a quite wonderful time. The regime and the herbs have supplied me with an energy that in purely physical terms I find quite inexplicable. I now need to see how I can integrate some of its aspects into my future life. I also want to know why these herbs have had such an effect on me.'

Day 40

'It's strange, in a way I have withdrawn from both Ben and my daughters. I feel more remote and strong. Perhaps this is necessary to redefine myself – to be more self-resourceful. I can grow back to them later from a stronger base.'

Day 41

'For me now, cancer is over – cancer of the breast, which was at the base of my frustrated female needs of territory, family and above all, a feminine perspective. And also it was a 'spiritual cancer' due to neglect and ignorance since relinquishing my Catholicism. I am now going to grow into that dimension that I have discovered with such bliss and happiness – that is a precious opportunity – Danke, Herr Breuss!'

(For more information of this Diet, see 'Chapter notes' below and Chapter XIV.)

Now I needed some explanations and I intended to find them. The forty days had passed and I returned to Basel. The relentless rounds of check-ups and tests continued but I was planning my exit. I negotiated working on a freelance basis and had a couple of projects with Ciba-Geigy UK. This gave me much more freedom and as Ben was travelling so much, I saw no reason to be alone in Basel.

During trips to England I researched and found a suitable Herbalism diploma course – by correspondence until the third year. This seemed to be the best starting point to understanding the healing properties of herbs. Because of my qualifications I could omit the foundation year. To do a correspondence course for the time being was an excellent way to go forward whilst waiting for Ben to find something that he wanted to do in England.

But during this time we were also putting both energy and enthusiasm into Chevenoz. We knew that to leave Basel did not mean to leave Chevenoz too. I had more time and a lot more energy. That summer we developed the terrace area, found and erected the stone table and landscaped the area around the house. The garden was definitely taking shape. We already had currant bushes in the vegetable garden and had a bountiful crop of redcurrants that year. At the end of the summer we were seriously looking for a way of leaving Basel and returning to England. I had started reading my way through Jung's 'Collected Works'[5] that Routledge had revised and published in a more attractive and approachable form. I also started the course with the School of Phytotherapy near Hailsham in East Sussex.

Working freelance gave me a lot of spare time. Work that had taken me five days now could be done in less than three. This gave me ample time to garden in Chevenoz, but I also wanted to be creative in other ways. I truly believe that one's Inner Life is deeply influenced by enduring childhood memories, and one of mine was of happy days sitting on the floor in my mother's sewing room – perhaps picking up pins on a magnet and marvelling at its power, perhaps going to her tall materials chest with its long drawers of beautiful silks and materials, or perhaps 'picking up spots' (i.e. gathering the material) in preparation for her smocking of the yokes of our pretty Viyella dresses. My mother's family had been Paris-trained master tailors and my mother made exquisite children's smocked or embroidered dresses for a shop on Regent Street, London. Whenever she had finished a dress and all cottons had been snipped, it had been carefully pressed and any slightest imperfection had been rectified, we used to crowd round it with admiration and covetousness. Some of those beautiful silks had come from India, where my Uncle Charles had travelled for years as a young 'box-wallah', trading and making connections with Indian tailors and clothing merchants. These silks were of such rich and sumptuous colours and, by post-war utility standards, felt heavenly. I adored them. So that year I also did a sewing course in quilt making at Liberty's. I knew Liberty fabrics were the best I could work with and was entranced by them. With a large amount of beautiful scraps of Liberty Lawn fabric given to us freely at the end of the course, I returned to Chevenoz to make my first quilt. Dr Peters was right about a number of things (creative activities and hobbies, for instance), for which I will be eternally grateful. I embarked on the quilt making, letting my anger seep away and creating something beautiful – a huge quilt for Gail's bed. And it was the right sort of creativity for me at that stage: meticulously cut strips sewn sequentially to make squares, which were then joined to form a greater whole – nothing too demanding or deeply creative. But the beauty of the Liberty fabrics and the assemblage of the basic squares was challenging, and then the way the colours of the basic squares changed when they were placed alongside other squares was engrossing. And working with and touching these beautiful fabrics was a joy. These skills were in my blood and it suited me.

During that year I read Jung – on and on. I read about the nature of the psyche, development of the personality, psychological types, dreams, and this all led further into the 'Collected Works'. But it was dreams that fascinated me most. Having been a vivid dreamer from childhood, I had completely forgotten how to remember them! Sometimes I could recall vignettes from particularly strange or vivid dreams and would recount them as peculiarities or funny stories. I never took them seriously. But now I decided to witness them, to respect them and to record them. In the early days I would struggle to hang on to those elusive threads before they sunk back into the depths or the ether, never to be recalled. I got to a

Gail's quilt from the Liberty material freely given at the end of the sewing course.

point of actually feeling them slither away – like a recoiling snake down a hole. I tried various techniques – lying on my back on waking with my eyes closed and instantly recalling, sleeping with my dream book and pen under my pillow, going to sleep with the firm intention of recalling the dream on waking. Eventually I could do it. But that of course was only a small part of it. Interpretation was a completely different matter. My early dreams were interesting to me but often without a lot of meaning or significance. I could understand the feeling part of them – the fear, the anger, the confusion – but the symbolism took me years to interpret.

A series of dreams I recorded soon after my beetroot regime were significant to me:

> 'I am lying in a tight box face up and am struggling to escape. I cry out for help. A man stands over me and prevents me from getting out or from making any noise. I am completely powerless...'

Then the next night:

> 'I am lying in a bath full of water. After a while my mother Dee comes in the room. I can't remember whether she rolls me over and puts my head under water or whether she pulls it out of the water...'

And a few days later:

> 'I am sitting astride a long thin boat (submarine?). It is facing the wrong direction. The young pilot goes to the helm and swings it through 180 degrees very gracefully and sweeps us out to sea. As the boat clears the harbour walls it keels over and I see it has a large gashing wound in its side...'

It seems that I was going deep into Water. There were definite stirrings.

The following spring, Ben and I returned to England for a busy three weeks. We were going up to the Lake District, where there was a prestigious three-day symposium sponsored by the Rank Foundation. Ben was a guest speaker and Clare and I were going as 'conference wives'. Since we knew several of the speakers well, and also the region, we aimed to have a great time – and so we did. We walked on the fells and in the bluebell woods and wandered in Wordsworth country with golden daffodils and stars. When we returned to London we then celebrated Jo's 21st birthday with a picnic on the sand dunes at Wittering with the skylarks singing overhead. Happiness was returning and infusing me. I needed England and my family. Ben and I made a firm commitment to work towards our return.

In September, Gail and I went to Crete together. It was here in this ancient place that I started to perceive things differently – an *Entstehen*, as the German language understands it. How strange we don't have a word for it – the closest translation is 'coming into being'. While there, we walked the deep Marian Gorge to the sea at Agia Roumeli. It seemed like a rite of passage. Those deep vertical rocks and the strange feeling between them were astounding. We also visited the temple of Knossos with its mosaic dolphins and there I met the prince-god and his irises. I was also very drawn to the ancient myths with gods and goddesses loving and fighting. These were uncharted waters for me.

I then returned to Basel and Chevenoz, where I worked freelance for Ciba-Geigy, maintaining my salary and doing the work with plenty of time left for other activities. The correspondence course with the School of Phytotherapy constantly surprised me – for all my training in classical botany and then biochemical research, I hadn't realised how important plants were as medicines. I had a few childhood memories of cherry linctus for coughs and occasional doses of syrup of figs administered during long periods of bed rest for illnesses like mumps. Did we use oil of wintergreen for sprains or was that for the animals? Also, here in the course of herbal medicine, there was little separation between foods and medicines. The first twenty plants we studied included mustard, horseradish, mint and fennel. These were foods in my mind, but I was coming to realise that herbs especially crossed the great divide. I also became aware that quite a few of the plants we were studying were growing wild on the plot in Chevenoz and I decided to create a herb garden. In particular I found that my beloved herb robert (*Geranium robertianum*), which had been an important ingredient of my beetroot diet, thrived on the plot.

The two things that I felt I really had to do were to find someone who could lead me into Jung's work and also to understand the monumental changes that took place in me while on the Breuss Diet. Talking to colleagues in Basel, it was suggested that I could do a training analysis at the Jungian Institute in Zurich. This was regarded as a 'respectable' way of justifying delving so deeply into oneself and bore no stigma of 'needing' to do so on mental/emotional health grounds. But I felt that I really needed to do this work in English to benefit from the subtleties of my mother tongue. I could see my future back in England. But

Ben was still heavily engaged in his work in Basel so I needed an interim plan. I had a meeting with Professor John Durant at Imperial College to discuss if I could do a Ph.D. with him on some aspect of dialogue on the benefits and risks of pesticide use. Following on from my master's degree course on Social Aspects of the Biosciences, this was a promising way forward. If I could get funding it seemed possible that I could do it between Ciba-Geigy in Basel and in London. This could be done alongside the Phytotherapy course. There were a lot of other options too. London offered so many possibilities for self-development and creativity – both things that I now craved.

In May 1993, Ben received a letter inviting him to apply to his former place of work for the post of Director. It came out of the blue! This was what we needed to return to the UK. By August, Ben had been offered the job. From then on things moved fast. I abandoned the idea of a Ph.D. that would bind me to Ciba-Geigy. We had to finish up our work projects, exit our flat in Basel, arrange for my continuing treatment and check-ups with a hospital in London, and find a way to combine a life in England with the work I wanted to do in the garden in Chevenoz. Once again there was a lot to arrange.

With our exit in view, we now planned packing up our things in Basel and a highly complicated move to England via Chevenoz before Christmas. The week before we left Basel, I orchestrated the move with a British removal company from the flat in Basel to Chevenoz, and then onwards to London. As always, leaving a Swiss flat was a meticulous affair (with standards of cleanliness and good repair upheld with cautions and high fines if they are not met). The furniture was carried out down four flights of stairs, the flat was cleaned, I checked the state of the kitchen taps for limescale (required on the lease), and then picked up the last remaining broom, flung it in the van and directed the removal van to the autoroute towards Bern, Montreux and then France.

Having raced the van to the house in Chevenoz, I arranged for the necessary furniture exchange, cooked lunch for the three strong young removal men and set them off on their way to a storage depot in England. The next day I returned to Basel and on December 17 spent the afternoon in the *Fremdenpolizei* (the police department concerned with residents' permits and non-Swiss financial affairs), completing our dossier to forfeit our precious Swiss Residents' Permits and pay our taxes – as few as possible. At the end of that afternoon, having discussed our affairs in German and occasional Basel dialect, I whistled through my front teeth and skipped down the beautiful spiral stairs, with passports stamped and pension lump sums unsullied. I noticed that I had got a parking ticket while upstairs with the *Fremdenpolizei*. Ben, who had worked overtime for the last month, was now back from the States and we left Basel immediately and drove up to Sélestat in Alsace, France, where we stayed the night in a lovely hotel and ate a splendid dinner. This was the end of an era.

Chapter notes

1. Jung, C.G. Memories, Dreams, Reflections. 1963, Fontana Press. ISBN 0-00-654027-9

2. Breuss, R. The Breuss Cancer Cure. (Translation from German.) 1995. Alive Books, Canada. ISBN 0-920470-56-4

The Herbs:

Tisane I: *Equisetum arvense* – horsetail; *Urtica dioica* – stinging nettle; *Polygonum aviculare* – knotgrass; *Hypericum perforatum* – St John's wort

Tisane II: *Salvia officinalis* – sage; *Hypericum perforatum* – St John's wort; *Mentha x piperata* – peppermint; *Melissa officinalis* – lemon balm

Tisane III: *Alchemilla alpina* – alpine lady's mantle; *Alchemilla vulgaris* – common lady's mantle; *Lamium album* – white dead nettle

Tisane IV: *Geranium robertianum* – herb robert

3. Watson, Lyall. Lifetide. 1979. Hodder & Stoughton. ISBN 0-340248-56-4

The quotes at the beginnings of the chapters that set me on my quest, which are all from Carl Gustav Jung's 'Memories, Dreams, Reflections' were:

'The collective unconscious is common to all; it is the foundation of what the ancients called the "sympathy of all things"'

And

'It is important to have a secret, a premonition of things unknown. It fills life with something impersonal, a numinosum. A man who has never experienced that has missed something important. He must sense that he lives in a world which in some respects is mysterious; that things happen and can be experienced which remain inexplicable; that not everything that happens can be anticipated.'

And

'The unexpected and the incredible belong to this world. Only then is life whole'.

4.   Segaller, Stephen and Berger, Merrill. The Wisdom of the Dream. The World of C.G. Jung. 1989. Shambhala Publications. ISBN 978-0877735120

5.   Jung, C.G. Collected Works (22 volumes). 1970. Routledge. ISBN 10: 0-710016336

Merlin and Nimuë. The Witch's tree (Sorbus aucuparia – Rowan). A copy (by the author) from 'The Flower Book' by Edward Burne-Jones[3].

III

The London years

'We must believe in a thing in order to fully understand
it. Everyone has experienced the mental condition of
being intellectually satisfied but not emotionally satisfied.
But the condition in which the mind is completely at ease
with itself and with the world is that of knowledge; and
knowledge is a blend of both Faith and Reason, or rather
a state in which these two are merged into a larger whole.'

'PHILOSOPHERS OF EAST AND WEST', REFERRING TO ST AUGUSTINE

Dream

I was with a large group of people and we were preparing for some grand
event. I met Lyndy (a friend of daughter Clare's) and her sister Nicci. They
were very excited and were dressing up in the most beautiful robes – golden
yellow and green. Suddenly we were all up on a huge stage and everyone was
in sumptuous costumes. I realised it was the staging of an opera. I was in the
centre of the group and we were moving together in formation towards the back
of the stage. When I reached the back I then turned around (like in a marching
band) and headed towards the front of the stage and everyone followed. As I
approached the audience, we all burst into a wonderful opera chorus.

Symbolism/connections: Lyndy was artistic. Previous we had a long
conversation about a second 'gap year' before going to university, during
which she wanted to paint. We discussed the role of art in society – was she
contributing? Nicci, her sister, was a medical student. Singing together was
being part of society.

On a trip to London a couple of months before leaving Basel, we found a house to buy in one of the Georgian squares in Islington. It was an elegant terraced house that had been lovingly restored by an American writer with a taste for expensive and beautiful artefacts and interior decoration. It had stained glass panelled doors, a wonderful attic/studio space, a bespoke kitchen with handcrafted cupboards and white marble work surfaces, and all the handsome proportions of a mid-sized Georgian house. It was interestingly decorated throughout with hand-printed wallpaper by a local Islington firm. It also had a small but wonderfully stocked and landscaped garden behind it – at the bottom of which stood a huge black poplar tree (male). The front of the house overlooked a square with plane, cherry and laburnum trees and lawns – a green space in the heart of London. This was to be our home for the next five years.

So, with Basel behind us, we headed for London. Since it was term time and there were no daughters around, we installed ourselves in their flat while we waited for the sale to go through. The purchase of the house was progressing with the usual dramas and impasses. What had been described as a hairline crack in a roof beam appeared in the survey as a fault in the main structure of the butterfly roof, and the whole beam needed replacing. But other things went well, with carpets being removed, old pinewood floors being sanded and polished, a couple of walls being removed. We visited the wallpaper factory and had more paper printed to patch-up and match the existing, and by February of the following year we were ready to move in.

These five years in London were perhaps the most productive in my life. This was a time of huge personal growth – and what a luxury that was. I had become a mother at a young age and all my endeavours in life had been made within the framework of myself and my family of husband and three daughters. Now I had the freedom, the time and the energy to pursue ideas that were hitherto off-limits. I also had the enthusiasm to go to these places and try to answer some questions that I regarded as essentially important. And I was back in an environment that was all so familiar. I loved London; I had already studied there twice. I understood what was going on around me, and when not in the flow, could persuade, charm or argue my way through most things – certainly something that I was not able to do in Basel! I soon discovered nearby Chapel Market and made it my business to get to know it and the stallholders well. The humour and lively banter of North London traders amused and enlivened me. Other wonderful shops were in Cross Street, with Mr Ferrari selling Italian specialities, Steve Hatt with his magnificent fish shop, the greengrocers in Essex Road trading (what?) all hours of the day and night. Then there was Camden Passage with its antiques and junk stalls. We had the Almeida Theatre on our doorstep, restaurants of every type and nationality, interesting shops and galleries. My life in Islington was lively and interactive and I enjoyed it immensely. My family was around me but not dependent on me. Ben was not travelling to distant places so was nearby most of the time. Our daughters arrived and departed as befitted their student lifestyles. I had sisters, friends and new colleagues nearby. These were all things I had missed in our years in Basel.

Besides the possibilities of my immediate life in Islington, London had so much to offer in terms of opportunities and possibilities for developing my interests and finding new ones. I set about constructing a life for myself. I suspected that to find a job as satisfying as the one I was leaving in Basel would be difficult. In any case, I had another agenda. I wanted to investigate the energy and superb feeling of wellbeing that I had experienced during the Breuss Diet and had also decided this was a time for me to give something back to society. So I set about finding a 'Bash Street Kid to Love'. During my first year back in London, I went to the Charities Fair at the Business Centre in Islington and went the whole way round looking for something to put my heart into. I found nothing, which distressed me considerably – it was all about legal matters and accountancy and aspects of charity work that I didn't feel I could contribute to. But just as I was leaving the vast Agricultural Hall, I came to a stall called REACH. They put people with skills in touch with charities who could use them. We talked for a while and they were sure they could find something for me and gave me a one-page application form. I took it home and filled it in. At the bottom of the page I saw in small print: 'REACH – Retired Executives Action Clearing House'. But I wasn't retired! I was still young, had lots of energy, had unfinished consultancy contracts with Ciba-Geigy and certainly didn't see myself in that category. I wrote a covering letter to that effect. Within a week they replied to my application with six charities that they thought could benefit from my skills and experience. All were interesting, but in that list was the Chelsea Physic Garden[1] – who wanted a receptionist. This wasn't what I had in mind, but here was THE Chelsea Physic Garden – the beautiful ancient Garden of the Apothecaries and home to a wonderful collection of medicinal plants. London's 'Secret Garden'.

So this was to be my 'Bash Street Kid' – an opportunity tailor-made for my agenda. Very soon afterwards I went to see the curator and on hearing that I was a botanist, she asked me to be a volunteer Records Officer instead. The job entailed working with someone who knew nothing about plants but a lot about computers. I would decipher the ancient handwritten details of the plant collection and then enter them onto the complex database that he had designed. This was a mammoth task that I started to undertake with the proviso that after entering twenty plants, I would go out into the garden to find them. The work was not exactly to my liking, but I could see how important it was for the Garden to get its records in order and onto a database that could be shared with other botanic gardens.

To give myself time for the Herbal Medicine Diploma coursework, I offered to work there two days a week. On those days I rose early to get across London before the rush-hour crowds and caught the Number 19 bus from Upper Street to the King's Road, Chelsea. This was a journey across the centre of London, past all those places dear to me – Red Lion Square, Holborn, Cambridge Circus, China Town, Piccadilly, Green Park, then down Sloane Street to Sloane Square, where my mother had always said that her parents had had their family tailoring business. I felt very much at home.

Being at the Physic Garden was fascinating and compelling. A new world was opening up to me. Making the database of the plants of the Physic Garden was laborious but I was doing it as a volunteer and could go at my own pace. The garden contained around 6,000 plants, which I slowly introduced myself to. My current botanical knowledge was restricted to a mostly European flora but now my knowledge base was expanding. The handwritten cards that I was required to decipher dated from around the 1930s and described each plant's nomenclature and synonyms (the various names it had had over time), its provenance (where it came from), its habitat (what sort of environment it preferred), its morphology (what it looked like) and occasional medical, economic and traditional usage. This was a huge body of knowledge for me to embrace. Besides the work, my colleagues were cultured, interesting, mostly gentle people – as so often gardeners and plants(wo)men are. The library of ancient floras and herbals introduced me to a vast wealth of herbal knowledge. Thus, my connection to the garden and its traditions had a profound influence on me.

Because of the prestige and location of the Physic Garden, there was a constant stream of interesting and knowledgeable visitors. Working in the curator's office brought me into contact with a lot of them and led to some very useful and interesting liaisons with scientists, herbalists and artists. I also made connections with Kew Gardens and we discussed how our database could add to their Endangered Species List. Then in 1996 we received a letter from the Botanic Gardens Conservation International asking if we could aid in the rebuilding and replanting of the Botanic Garden in Sarajevo, which had been destroyed in the Bosnian war. Because we now had the database, I was able to search the now extensive records and find nineteen plants in our collection that had authentic provenance in that region. These were offered to the new Botanic Garden. All these ideas added to my enthusiasm to study and develop ideas of my own.

The Chelsea Physic Garden was founded by the Worshipful Company of Apothecaries of London in 1673 for the study of plants and research. This beautiful little garden alongside the Thames in Chelsea was one of the first botanic gardens in Europe. The London apothecaries – who arrived by boat up the Thames from central London, came to identify and recognise the plants that were at their disposal to use in their trade: to know their mandrake, belladonna and, later, quinine plants. Very early on, in 1735, the plants at the Garden were identified and classified using a system devised by the Swedish botanist Linnaeus. Each plant was given a generic name (genus) and specific name (species) in Latin, and plants used by apothecaries were also given the name *officinalis*. As in most botanic gardens where plants were studied, the plants were arranged according to the classification: orders, families, genera and species, forming 'order beds'. These beds are still an important part of the Garden.

In the 18th century, a period of voyaging and discovery became associated with the Physic Garden. Philip Miller was Chief Gardener between 1722 and 1770 and became famed for his collections of plants from Europe, the Far East and the Americas – in particular, North American plants. A succession of influential gardeners and botanists continued this tradition. William Hudson became Demonstrator of Plants between 1765 and 1771. Prior to that, he had written 'Flora Anglica', classifying all plants with Linnaean nomenclature. Around this time, the most influential contact with the Garden was Sir Joseph Banks, a wealthy naturalist and botanist. Having been encouraged by Philip Miller, he set off on trips – first to Newfoundland in 1766 and then with Captain James Cook on HMS Endeavour between 1768 and 1771. On this long trip to Australia via Brazil and Tahiti with Daniel Solanger, Banks studied native floras. They collected around 1300 exotic plants in Madeira, Brazil, Tierra del Fuego, the Society Islands, New Zealand, Australia and Java, and eventually produced the 'Banks' Florilegium'. It took eighteen engravers between 1771 and 1784 to create the beautiful copperplate line engravings from 743 completed watercolours made on the voyage by Sydney Parkinson. The 'Florilegium' was not printed in Banks' lifetime and he bequeathed the plates to the British Museum. Many plants and seeds from these voyages were given to the Physic Garden. Other influential gardeners following on from Miller and Banks were William Forsyth and William Curtis, who wrote 'Flora Londinensis'.

In the 19th century, later collecting trips were made by three influential botanists: Robert Fortune, Curator of the Garden (1846 to 1848), made collecting trips to China and devised the 'Wardian Case' to transport living plants back home in good condition; his successor, Thomas Moore, Curator from 1848 to 1887, had a passion for ferns and during his time at the Garden increased the number of plants in the collection by 50%; and John Lindley, educator and orchid collector[2]. Under the influence of these three men, there was a distinct change in emphasis away from herb gathering and towards plant collecting – i.e. from medicine and healing to botany and horticulture. The current Chelsea Physic Garden has plantings of species brought back by these influential collectors – but in the process of collecting, these plants became separated from the traditional knowledge of their uses in healing and medicine.

My impression when I arrived at the Garden was that its emphasis certainly was not medicinal plants. Although a truly excellent place, its excellence lay more in its important historical plant collections; its National Collections – of *Cistus* and *Pelargonium* for instance; its membership of the British Florilegium with its floral art classes; its affiliation to the English Gardening School; its collaboration with the pharmaceutical company Glaxo, whom it supplied with plant material for research; its membership, volunteers and tours; and, not insignificantly, its superb café, catering and corporate hospitality. It had been forced to open its doors and support itself, which it certainly did.

It was Susan Minter, Curator of the Garden between 1991 and 2001, who had the wisdom to create initiatives to change this emphasis. She designed an impressive 'Garden of Medicinal Plants' that had areas dedicated to medicine from every region of the world, containing plants used by healers, shamans, witch doctors and herbalists over a period of 5000 years. She also designed the '*Officinalis* Beds' with representatives of the plants used by apothecaries between the 17th and 19th centuries; another bed of significant plants used in herbal remedies relied on by over 70% of the world's population; and finally, a bed of important plants that have influenced the production of 25% of all modern Western pharmaceuticals. In later years, a scented garden and aromatherapy beds were developed. Around a decade later these gardens were redesigned and significantly enlarged to include a garden of 'useful plants' and of vegetables. The

Garden now has a plant collection arranged in a way that can truly be described as the 'Garden of the Apothecaries'.

After three years, as the work with the database drew to a close (it would never finish!), I was offered a permanent position as Records Officer – an offer that I declined. I requested instead to become a volunteer gardener for a year. This was a rigorous and extensive training, for which I am extremely grateful. I followed the practices through all seasons, working with Jane – a gentle, meticulous and caring gardener who was responsible for seed gathering, cleaning, storing and then propagating and planting out in the garden. In the potting shed and adjoining room, we cleaned the collected seeds carefully with tweezers, sieves and blotting paper, and stored them, accurately labelled in brown paper bags in filing drawers. The calm atmosphere of loving concentration while listening to classical music on BBC Radio 3 impressed me deeply. The beauty of seeds with their secrets and potential was magical. And there was something primitive, yet completely necessary, about doing this work to preserve and enable continuation of life and our cultural dependence on plants.

The climate at the Chelsea Physic Garden was exceptional. The high brick walls that surrounded it conserved warmth in the garden so that it was considerably warmer than adjacent areas. On New Year's Day, successive curators have noted plants in flower, showing how early spring came to the garden. With the numerous glass- and hothouses there, propagation of annuals started early. Well-tried and meticulous methods were used to sow seeds: in small pots, covered with quartz gravel, irrigated effectively, in the light, stored in the fridge, in the dark, or put in whatever conditions promoted growth for that species. Wonderfully, the seedlings mostly emerged within two or three days and then came the laborious job of tipping out the seedlings, selecting ones to prick out into larger pots (five seedlings per pot) and setting them aside to grow further. The remaining seedlings were returned to their original pots in case the process failed and needed to be repeated. The speed at which the seedlings grew, once transplanted was impressive. Within a few hours the plantlets stood erect and the leaflets expanded, growing upwards to the light. Hundreds of species were treated in this way and were later moved to the cold frames to harden off and then transplanted in the order beds or suitable locations in the garden. Nothing was mechanised – everything was done by hand. It was here that I realised that my green fingers were a gift. Besides this, to produce more stock, seeds of perennial plants were sown and cuttings were taken at various times of the year. This was a fascinating procedure: learning which part of the plant to use, how to prepare it, how long it would take for root formation. It always amazed me how the process would spread around the pot – as if root formation in one cutting influenced the others in that pot (which, of course, it did). Jane tutored me in all these methods and I loved the work. As the year progressed, I learned how to plant out, to sow directly into the soil in small areas mapped out by sand markings, to thin out, to prune, to stake, and so many other gardening techniques (some were heavy – we were all very emancipated here…). When the beginning of June arrived and the Garden was looking at its best, I was ready to return to Chevenoz to work on my own garden.

Alongside these efforts, I was also putting in many hours of hard work with the Herbal Medicine course. The second year syllabus was mostly basic human anatomy and physiology. It was a lot of revision that I had to tolerate, but there was also a new world of information on herbal medicine that was exciting and interesting. How could I have previously learned so much about plants and about humans and not realised this deep healing connection between them? How could this knowledge have been reduced in an Honours Botany B.Sc. degree to a brief course on pharmacognosy in the third year of study?

The Jungian in Kew Gardens

A third item on my agenda for life in London was to find a Jungian analyst to work with. I had continued to read Jung's 'Collected Works' and much more besides and had now found something so intriguing to study – what it really meant to be a spiritual human being. A dear friend had told me of a Jungian who lived by Kew Gardens and I was intensely drawn to him. After discussion, I approached him and arranged an appointment.

On a spring morning I walked up a short driveway to his house in Kew Road, just outside the Cumberland Gate of Kew Gardens. My first impression of him was not positive. He was not at all as I had imagined (Jung-like, sitting behind couch?). I sat opposite him in his consulting room and told him my story, of my illness, of my early vivid dreams of cracking earth and burning haystacks and pitchforks. He took me on – for four years. Each Tuesday I visited Nicholas and then spent the rest of the day in the gardens at Kew – either reflecting on our discussions or studying and enjoying the gardens. It was usually both. The two processes became very intertwined and my work quickly became very engrossing. Nicholas's extensive library was at my disposal and I continued to read avidly and widely. The other main strand to the work was a comprehensive analysis of my dreams. Although so many of them were mundane, the 'Big Dreams' were of such momentous significance that I can't imagine how impoverished my life would have been if I hadn't caught them! The thought of some of them still fills me with such energy whenever I touch on them or have a glimpse of an image from them. Where do they come from?

Around this time I also discovered the Wellcome Library[4] on Euston Road and became a Reader to research British Pharmacopoeias and plants used as medicines. In effect, I became a student again, designing my own course. This all tied in well with the work I was doing on the Phytotherapy course and gave it an historical context. In the second year of the course we studied quite a large number of mostly European plants and their uses in modern herbal medicine. But already many of the more holistic approaches to herbalism were being discounted. Leading up to the new schemes of accreditation for herbalists, a huge reductionist programme was taking place and plants were being assessed by individual 'active ingredients' instead of the sum of their many benefits – both physiological and 'Other'. Our course was gearing up to become a B.Sc. university degree course instead of the much loved and cherished brainchild of a pair of dedicated Dutch herbalists and pharmacists – as Dr Hein and Mrs Annette Zealstra were. It thus needed more scientific credibility and test-worthiness. I wanted to go in a contrary direction. The course's approach was to be scientific and reductionist and akin to curing, while I was looking for something psycho-spiritual akin to healing.

Shamanic practices I

One day, sitting in Nicholas's waiting room, I 'idly' picked up a leaflet on shamanism. It was advertising a weekend course in Kew – an 'Introduction to Shamanism'. This was to be an 'experiential course' led by an American anthropologist and trained shaman – Jonathan Horwitz[5]. Since in many ways I was still 'pond-skating' in my initial work with Nicholas, and was deeply attracted to theoretical knowledge, to actually DO some of this work was problematical – emphasising the huge difference between 'knowing about' and 'knowing'. But there was something here that I found compelling, especially the primitive artwork featuring plants and animals on the brochure – and on impulse, I signed up to go.

My first course with Jonathan Horwitz was in a small hall near Kew Gardens station. It was a two-day beginners' course over the period of a weekend. About twenty-five people were present – all sorts: male, female, 'hippy', conventional, flamboyant, introverted, young and old – all standing in a circle, holding hands. Our aim was to learn the basic tool of the shaman – the shamanic Journey. Jonathan was (and is) a wonderful and inspirational teacher. Calmly, he set the scene, explained the technique and its aims and then set us to work. Using techniques to put inhibitions and unhelpful thoughts aside, we set off on our first Journey. That Friday night in a darkened hall, with sage incense burning, drumming, whistling, dancing and rattling, the aim was to leave this 'Ordinary Reality' behind and reach a trance state in which the Spirits' presence became apparent. This was a considerable challenge!

Our first Journey was to find a Spirit Guide to accompany us on all future Journeys – a seemingly simple task. During that thirty-minute Journey, guided by Jonathan's constant drumming, amid the doubts, fears of failure and ridicule, and despair, and then later, optimism, intrigue and fantasy, I made contact with a creature – so commonplace and so beautiful – who has been my Spirit Guide for the last twenty years and with whom I commune in this worldly Ordinary Reality and in the Spiritual Non-Ordinary Reality in a way that brings the two worlds so close together that they can seem to merge. In those days I could never have imagined such a bond being forged.

During that weekend we interspersed Journeying with learning the basics of core shamanic practices and with discussions of outcomes and interpretations. The aim was to invite and make contact with a Spirit Guide, and since so much of shamanic work is about power, a Power Animal to help in this work. The work was carefully paced and the techniques were meticulously described and practised – but all done in a very organic way. As in dream-work, after a Journey, the 'happenings' were recorded as fully as possible and only later was anything discussed or any connection and meaning given to them.

The early courses that I went on with Jonathan were aimed at developing the techniques of Journeying to the three Worlds – the Upper World, the Lower World and the Middle World, and to strengthen relationships with the Spirits. For me, this was no easy task. To connect with the Spirits – or as Jonathan described them, 'bundles of cosmic energy in forms we can recognise' – took me outside my comfort zone. I offered considerable and lasting resistance to it. But the compelling and supporting nature of this 'Spirit-ful' work carried me through. What came later, when the basics were established, was delightfully easy to assimilate, with some amazing outcomes. It was years later that my shamanic work extended to working with plants.

Looking back on those early courses and activities, I realise that my greatest challenge was to overcome huge inhibitions. I already had strong connections with the natural world and could work well with my dreams. In my childhood I believed in (and also believed I saw) fairies. In a Georgia O'Keeffe sort of way, I knew the numinous inner world of flowers: irises, tulips, roses and peonies. During my Catholic upbringing angels were commonplace, and I had my own guardian angel with whom I had a negative as well as a positive relationship. The devil was powerful too and I always felt really sorry for wondrous Lucifer (the Bringer of Light). I also knew that when I looked at birds for a time, they responded. My childhood life in our wonderful garden was Spirit-ful, perfumed and imaginative. Perhaps it was because of this, and my later more 'mature' rejection of most of it in the name of science and the study of the material world, that I feared I was being childish and immature again. The arch-critic in me ridiculed such actions and questioned my mental stability and sanity. So, I needed to overcome these ideas and, like most of the others around me, develop trust – both in Jonathan and the practices – and also to construct a rigour and have an open mind. With time, this has happened.

Becoming a dispenser

Another strand to my London activities that tied in well and influenced me considerably was my interaction with a local herbalist. I responded to an advertisement in a herbal medicine journal looking for a dispenser of herbal tinctures. As his practice was very near where we lived in Islington, I made contact and arranged a meeting in an apartment on a Victorian tenement housing estate in Holborn. I was amazed that such activities could go on in such a location, but it was here that I met a dedicated young French herbalist with two practices in London and in great need of someone to help him dispense the complex mixtures of tinctures that he prescribed for his patients.

Work with Antoine was interesting and meaningful. He used both European and Chinese herbs and was able to combine the two systems of healing effectively. Certainly, the smells of those tinctures made a deep impression on me and I decided to also look at Chinese medicine as a methodology. I started to read a book – 'The Web That Has No Weaver' by Ted Kaptchuk[6]. Here was a comprehensive system of healing (to my mind, far more extensive in its range than contemporary Western medicine) that could effectively treat the human body and condition to bring about healing and wellbeing, and yet could only be transposed onto the system of Western medicine in very few instances. It had definite similarities with ancient Western herbalism in that it related to the Elements of the Earth and human emotions and Spirit. But over time, Western medicine had eliminated these aspects to a great extent. I became intensely interested in this work with Antoine.

Two afternoons a week, I entered his little office on his tenement balcony. I was surrounded by rows of concentrated extracts and tinctures of both Chinese and Western herbs. Everything was meticulously labelled and stored, but conditions were cramped. Working from his treatment notes and prescribed recipes for 'patient-appropriate' medicine, I dispensed complex mixtures of tinctures into 500ml or 1000ml bottles to be posted to or collected by his patients. Gradually I came to recognise the herbal extracts by name, and also by smell. Researching the tinctures, I gradually understood how he was using them and this tied into the theoretical work I was doing on the course. I immersed myself body and spirit in these herbs and came to love them all – especially the Chinese peonies.

The use and efficacy of these herbal tinctures was not governed by the rigours of modern pharmaceutical drug testing. Dosage of these herbal extracts was recommended by a standard text, the 'British Herbal Pharmacopoeia'[7] – a relatively modern edition compiled by a small number of expert herbalists. In many ways, this was causing the reductionist influences on the way herbs were being used. It was a process of standardisation. By contrast, treatment by individual herbalists was often based on the experience of the herbalist. In these cases, the efficacy of these herbs had to be measured empirically – by descriptions of the benefits received and thanks proffered (as in the Breuss Diet booklet as well). Antoine also got these empirical results and noted them, or he would tell me enthusiastically of a remarkable recovery someone had made. Often the treatments took weeks to be effective – far longer than people would expect to wait using allopathic (conventional) treatments. But perhaps this was the nature of healing? For me, there were a lot of question marks. Very often Antoine would have to assess his results by the non-reappearance of his patient!

Overall, I was very impressed by these tinctures and the ways they appeared to work. But there was something about the sameness of those stock bottles and the lack of freshness of the brown preparations that displeased me. They all seemed so far away from the original plants. It was later, on a visit to a leading British tincture producing company – of both Chinese and Western herbs, that I understood the problem. There were bundles of uniformly brown dried herbs from all over the world (and especially China) and vats of plants steeping in alcohol, waiting to be pressed. To my mind they all lacked 'vitality'. Since I had found several of the plants in Chevenoz, I decided to start to cultivate them in the garden and to make tinctures. I used the 'British Herbal Pharmacopoeia'[7] as the standard textbook for recipes and preparation methods. I had also made contact with a leading herbalist in London who ran discussion groups for herbal medicine students. He encouraged me make some high-quality tinctures as he also questioned the quality and purity of some of the existing ones on the market. He suggested I made them with fresh herbs as he considered them to be more powerful.

So I kept myself very busy in London, but in the summer returned to Chevenoz for three months. We had gone there at regular intervals during the spring and I had managed to do what I called 'remedial gardening'. Although plant growth in late May and early June was phenomenal, resulting in weeds up to waist height, the basic layout and plantings were fairly easy to recapture. The Chelsea Physic Garden sold off its surplus plants and I became a habitual buyer. On every trip to France, I had cases and bags of plants – which luckily in those days were accepted by British Airways or Swiss as hand- or hold-luggage. Within the family I was called the 'Bag Lady'. These plants mostly thrived in their new environment, growing larger and more luxuriantly than their London relatives.

I worked hard and in September returned to London, satisfied that real progress had been made with the herb garden and plantings of important medicinal herbs. I was now ready for more research and input of ideas, and became very interested in the activities of the Scientific and Medical Network (SMN)[8]. The organisation, formed in 1973, describes itself as:

'a leading international forum for people engaged in creating a new worldview for the 21st century. The Network brings together scientists, doctors, psychologists, engineers, philosophers, complementary practitioners and other professionals, and has Members in more than thirty countries.'

The following spring, I attended their 'Mystics' and Scientists' Conference' in Winchester. Here I met a large number of science-related people with a will to come together and attempt to bridge the gap between science and spirituality. In particular, I appreciated the book reviews in their magazine, 'Network', by David Lorimer (Programme Director). David's capacity to source and review so many books on so many themes was impressive. He introduced me to a vast library of books to widen my horizons and challenge my ideas. I was an active member of SMN for many years and made some interesting friendships and acquaintances.

So during this time I was an avid reader. Besides Jung, I studied Freud and others, and then extended my reading to Marie Louise von Franz and second-generation Jungians like James Hillman, Marion Woodman, June Singer and Barbara Hannah. A book that had a profound effect on me was 'Saving the Appearances' by Owen Barfield[9]. I was very drawn to his ideas of Consciousness and how we make sense of our reality – covering our use of images, symbols, idols and language. These ideas were especially important in interpretation of my dreams and in Non-Ordinary Reality, in shamanic work. The book gave my new ideas a basis and a coherence. I also read widely from Nicholas's library and again I was able to bring together aspects of herbal medicine and a more psychological and spiritual approach to life.

It was only during the following year's study that I began to have real difficulties with the Phytotherapy course. I was still dispensing for Antoine and watched his blending of Chinese and Western herbs – with what seemed like a predominance of Chinese herbs. I was also observing sessions at a herbal practice in South London and saw the number of patients presenting illnesses for which Western medicine could offer them no solutions – what I regarded as emotional/psycho-spiritual problems, and also chronic illnesses. It was beginning to occur to me that the Chinese medicine model was more able to deal with these problems than the Western herbalism system. And this was strange, as ancient Western herbalism had also seemed able to treat the 'whole' person – with body ailments and ailments of the Soul and emotions and also of the Spirit. It was these latter conditions that were being reduced in modern Western herbalism – for instance, to nervous diseases, or requiring stimulus or calming – i.e. being given a simple physiological basis. The practice was being subjected to separation and reductionism as allopathic medicine had been. It no longer treated the whole person.

In my Jungian work with Nicholas, I was delving deep into my dreams and developing my own symbolism for their interpretation. I was becoming more willing to balance logical and rational thought processes with my feelings (physically, intuitively and emotionally) about the situation or decision. This was an advance for someone who, by training, had been taught that thinking and logic were the processes leading to knowledge. I was also working with Jonathan and studying different aspects of shamanic practice, so often I would be judging my own wellbeing by my Power levels and intensity of Spirit. In particular I was aware of connections – whether synchronistic events (two of us picking up the telephone to speak to each other at the same time) or something in Nature appearing in front of me as I was talking to someone about it, etc. These things could be given a rational explanation – by chance, by being subjective rather than objective. But they could also have other explanations if perceived in a different way. I became very open to new ways of knowing.

Towards the end of my second year on the Phytotherapy course I wrote an essay that I considered to be a statement of my current thinking concerning the psycho-spiritual aspects of illness and the healing process. The subject matter was the interactions of Man and the Environment. I wrote a very long essay, well researched and referenced, and I was satisfied that it answered the question. I included both ecological and shamanic ideas of connection. Eventually my marked essay was returned with a grade C+ (definitely the first ever) and an irate comment across the top page that I could have omitted the first seven pages and should have included the effect of deodorants on human skin! Clearly I was way off course, according to this tutor. In later discussion with him, he told me that my way of thinking was not part of the scientifically based coursework, nor the direction in which herbal medicine was heading. This was what I had suspected for some time. After long deliberations, reluctantly I resigned from the course. But, still very committed to using herbs for healing and seeing myself as a dispenser of beautiful herbs, there was another, if not preferable, way forward. An advertisement in the Herbal Times for a Herbal Study tour in Provence that summer by a leading aromatherapist, Gabriel Mojay, was part of it. Researching him, I read his book 'Aromatherapy for Healing the Spirit'[10]. In this book, besides describing his philosophy and where his ideas come from, he wrote treatises for around thirty essential oils. For each plant he described the whole spectrum of properties – biochemical components, Western pharmacological properties, a description of the plant to include its nature, and how it could affect the human psyche in the healing process. It also outlined a systematic approach to utilising the psychological benefits of essential oils according to the body-mind relationships of Oriental medicine. So, like Antoine, Gabriel was able to use aspects of both traditional Western herbalism and Chinese medicine in describing the healing properties of plants.

I applied to go on the Provence study tour immediately. In the hope that this would satisfy my enthusiasm for a holistic approach to herbalism, I also applied to study with Gabriel Mojay on his one-year Traditional Herbal Medicine and Aromatherapy course starting in London that autumn. The study tour was inspirational and informative – in the Maritime Alps, not so far from my garden in Chevenoz, studying the native flora, visiting distilleries in the lavender-growing region, picking *Calendula* flowers for herbal preparations, seeing a small-scale still in action, visiting a Dutch cooperative of herb growers and a company making beautiful herbal products, I could see my way forward clearly!

The Aromatherapy course was held in Regent's College in Regent's Park. Gabriel was principal of The Institute of Traditional Herbal Medicine and Aromatherapy[11] and had amassed excellent staff to assist him in teaching the course. Each weekend, around twenty-four students gathered for intensive lectures and massage tuition. During that year we learned a system of acupressure massage using essential oils therapeutically. Alongside this practice, we studied the oils systematically – their preparation, their biochemical properties and then their therapeutic properties. The work was exacting.

From this course we also learned about basic still design and techniques to prepare high-quality essential oils. So I was en route to designing my own still. The quality of the teaching and lecture materials and the presentation of the whole course were excellent. We also had massage partners and practised both acupressure massage techniques and the use of different oils during the week. My partner was a young Japanese woman whose understanding of Qi energy and Chinese medicine was grounded and deep, and who had very strong thumbs. She was a blessing to me in so many ways.

By the time the course ended our five years in London were drawing to a close. I had a few more months to take advantage of the opportunities that London offered before I immersed myself into my future project of growing the highest quality herbs for herbal preparations to be used by herbalists and aromatherapists in the UK. In effect I would become an arch-dispenser and also a distiller. I had studied enough and seen enough to realise that Chevenoz was ideal as a place to grow the herbs, with conditions and facilities to prepare dried herbs, infused oils, floral waters and essential oils. I was well equipped and motivated to do these things.

During that last year, I searched out future markets for my products and sourced equipment for my preparations. I continued to research possible products and in this regard, I turned to that fountain of information in the Wellcome Library. Their collection of British Pharmacopoeias and also French and German ones was invaluable, giving botanical information as well as cultivation methods, preparation methods, and concentrations and dosages to use. Doing this research made me realise how very quickly – within a space of perhaps two or three generations – we in the UK had lost the healing connection with plants. Indigenous plants had been replaced by exotic plants from the colonies and distant markets, and then later, those plants had been replaced by products of the chemical and pharmaceutical industries – the poisonous compounds of arsenic and mercury, the antibiotics, and finally the development of the wide spectrum of synthetic drugs that now comprises the modern pharmaceutical industry. Interestingly, the French Pharmacopoeias – and the German ones, to a lesser extent – kept their plant preparations much longer than we did, and many of them are still in use.

My searches for equipment led me to a delightful supplier of glassware just south of the Thames under the arches of London Bridge Station. Its name was French Flint and Orm Co. after the newly invented French flint glass that they started to import in 1824. For around two hundred years, they had been suppliers of high-quality glassware to the food, pharmaceutical and cosmetic industries. It was here, in their dingy showrooms and warehouse, that I spent time looking at and selecting the glassware to use in my preparations. Already at this time I had the concept of high energy – which I would later call 'vitality' – that I wanted to preserve in my plant products. I felt that glass would be the best material to work with. I selected smaller quantities of glass jars and bottles for finished preparations and also larger quantities of 4.2litre and 1.7litre wide-necked glass jars for my infused oil preparations. These were all delivered to Chevenoz. A research laboratory was closing down and I contacted them to see if I could purchase some of their fine and old-fashioned laboratory glassware. A visit later, I drove away with a car boot full of the most wonderful large round-bottomed flasks for distillation, measuring burettes and pipettes, beakers, measuring cylinders of all sizes and separating funnels – all the classic tools of my ancient trade. Besides these, I got German 'midwife scales' accurately weighing up to 10kg with a flat bed ideal for weighing babies and herbs, a large guillotine for chopping herbs, tripods and clamps. I had, in effect, purchased a mini laboratory.

There were other parts of this jigsaw to fashion but some of that would come later. I made contact with some possible future markets for my products and I was constantly aware that I needed to find like-minded people who would assess the products for their therapeutic properties on a wide scale. I found two London herbalists who were interested in my future tinctures; I found skin cream makers interested in my infused oils; Joe Nasr of Avicenna Herbs[12] became a long-term recipient of the infused oils; and I made invaluable contact with Charles Wells of Essentially Oils[13], who took an interest in what I was trying to do and arranged assays and analyses of my essential oils and floral waters. Later he bought large quantities of many of these.

My last area of research was to source high-quality seeds of known provenance to grow. Chelsea Physic Garden was my first port of call; also Jeremy Cherfas, who had developed a delightful company on the Somerset Levels growing less well-known vegetables and herbs and then selling the seeds[14]. I then needed to find lavender and rosemary cuttings/plantlets for cultivars well suited to my growing conditions. This was a longer-term project that took several years to fulfill.

I was then ready to start '*Le Grand Oeuvre*' in Chevenoz. It was never intended to be a huge and successful business – much more a pilot and research project, a process to design and create a range of beautiful herbal products to heal bodies and Souls and an adventure and experiment on myself.

Chapter notes

1.   Chelsea Physic Garden, 66 Royal Hospital Road, Chelsea, London SW3 4HS. https://www.chelseaphysicgarden.co.uk

2.   Minter, Susan. The Apothecaries' Garden – A History of the Chelsea Physic Garden. 2000. Sutton Publishing ltd. ISBN 0 7509 2449 7

3.   Burne-Jones, Edward. The Flower Book. 1994. Taschen Verlag GmbH. ISBN 3-8228-9043-X

4.   Wellcome Library, 183 Euston Road, London, NW1 2BE. https://wellcomelibrary.org/

5.   Jonathan Horwitz, Scandinavian Center for Shamanic Studies. www.shamanism.dk

6.   Kaptchuk, Ted. The Web that has no Weaver – Understanding Chinese Medicine. 2000. Contemporary Books/McGraw-Hill. ISBN 0-8092-2840-8

7.   British Herbal Pharmacopoeia 1983. Published by British Herbal Medicine Association. ISBN 0 903032 07 4

8.   Scientific & Medical Network. https://explore.scimednet.org

9.   Barfield, Owen. Saving the Appearances. Second edition. 1988. Wesleyan University Press. ISBN 0-8195-6205-x (paperback)

10.   Mojay, Gabriel. Aromatherapy for Healing the Spirit. 1997. Gaia Books Ltd. London. ISBN 978 0 89281 887 8

11.   Institute of Traditional Herbal Medicine & Aromatherapy (ITHMA). 2018. www.aromatherapy-studies.com

12.   Nasr, Joe. Founder of Avicenna Herbs. http://www.avicennaherbs.co.uk/

13.   Wells, Charles and Jan. Founders of Essentially Oils. Chipping Norton, Oxon. No longer operational.

14.   Cherfas, Jeremy. Formerly founder of Future Foods, now a science communicator. www.jeremycherfas.net

Emblem of the Apothecaries of Laon – the serpent and the rod

'Health depends on being in harmony with our Souls.'
Dr Edward Bach

'We still do not know one thousandth of one per cent of
what nature has revealed to us.'
Albert Einstein

IV

Plants as medicines

Plants have been used in healing throughout the world and until quite recently in the West, medicine was seen as sacred knowledge. The World Health Organization logo represents the Rod of Asclepius – a snake-entwined staff – over the Earth, contained within the laurel wreath of victory. The Apothecaries of Laon (a town in north east France) have used a similar motif since the Middle Ages. The Greek god Asclepius was one of Apollo's sons and with him shared the title *Paean*, meaning 'the healer' (the plant species *Paeonia* – peony – is named after them and is used extensively in Chinese medicine). The staff is the rod of connection between the gods and mankind and is used in this instance to strike out disease. It is akin to the magician's wand. The snake represents the powerful life force and spirituality that brings about healing. Honouring this idea, sacred snakes were always kept in healing temples known as Asclepeions, where the sick and injured congregated. In these temples, sacrifice, ritual and offerings to the gods were all part of the healing process.

World healing systems

With the exception of modern Western medicine, the concepts of connection and balance have always been central to these systems. Whether American Indian, Mediaeval European, Islamic, Ayurvedic or Chinese (to name important ones), the systems have sought to find imbalances or patterns of disharmony within an individual. A third component, a force or power, can be invoked by healer/priest/magician/shaman who has at his/her disposal a 'medicine bag' of herbs/minerals/artefacts to be used in healing. For all these systems that have an energetic basis, the modern term 'energy medicine' has evolved. In it, every individual has a unique make-up or constitution that determines the innate strengths and weaknesses the person is born with, and thus the types of disease he/she is prone to. A sick person presents a terrain (which is his/her general condition or imbalance) and it is here, and not at the symptom level, that treatment is effective.

Plants have always played a central role in this therapeutic process. This has been recorded in texts from Ancient Egypt; Greek and Roman texts (e.g. those of the Roman army general Dioscorides, who identified many healing plants for use on battle grounds); later, from the Islamic world and the work of the Persian physician and alchemist Avicenna; and even later, from those of the Swiss botanist and physician Paracelsus. Common to many of these highly developed and complex systems is the idea that a plant can be defined energetically – as Hot, or its polarity Cold, thus describing the Warming and Cooling capacities of the plant, and also Moist or Dry. By matching the energetic profile of the plant with the imbalance within the person, healing can be initiated.

The Correspondences in mediaeval herbalism

Traditional early mediaeval European herbalism was based on the polarities Hot and Cold and Moist and Dry. These were considered to be the first principles of Nature, and the four Elements of Fire, Water, Air and Earth, which make up all matter, were thought to manifest two primary qualities (e.g. Fire was Hot and Dry). The model had three central concepts: balance, connection and Spirit. Its central tenet was that everything was connected. A human being was seen in the context of its environment and as a microcosm of the heavens: 'As above, so below'. Highly influenced by ancient Greek philosophy and Aristotle in particular, the model was based on a life-giving principle or vital Spirit called *pneuma* (meaning 'air', 'breath' or 'Spirit'). This was the Western equivalent of *prana* (in Ayurvedic medicine) and Qi (in Chinese medicine) and was drawn into the body as life-giving air and sucked from the lungs to the pumping heart. Here it mixed with the 'light' portions of the blood flowing through the heart and formed the *pneuma*, or vital Spirit, which then coursed through the body. Culpeper called this *pneuma* the 'Breath of God' which infused the whole body with Spirit and also balanced the four Humours within an individual – the liquids Blood, Phlegm, Yellow Bile and Black Bile. These governed a person's constitution and health. The Humours were governed by organs in the body and influenced the personalities: whether sanguine, phlegmatic, choleric or melancholic. These Humours also related outwards to the four Elements. Plants

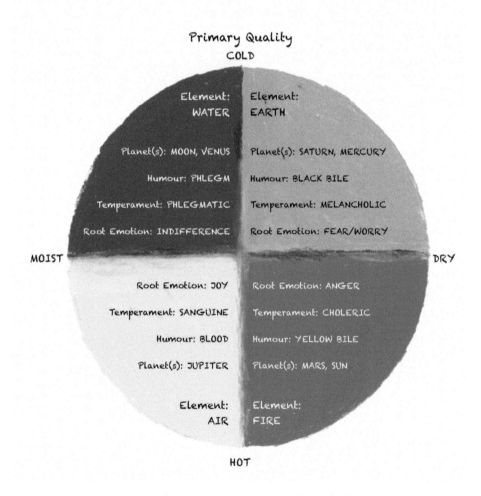

The Correspondences in Mediaeval Herbalism
(according to Culpeper)

Primary Quality
COLD

Element: WATER

Element: EARTH

Planet(s): MOON, VENUS

Planet(s): SATURN, MERCURY

Humour: PHLEGM

Humour: BLACK BILE

Temperament: PHLEGMATIC

Temperament: MELANCHOLIC

Root Emotion: INDIFFERENCE

Root Emotion: FEAR/WORRY

MOIST

DRY

Root Emotion: JOY

Root Emotion: ANGER

Temperament: SANGUINE

Temperament: CHOLERIC

Humour: BLOOD

Humour: YELLOW BILE

Planet(s): JUPITER

Planet(s): MARS, SUN

Element: AIR

Element: FIRE

HOT

Diagram of the Correspondences in mediaeval herbalism

played the important role in this connection, having the capacity to correct imbalances between the Humours and the macrocosm of the heavens.

These ideas underlay herbalism until the Middle Ages, as is seen in the important herbals of those times (e.g. the Physicians of Myddfai[1], John Gerard[2], Nicholas Culpeper[3]). In his herbal, Culpeper developed this idea a stage further and related each herb to a heavenly body or planet that governed it, a constellation and an Element (e.g. St John's wort (*Hypericum perforatum*) was ruled by the Sun and was under the influence of the constellation Leo and the Element Fire).

Following from later ideas of the Renaissance, Descartes and Francis Bacon, studies of the anatomy of the human body and the discovery of the circulation of the blood by William Harvey, the human body was seen to be a 'machine' separate from the mind, which had spiritual connection. The concept of *pneuma* lost its importance as the balancing and healing connection between man and the cosmos. This separation continues to this day but the theme has been revisited, especially by those searching for an energetic or spiritual basis for modern medicine. A recent description of these ideas and the ancient relationship between herbs, the planets and the Elements can be seen in Scott Cunningham's deeply researched books: 'The Encyclopedia of Magical Herbs'[4] and 'Magical Aromatherapy'[5]. Here 'magic' is defined as *'the practice of causing change through the use of powers as yet not defined or accepted by science'*.

Although these publications reach out to the 'New Age' market, they nevertheless reach back to much traditional knowledge and incorporate the concepts of correspondences and connection between all living things. It's my belief that the Power 'as yet not defined or accepted by science' is an energy/Qi/ *prana*/*pneuma*/vitality, or even grace (which could be the Christian equivalent – which gave the saints halos as an indication of God's blessing). As yet, we do not have a scientific hypothesis to describe it, or an instrument to measure this force that permeates the universe.

The Correspondences in Chinese medicine

Chinese medicine of around 200 A.D. as documented in the text 'The Pharmacopoeia of the Heavenly Husbandman' lists 300 plants used at that time. In Chinese medicine to this day, many herbs are used in combinations specific to an individual's needs and 'disposition'. These complex blends aim to restore balance of Yin and Yang states within the body.

The Correspondences of the Five Elements in Chinese Medicine[6]

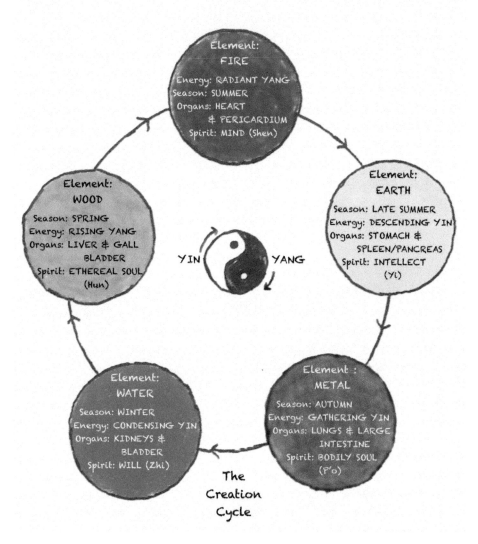

Diagram of the Correspondences of the five Elements in Chinese medicine[6]

This Yin-Yang concept is based on the polarity of opposites. They are neither forces nor material entities but are ways of describing how things function in relationship to each other and to the universe. They describe the dynamic process of change. Qualities are attributed to both Yin and Yang: Yin is more substantial and material, Yang more unsubstantial and immaterial; Yin condensing, slower, descending, cooler, more moist, and Yang expanding, faster, rising, warmer, drier. As with all polarities, neither can exist without the other. An aspect of Yang is Qi – the universal force connecting the universe, the body and the mind. Within the body it is channeled along lines, or meridians, bringing balance to energetic excesses or deficiencies, to heat and cold, to dryness and damp within the organs of the body. In this holistic system there are correspondences between the organs, the Emotions and then the Spirit concepts of Qi (energy), Shen (the Spirit), Bo (Bodily Soul), Po (Ethereal Soul) and Zhi (the Will) – every aspect of what is considered being 'human'. Herbs in this system have the capacity to tone, to strengthen Yin or Yang in the various organs, including the Blood, and to heat or to cool in order to create harmonious balance. Importantly, this balance reflects the relationships not just of the individual within the environment, but of the Elements, the Seasons, the whole of creation.

Although the terminology of these two systems is markedly different, they both depend on balance and connection and the presence of a vital and dynamic force emanating from 'on high' and permeating everything. Good health depends on this balance, both of the organs of the physical body and the state of the emotions and Spirit. Both these medical systems are recognised and well-documented in the Western world even though they have few parallels in Western medicine – other than the concept of balance and how it can be achieved within the physical body. The concept of physiological homoeostasis (the concentrations of molecules in biochemical pathways staying the same) and feedback loops, which can correct imbalance, involves only the physical body and not the emotional and spiritual states of the individual.

Of other world healing traditions the most ancient is Ayurveda (Sanskrit for 'the knowledge of life and longevity'). It has been practised in the Indian sub-continent, since the 4th century BCE. Classical Ayurvedic texts describe how knowledge of healing was passed from the gods to the sages and thence to physicians. Ancient texts describe over 700 plants used as foods and as medicines. Again, the basis of this practice is balance – of the Humours, or *Dhosas*, of Wind (*Vata*), Bile (*Pitta*) and Phlegm (*Kapha*) in the human body.

Each *Dhosa* contains all five Elements of Water, Fire, Air, Earth and Ether – which again need to be in balance. Imbalance causes disease. A vital principle or life force called *Prana* originates from the Sun and connects the Elements within the human body. This *Prana* can be inward moving, outward moving or circulating – known in yoga as the Three Breaths. Within the body, *Prana* moves through channels called the *Nadi* and is the dynamic force that causes the balance or imbalance – thus determining health.

Shamanic perspectives of connection

But another system, traditional shamanism of Aboriginal people, involves ancient techniques to achieve and maintain wellbeing and healing of individuals, within communities and for the environment. Central to all these belief systems is that everything is connected. Their mostly undocumented methods – from cultures differing in so many aspects of life and environment – have remarkable similarities.

In earlier times it had been the role of anthropologists to record and interpret these methods for western cultures. In such an account, written in the 1950's, the native tribes of the Colombian Northwest Amazon rainforests believed that illness was a direct consequence of an individual upsetting a certain aspect of ecological balance[7]. The delicate balance between the natural environment, society and the individual meant that any disturbance, however small, affected the whole. Such beliefs and practices were common to many indigenous populations. More recently, within surviving populations, especially Native Americans, individuals have documented their practices and communicated directly with Westerners to explain their belief systems and practices regarding the environment, community and spirituality[8].

The American anthropologist Michael Harner lived with and studied many of these cultures. From the cultural similarities he had researched, he developed 'core' shamanic practices, i.e. those practices common to many different indigenous populations. Later, he created the Foundation for Shamanic Studies in Connecticut, NY to teach these methods in a modern context to Westerners. In his book ' The Way of the Shaman'[9] he describes how these people use highly developed 'non-technological' aspects of the human mind that extended to other realities, and give different explanations of both disease and healing. Although the language is quite different from the two Correspondence systems cited above, the basis of all these practices is balance and how it can be disturbed. In shamanic terms, this is caused by energy loss (described as Soul or Power loss) or energy gain (described as an Invasion by a malevolent Spirit) – both events causing ill health and needing to be rectified. Plants are used extensively in these cultures both to alter states of Consciousness in order to increase awareness and knowledge and as medicines. These plants are often identified in trance state – as seen in practices of the Native Americans[10]. It will be to these explanations that I return on several occasions later (see Chapter VII).

In other cultures, over 800 plant species are listed in South African herbals of the Zulu, Xhosa and Sotho tribes. Indonesian herbal practices are ancient and use up to 3000 different plant species. The World Health Organization still strongly supports traditional medicine and assesses that 80% of the world's population depends mainly on traditional and indigenous systems of health care using herbal remedies.

This very brief comparative account of healing systems in different cultures and times in human history only touches on their similarities in order to emphasise the difference between them and our system of modern Western medicine and surgery. After so long, the Cartesian separation of Mind and Matter in Western philosophy in the late 17th century has resulted in a mechanistic and material description of our modern world, our bodies and how we heal ourselves. In particular, we have turned away from plants and a deeper connection with them, either magical/shamanic, energetic or based on traditional knowledge. Instead of considering herbs as our healers which are in close connection with the Elements and the Power of the universe, and using herbal medicines close to their natural state according to tradition, we have taken another approach.

The Hippocratic Oath, sworn by all newly qualified physicians in the Western world, until the mid-20th century started with the appeal:

'I swear by Apollo, the Healer, by Asclepius, by Hygieia, by Panacea, and by all the gods and goddesses, making them my witnesses, that I will carry out, according to my ability and judgement, this oath and this indenture...'

But in the 1960s, the wording was changed to require *'Utmost respect for Human life from its beginning'*, making it an oath no longer taken before the gods, but before people. This was a highly significant change. Besides removing this element from the healing process, in Western medicine, gradually plants have been removed as well.

Chapter notes

1. Breverton, Terry. Physicians of Myddfai Cures and remedies of the Mediaeval World 2012 ISBN 978-0-9574894-1-7

2. Gerard's Herbal. The History of Plants. Edited by Marcus Woodward 1994. Published by Senate, an imprint of Studio Editions Ltd. London. ISBN 1 85958 051 3

3. Culpeper, Nicholas. Culpeper's Complete Herbal 1992 Bloomsbury Books under licence from Omega Books. ISBN 1 85471 140 7

4. Cunningham, Scott: Encyclopedia of Magical Herbs. 1997 Llewellyn Publications, Minnesota, USA ISBN 0-87542-122-9

5. Cunningham, Scott: Magical Aromatherapy. 1996 Llewellyn Publications, Minnesota, USA

6. Mojay, Gabriel: Aromatherapy for Healing the Spirit 1997 Gaia Books Ltd, London ISBN 978 0 89281 887 8

7. Reichel-Dolmatoff, Gerardo: Rainforest Shamans 1997 Green Books Ltd, Totnes, Devon. ISBN 0 9527302 4 3

8. Colorado, Apela: Woman between the Worlds: seeing through the eyes of Indigenous people. 2012 Hay House UK Ltd. ISBN 1848501196

9. Harner. Michael, The Way of the Shaman 3rd edition, 1990 Harper & Row ISBN 0-06-250373-1 also https://www.youtube.com/watch?v=fbGbp-QEjCk

10. Kimmerer, Robin Wall: Braiding Sweetgrass: Indigenous Wisdom, Scientific Knowledge and the Teachings of Plants. 2013 published by Milkweed Editions ISBN 978-1-57131-335-5

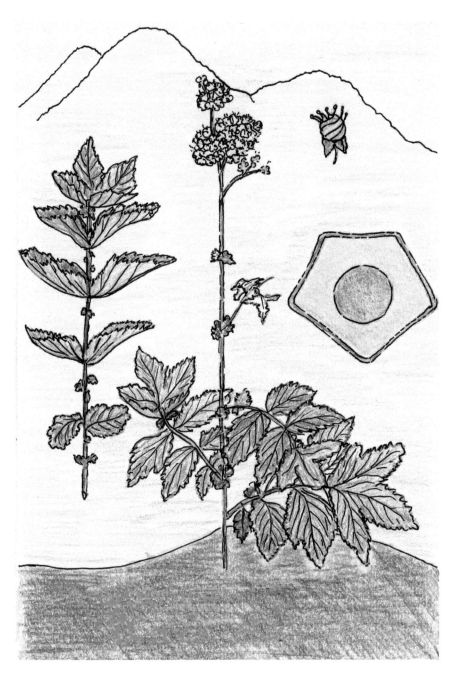

Meadowsweet (Filipendula ulmaria – formerly Spiraea),
which contains the chemical basis of aspirin

V

The separations: from traditional medicine to the development of modern pharmaceuticals

*'Any spiritual practice that we do, since it accumulates
'merit', will help prolong our lives and bring good health.
A good practitioner, through the inspiration and power
of his or her practice, comes to feel psychologically,
emotionally and spiritually whole and this is both the
greatest source of healing and the strongest protection
against illness.'*

SOGYAL RINPOCHE, 'THE TIBETAN BOOK OF LIVING AND DYING'

From the apothecaries to the spicers and the grocers

It is a long and tortuous path from the traditional medicine of the mediaeval British Isles to where we are today. In the early days, the herb gatherers (predominantly 'wise women' and later sometimes branded as 'witch doctors') had direct contact with the living plants and their habitats. They were the foragers and the collectors who knew what to look for, where to look and where to find it, and also how to protect what they knew was valuable for their livelihoods and their health. They brought their wares to the apothecaries. The word 'apothecary' comes from the ancient Greek word meaning 'storehouse'. Apothecaries were places for storing wine, spices and herbs. In late 13th century London, the apothecaries, alongside the pepperers, were members of the livery company – the grocers. These traders dealt with supplies and sold *en gros* (wholesale). Later, the spicers joined with the apothecaries to become the spicer-apothecaries selling spices, confectionery, perfumes, spiced wines, herbs and drugs – which they compounded and dispensed to the public. In 1617, the apothecaries split off from the grocers and by Royal Charter became their own Worshipful Society of Apothecaries of London[1]. They acquired the guesthouse of the Dominican Priory of the Blackfriars – now called Apothecaries' Hall. For centuries up until 1922, the Society of Apothecaries manufactured and sold medicinal and pharmaceutical products at the Hall.

Traditional medicine between the 17th and 19th centuries relied on plants – known as 'simples' and the apothecaries used them for treatments in many different forms – as dried herbs or parts; as extracts of these in water, alcohol or oils; as essential oils and waters; and as formulations into unguents, ointments, liniments, creams, powders, pills and lozenges. These classic preparations still featured in the British Pharmacopoeias of the 20th century.

The collecting expeditions of the Chelsea Physic Garden were going on around the time of the Industrial Revolution and a time of great sociological change. The chemical industry was developing ways of using Earth's abundant resources: industrial processes of metal extractions, syntheses of products for large-scale industrial use and, in particular from the point of view of medicines, the development of the aniline dyes. In 1856, while trying to synthesise quinine, a British student, William Henry Perkin, discovered mauveine, which became the first synthetic dye at that time suitable to dye silk 'mauve'. This led to the development of a massive dye industry, especially in Germany and in Basel in Switzerland. This industry later produced disinfectants and antibiotics and, considerably later in 1908, sulphanilamide was synthesised – the first agent to exhibit broad-spectrum activity against systemic bacterial disease. These products had profound implications. This was the beginning of the pharmaceutical industry with its overwhelming influence on Western medicine. What followed was a major disconnection between health and plants.

In 1858, the Medical Act of the United Kingdom was passed and gave rise to the development of the British Pharmacopoeia (BP), first published in 1864[2]. It contained a comprehensive list of all plants and substances in use by pharmacists throughout the UK and replaced the individual pharmacopoeias of London, Dublin and Edinburgh. In it were descriptions of the plants and also their formulations in common medical use. New editions of the British Pharmacopoeia were published at intervals until 1993. With each new edition, a list was issued of additions, and also of deletions of entries no longer considered part of the BP. Little reason for these deletions was given. Later, in 1903, the Council of the Pharmaceutical Society decided to address this problem and to produce a reference book giving guidance on prescribing and dispensing medicines throughout the British Empire. The first edition was published in 1907, entitled the 'British Pharmaceutical Codex' (BPC)[3] and further editions were published regularly. Early editions were designed to supplement information in the BP by providing information on the actions and uses of drugs. They also provided formulae and standards of materials not included in the BP. In 1972, as a result of the 1968 Medicines Act, the General Medical Council recommended that there should be one source of information and the BPC was discontinued. The next edition was 'The Pharmaceutical Codex' published in 1979, and this was later replaced by 'Martindale: The Extra Pharmacopoeia' and the 'British National Formulary'.

While studying herbal medicine, I came across all these publications at the Wellcome Library, and as I delved deeper, I realised that over a period of around 130 years, plants were systematically removed from these volumes and inorganic salts, synthetic molecules and very different formulations had taken their place.

As a summary, the 1864 British Pharmacopoeia was made up of around 60% plant-based entries. Of these original 138 plant species, 48 were native British plants/cultivated in Britain or in very common use. They were formulated traditionally as herbs, tinctures, oils, infusions and syrups, etc. From this starting point, I was in a position to chart the fate of these plants over time. At intervals over a period of 126 years, fifteen new editions of the British Pharmacopoeia were published – each with additions and deletions of formulations. I could thus survey the plant deletions of each subsequent pharmacopoeia as seen below.

Deletions of plant-based formulations from British Pharmacopoeias 1867–1993

Year	Number of deleted entries
1867	3
1885	11
1914	104
1932	187
1948	59
1953	56
1958	24
1963	18
1968	7
1973	9
1980	8
1988	21
1993	134
Total	521 entries

Note: a plant species was sometimes represented in the BP in several different formulations.

There were occasional additions as well, but these were insignificant compared with the systematic deletions of plant formulations. This research charts the huge changes in the British Pharmacopoeia that were taking place during the 20th century. From 1885 until 1993, there were 521 deletions of plant-based formulations. In 1885, some very toxic and important European plants in various formulations were removed, and in the 1914 edition, 104 different formulations of plant products representing fifty-seven plant species were removed. This was followed in 1932 by the removal of 187 entries of plant-based formulations, representing 101 plant species. Formulations of plant species were being replaced by other formulations and ways of treatments, and also by many non-plant-based products. There were a considerable number of additions to the BP but very few of these were plant-based ones. The plants that remained were predominantly the most potent ones (e.g. those containing glycosides, from which important modern drugs used in cardiac disease and treatment were synthesised). The final edition of the British Pharmacopoeia in this form was in 1993. This edition contained fifty-two plant entries. As shown in the table below, twenty-three of them were significant biologically active entries. The others were predominantly pharmaceutical aids like fillers, gums, starches, oils and flavours.

List of important plants/extracts in index of BP 1993

Index name	Species name	Properties/use
Acacia*	Acacia Senegal L.	laxative
Alexandrian Senna fruit	Cassia senna L.	stimulant laxative
Anise & Oil*	Pimpinella anisum L.	carminative & flavour
Barbados Aloes*	Aloe barbadensis Miller	laxative
Belladonna herb*	Atropa belladonna L	antispasmodic
Cardamom & oil*	Elettaria cardamomum Maton	carminative & flavour
Cascara	Rhamnus purshianus DC	stimulant laxative
Chinchona bark*	Chinchona pubescens Vahl.	bitter
Clove*	Syzygium aromaticum (L.) Merrill	carminative & flavour
Digitalis leaf*	Digitalis purpurea L.	anti-inflammatory & analgesic
Fig*	Ficus carica L.	demulcent
Gentian*	Gentiana lutea L.	bitter
Hyoscyamus* Leaf	Hyoscyamus niger L.	antispasmodic
Ipecacuanha	Cephaelis ipecacuanha (Brot.) A. Rich	expectorant, emetic

Ispaghula husk	*Plantago ovata Forssk.*	anti-diarrhoeal; bulk-forming laxative
Linseed*	*Linum usitatissimum L.*	demulcent
Opium*	*Papaver somniferum L.*	narcotic analgesic
Rhatany root*	*Krameria triandra Ruiz & Pavon*	astringent
Rhubarb*	*Rheum officinale Baillon*	laxative
Senega root*	*Polygala senega L.*	expectorant
Squill*	*Drimia maritima (L.) Stearn*	expectorant
Stramonium Leaf*	*Datura stramonium L.*	antispasmodic
Valerian*	*Valeriana officinalis L.*	sedative

23 entries
* denotes presence in BP 1864

A detailed account of this research is documented in Appendix 1, Tables I-VIII:

I.   Plant species present in the British Pharmacopoeia 1864
II.   Native British plant species in Table I
III.   Formulations of plants in Table I
IV.   List of British Pharmacopoeia deletions from 1867 to 1993 (arranged chronologically)
V.   List of British Pharmacopoeia deletions from 1867 to 1993 (arranged alphabetically)
VI.   Number of deletions from each British Pharmacopoeia between 1858 and 1993
VII.   Remaining plants/extracts in the index of BP 1993
VIII. For comparison, I have also included plant entries in the French Pharmacopoeia between 1818 and 1937

These tables can also be found at www.apothecaryplants.org.uk

Since my original investigation was to see the relevance to modern Western medicine of plants I intended to grow and products I was planning to make, important deletions included juniper oil and spirit of juniper; spirit and tincture of lavender; rose oil, water and cream of *Rosa damascena* and the infusion, syrup and petals of *Rosa gallica*. In 1958, lavender oil was removed from the BP.

I spent a long time perusing these old books and besides the analysis, I became acutely aware of the ongoing trend of removing plants from our national healing pharmacy. As our knowledge of them and our dependence on them waned, plants were losing a deep significance in our culture and in our psyches. This was the major disconnection. Plants were no longer the basis of our British pharmacy, as they had been replaced by inorganic substances and synthetic chemicals manufactured by the pharmaceutical industry. Although these companies were often interested in medicinal plants and synthesised their active ingredients, these were to be tested in the allopathic drug model of single active ingredients. This is very different from the holistic effects of a herbal treatment with many biological actions. Thus the nature of healing changed intrinsically.

The roots of modern herbal medicine

But alongside all this activity of deletions of plant entries and standardisation and regulation to produce the British Pharmacopoeia, British herbalists were still active, although separate from mainstream medicine. The National Institute of Medical Herbalists[4] was established in 1864 by a small group of herbalists in the north of England. They have since become the established body for describing and maintaining standards of practice for herbalists throughout the UK.

Most herbalists would agree that a herb acts in its entirety, working on the body in many different ways, all of which contribute to the healing process and general health. Nevertheless, different plants can be categorised by their most characteristic modes of action (as is done with all Western medicines), and thus can be grouped together in a 'natural pharmacy' to aid prescriptions. There are many categories but the chief ones are:

Category	Mode of action	Plant e.g.
Anti-spasmodic	To ease spasms or cramps in muscle	Chamomile

Aperient/Laxative	To relieve constipation	Fig, Sorrel
Astringent	To produce mucilage to tone smooth muscle e.g. of Alimentary Canal	Rose, Blackberry leaves
Aromatics	To aid digestion, to disinfect the respiratory tract	Peppermint, Ginger, Fennel
Alterative	To help support the body's immune system	*Echinacea*
Adaptogen	To help the body restore balance, withstand stress	Holy Basil
Bitters	To stimulate digestion and secretion of gastric juices	Dandelion
Carminative	To relieve flatulence	Cardamom, Caraway
Calmative	To relieve muscle tension and spasms	Chamomile, Valerian, Lavender
Cardiac tonic	To regulate the smooth rhythm of the heart	Hawthorn berries and flowers
Demulcent	To coat and protect the mucus membranes of e.g. the respiratory tract	Marshmallow, Mullein
Diaphoretic/ Sudorific	To raise body temperature as a stimulant, to cause sweating	Elderflower, Ginger
Emetic	To induce vomiting	Heartsease

Emollient	Similar to demulcents but used topically to treat skin eruptions	*Aloe vera*
Expectorant	To aid expulsion of mucus from the lungs	Mullein, Horehound
Febrifuge	To reduce fevers	Birch bark and leaf
Nervine	To support the nervous system	Skullcap
Laxative/Purgative	To empty rectum and colon	Senna
Styptic	To staunch blood flow	*Calendula*
Tonic	Nutritive to support and strengthen systems	Nettles
Vermifuge/Anti-thelmintic	To expel 'worms' (e.g. tapeworm/flukes) from the body	Vervain
Vulnerary	To support healing of wounds and inflammation	*Calendula*

In-depth information on these categories can be found in the herbal, written in 1931 by Mrs M. Grieve[5]. This impressive piece of work gives details of actions of individual herbs and also notes active ingredients in chemical terms. All these studies and analyses were going on as the British Pharmacopoeia was systematically rejecting plants from its lists.

Considerably later, in 1964, the British Medical Herbalists Association[6] was established. This was at a time of increasing regulatory control, when herbal medicine was facing a very uncertain time in the UK. Influenced by the 1968 Medicines Act, this body later developed a Scientific Committee of Herbalists who started work on the production of herb monographs for a British Herbal Pharmacopoeia. The first volume was the 'Herbal Compendium'[7] which was published in 1971, and later, in 1983, the second volume – the 'British Herbal Pharmacopoeia'[8] – was published. This volume included 232 herbal drugs. (It was updated in 1996 and a second compendium was produced in 2006.) It was considerably later, in 1996, that the National Institute of Medical Herbalists devised an accreditation scheme for members, and in 2004 it became affiliated to European groups. There was then a marked revival of herbal medicine in the UK, accompanied by new university degree courses and considerable support from the NHS. But in an atmosphere of high regulation and legal requirements, there was constant pressure from pharmaceutical companies for authentication and regulation of herbal usage on their terms and according to their devised, and very costly, methods of testing and trialling of a single biological active ingredient with a physiological effect on the body. This enabled them to develop a rigorous system of testing for efficacy and risk and ultimately to patent these molecules – which was necessary to recoup the vast expenses involved. Their drugs were all based on single active ingredients, whereas a herbal remedy contains a large number of active molecules that all act on the body simultaneously. This makes such testing impossible. They could not exist under the same rules.

But this wasn't the only difference between modern herbalism and Western medicine. Herbalism has always retained strong links with traditional knowledge of its culture. It is a system based on looking at the individual in her/his totality and seeing disease as an imbalance in the patterns of harmony that maintain health, rather than treating the symptoms of the disease. This holistic approach includes the connections of an individual with her/his environment – an idea shared with other holistic therapies that became grouped together as complementary and alternative medicine (CAM). These are very diverse treatments that fall outside of mainstream healthcare and several of them are plant-based (e.g. aromatherapy, homeopathy).

A British Medical Journal definition of CAM is:

'... a broad domain of healing resources that encompasses all health systems, modalities, and practices and their accompanying theories and beliefs, other than those intrinsic to the politically dominant health system of a particular society or culture in a given historical period.'

The BMJ also stresses that there is a difference between complementary and alternative medicine in that complementary medicine can be practised alongside allopathic medicine, whereas alternative medicine is a substitute for it.

Since around 2003, there has been a huge expansion in CAM practices. Holistic therapies have been recognised as beneficial in many areas, especially for the treatment of stress and many of the chronic diseases where mainstream healthcare has very limited success. Despite the apparent lack of rigorous evidence, complementary medicine has also become increasingly legitimised. It is taught in universities, receives considerable funding from the NHS, and is recommended by the World Health Organization. Most importantly, it is supported by a large proportion of patients who receive conventional treatments within the NHS and are seeking a more holistic approach.

But of course, complementary medicine has not been without its detractors – perhaps the most noteworthy being Professor Edzard Ernst, who was appointed the first Professor of Complementary Medicine at the University of Exeter in 1993. His aim was to apply scientific scrutiny to the field of complementary and alternative medicine. After carrying out clinical trials, writing many reviews and doing meta-analyses on other people's results, his damning conclusions were that there was little evidence for the success of CAM – in fact, that 90% of treatments didn't live up to the claims and expectations made for them by their alternative therapists.

In her popularist book 'The Suckers'[9] another detractor, Rose Shapiro, questions the effectiveness of CAM treatments, claiming that:

'The sick clearly long for their symptoms to carry more meaning than the prevailing mechanistic model allows.'

And:

'The patients who seek alternative practitioners are often described by doctors as "heartsick": they suffer from chronic illnesses that respond poorly to conventional treatments or from a constellation of symptoms that are not easily diagnosed or treated. The problem is that… headaches, heartaches, backaches, aching feet, fatigue, anxiety and those vague burning pains in your legs at night – are the nemeses of real doctors. Many people have these symptoms but the cruel truth is there is no reliable cure for any of them.'

But it seems this is not the case. The demand for many of these therapies has continued. So herein lay the problem: modern Western medicine provides cures for many symptoms of illnesses and prolongs life in so many spectacular instances but does not address the fact that disease in its entirety is a much deeper human phenomenon. It involves an imbalance, a loss of connection and a fragmentation of Wholeness. It is these latter elements that complementary practices seek to remedy.

'Healing is a much deeper phenomenon than a single plant chemical, and involves all of what it means to be human[10].'

Another separation – food from medicine

The separation of the London spicer-apothecaries from the grocers so long ago has had deep and long-lasting implications for society. It divided food from medicine. Traditional medicine from many other cultures does not make this divide. In Ayurvedic and Chinese medicine – both holistic healing models where health and disease are seen as a continuum – foods are an intrinsic part of balancing the needs of the individual. But by contrast, in many Western cultures, this divide has become extreme and populations have become estranged from plants – both as food and as health promoters. Diets in the UK had become so dependent on processed foods that were low in vegetables and fruit that a campaign was sponsored by the NHS Department of Health looking at possible health detriments of such diets and what benefits were to be had by eating fruit and vegetables. They reported their findings in April 2014. The results of this Health Survey for England, using information from more than 65,000 randomly selected participating adults, prompted a national campaign to promote eating five portions of fruit and vegetables each day!

The development of synthetic vitamins

Another area where we have lost connection with plants and where they have been replaced by synthetic chemicals is in the development of vitamins. In 1911 a Polish biochemist, Kazimierz Funk, was researching why people eating brown rice were less likely to suffer from the disease beri-beri than those who ate refined milled rice. He succeeded in isolating the substance present in brown rice that protected from the disease and he called it a 'vitamine'. This word was a fusion of 'vita', meaning life, and 'amine' – a chemical compound and building block of proteins. Later it was discovered that the molecule was not an 'amine' so the 'e' was dropped from the word and thus 'vitamin' came into being. The substance was later found to be vitamin B3 niacin. Funk went on to discover other B vitamins. Most of the thirteen vitamins crucial for human nutrition and health – vitamins A, D, E, K, C, and eight B vitamins – are plant-based (except B12 and vitamin D).

This was a time when nutritional diseases were an important sociological phenomenon that needed some action – in institutions, in children living in poverty, in sailors surviving long periods at sea, in soldiers with wartime rations, etc. A huge amount of medical and biological research took place, looking at the specific food sources of vitamins, and later (especially in the war years), the vitamin requirements of people of different ages and with different lifestyles. It was also discovered that the processes of bulk food production destroyed many of these essential vitamins – hence the production of synthetic vitamins used as food additives. The sale of vitamins has reached an all-time high, with 46% of the UK population (and 65% of all adults) in 2016 being regular daily vitamin and supplement users. In many cases, these supplements are synthetic plant products, far removed from the living plants on which they are based.

This was the nadir: the separation of humans and plants as medicines, as food and as a vital force i.e. vitamins. But alongside these long-term developments, a huge effort has been made to reconnect with plants in a more holistic way. This is demonstrated by the work of the botanic gardens in recent years. Kew Gardens has put emphasis on educating both young and old in the uses of plants at all levels: as food, as fibres for weaving and building, as medicines; in ecology and environmental considerations; and in our dependence and connection with them. This has also been done superbly at the Chelsea Physic Garden with their re-designed World Medicine beds, and also at Brooklyn Botanic Garden in New York, where a newly designed children's garden has been opened alongside an extensive native plants garden, a large vegetable garden, and a water garden where aspects of water usage and conservation, ecology, environment and climate change are all considered. In the UK, the Royal Horticultural Society has made great moves forward to change the emphasis of their magazine 'The Gardener' to include: aspects of growing vegetables – the best varieties for taste, as near 'organic' as they can feel comfortable with; schools' programmes to teach children how to grow vegetables and the benefits obtained; the aesthetics, enjoyment and health benefits of gardening; and horticulture as 'Connection'. The National Trust, The Woodland Trust and National Parks all emphasise the aesthetic and spiritual values of communing with trees, plants and Nature – our need for connection with the natural world for mutual benefit.

New ideas of health and disease

The scientific paradigm that has brought such monumental changes to our lives in the Western world has also brought about chronic health and environmental problems that require our immediate attention.

Both Western medicine and, in many instances, modern herbal medicine too, have become disciplines for healing only the physical body. Aspects of healing the emotions and the Spirit using plant energies are no longer regarded as important in these systems. Nevertheless, patients have searched for complementary therapies so that they are able to heal in their entirety.

Many areas of medicine now speak of a Third Era, in which the enormous benefits of modern medicine and surgery can be used alongside holistic approaches to health and wellbeing. In this model, human disease is no longer regarded as the symptom (as it is currently in Western medicine), but as a condition that reflects an imbalance or lack of harmony within the whole person (and her/his environment), which could be described as a sickness of Body, Mind, and Spirit and lack of connection. Very often, plants can heal all of these in ways that Western medicines cannot. The use of plant medicines and therapies could thus play an increasingly important role in the new working model. This would have the additional advantage of healing an environmental disease – the disconnection of humans and their green mantle, the plants that cover the Earth's crust and totally sustain us.

And here I turn back to my garden in Chevenoz, where my aim has always been to cultivate the finest herbs in conditions which conserve their physical, energetic and spiritual properties to be used for healing and also conserve the health of this beautiful land. I thus became the gardener, dispenser and eventual distiller of *Herbes de Chevenoz*. My contribution.

Chapter notes

1.   Society of the Apothecaries. http://www.apothecaries.org/charity/history/our-history

2.   British Pharmacopoeia 1864. Spottiswoode & Co for the General Medical Council

3.   British Pharmaceutical Codex 1949. Spottiswoode & Co for the General Medical Council

4.   National Institute of Medical Herbalists. https://www.nimh.org.uk/

5.   Grieve, Mrs M. FRHS: A Modern Herbal. Edited by Mrs C.F. Leyel. First published in 1931 by Jonathan Cape. Current edition published in 1994 by Cresset Books. ISBN 1-85501-249-9

6.   British Medical Herbalists Association. https://bhma.info/

7.   British Herbal Compendium Volume I. Edited by Peter R. Bradley. 1992. Copyright British Herbal Medicine Association. ISBN 0 903032 09 0

8.   British Herbal Pharmacopoeia 1983. Published by British Herbal Medicine Association. ISBN 0 903032 07 4

9.   Shapiro, Rose: The Suckers: how Alternative Medicine makes fools of us all. 2008. Vintage Publishing. ISBN 1846550289

10.   Marciano, Marisa. Naturopathic Herbalist. Vancouver, Canada. https://thenaturopathicherbalist.com/about-3/dr-marisa-marciano/

Grass of Parnassus growing in the Alps in perfection and full connection – with history, with imagination, with culture and with its environment.

VI

Creating the herb garden

*'It is the unexplainable thing in nature that makes me feel
that the world is big far beyond my understanding'*
GEORGIA O'KEEFFE

This beautiful little plant was named *Parnassia palustris* in the mid-18th century by the Swedish botanist Carl Linnaeus. In modern times, Richard Mabey, in his 'Flora Britannica', traces the name 'grass of Parnassus' back even earlier to 1576, when the Flemish botanist Matthias de l'Obel referred to '*Gramen Parnassi*'. This was translated into English in 1578 by Henry Lyte. In herbal medicine, *Parnassia palustris* has been used to treat disorders of the liver, and an infusion of leaves to dissolve kidney stones. It is still of interest in current medical research.

Parnassus is a mountain towering above Delphi in Central Greece. It was sacred to Dionysus and Apollo and, according to Greek mythology, where the Muses lived. Parnassus became known as the home of poetry, music and learning. Cattle grazing on Mount Parnassus developed a taste for this succulent little plant that grew near water in the lush meadows – hence its Latin species name '*palustris*', meaning boggy.

Around the age of nine, at school we were all issued with a little green poetry book entitled 'The Grass of Parnassus – An anthology of poetry for schools' with an introduction by Sir John Squire[1]. On the simple hardback green cover was a white imprint of a grass of Parnassus plant with a single flower. For me, the book cover always gave more pleasure as I ran my finger up and down the outline of the plant than the content (which was designed to bring back poetry and culture to the post-war era of deprived children, and certainly had its share of male-centered patriotism).

I wanted the plants in my garden to have full connection with their environments and histories too. I saw this as a way of preserving their vitality and power. So I needed to consider how I could combine my knowledge of herbal medicine with my training and opportunities as a botanist, gardener and land-owner. My first consideration was how to select the plants to grow – and here I had two main sources: the beautiful plants that I was bringing over with each visit from our desperately overcrowded garden in London and from the Chelsea Physic Garden; and then I was also aware that plants that I had studied on the Phytotherapy course were actually growing wild around the house. So rather like the Chelsea Physic Garden itself, I decided to make my garden a mixture of garden plants and medicinal herbs – a fusion of beauty and healing surrounded by magnificent Alpine scenery with its crystal-clear water and sparkling air. This was the environment that my plants would connect with.

That autumn I created the first flowerbed on a large area bordering our east perimeter fence. I called it the 'nut garden'. After days of ploughing up the meadow grasses with my little cultivator, then treading down the sods of earth with a sideways marching step as I had learned at the Physic Garden, then cutting the edges with a spade, I had a long triangular bed with an existing backcloth of plum trees and three small pine trees. I found hazelnut and yew saplings and elderberry bushes around the plot, so added them to form a small protective spinney to frame the garden. I wanted it to be a fusion of cultivated and wild species, so I mixed acanthus, day lilies, cephalarias, irises, tree and bush peonies, agapanthus, white and yellow asphodels, rose species, crocosmia, hostas – all from London – with the wild sanicles, meadow sage, salad burnet, aquilegias, meadow geraniums, alchemilla, red and white campions, foxgloves, St John's wort and centaureas. They grew fast and the next year was a riot of huge clumps of colour and foliage at the back, with smaller meadow plants at the front – an 'eclectic choice', as a garden designer friend called it. And it worked. It was magnificent! In that climate and those conditions, plants grew as I had never known before. Here, plants that had looked impressive at Chelsea were half as large again, flowers were so plentiful and their colours so much more intense, the leaves deeper green. The sheer good health and vigour of those plants was remarkable.

This was my observation and it was considerably later that I read in 'Habundantia'[2] that indeed the growing conditions in La Vallée d'Abondance are extraordinary. As with all mountainous regions, rainfall increases with altitude. So annual rainfall in Thonon at altitude 375m is 992mm and in Abondance at

1000m is 1561mm – Chevenoz is 850m above sea level. This rainfall is spread throughout the year and summer rainfall usually coincides with increased and often continental temperatures. But in addition to this abundant rainfall, here the quality of the soil is also superb, especially the post-glacial fine alluvial black earth and crystalline deposits; and the quality and intensity of the sunlight encourage rapid growth of vegetation – to an extent that is often surprising to witness. These are truly excellent conditions for cultivation. And besides, this land has a quality that I call 'magic'. Its air quality and light intensity give it a surreal clarity and glow, and the variation and intensity of the weather conditions show the benevolent and also the cruel side of Nature. Day by day, theatre is played out between the Elements – Earth, Air, Water and Sun – and the Earth's green mantle.

Following on from my successes with the nut garden, and because I ran out of space, I then designed and created a second bed nearby. This was on a slight slope down from the terrace area. We planted a beautiful little rowan tree (*Sorbus aucuparia* – 'for the birds') between the stone table and this bed to give dappled shade to the table and also to a long slate slab that we found in the ground nearby. We named it the 'King and Queen seat' to remind us of the Henry Moore seat that we were so fond of. Although seldom regal, we sat here seeking rest and tranquility after our gardening efforts for many years to come. These large naturally occurring slate slabs were commonplace in Chevenoz. In the graveyard surrounding the old church they had been used as gravestones, and after the de-consecration of the church and graveyard had found their way to other places – with other uses. The ones we found on the plot we used structurally in the garden and as venerable thresholds to the various French doors and entrances around the house. We also made stepping stones down from the front of the house to the lawn created from the newly purchased orchard land.

The second garden already contained a sumach tree and in the shady parts was ideal for new plantings of solomon's seal, ferns, hellebores, meadowsweet, veronicastrum and other shade-tolerant plants. The sunny lower part had beautiful *Iris sibirica*, day lilies, peonies, Japanese anemones and lavender bushes around the seat. Other plants just arrived. Wild marjoram, creeping thyme, ragged robin and geraniums all came in from the meadow. From the beginning, this garden was also a beautiful fusion of the wild with the cultivated.

These two beds changed the nature of the meadow considerably – it was becoming a garden. But that was short-lived. By early November the frosts arrived, and apart from the evergreen yews and pine trees, most other plants died down. A temperate green winter garden wasn't to be. It became an autumnal ritual of strimming and clearing the dense summer foliage and preparing the soil for its covering of frost crystals and later ermine mantle. In common with my neighbours, all garden work in Chevenoz ceased from November to May. Temperatures plummeted, the ground froze hard and life processes shut down. It was winter.

During the previous summer I had attended the School of Phytotherapy Summer School – a week-long course in East Sussex. The aims of the course were to consolidate the learning done by correspondence during the year, to meet the tutors and to do some practical work. At the end of the course, one of the teachers and directors, Annette Zealstra, had offered us seeds from her beautiful herb garden with the proviso 'Donné c'est donné' – to do what we liked with. I collected small quantities of several interesting aromatic herbs, again with the idea of bulking them up for future cultivation. I came away from that course feeling positive and enthusiastic. It was on this course that I met Joe Nasr – a charismatic and highly skilled teacher and herbalist who had been trained at the school. At the end of the course I was asked if I could give him a lift back to London, and this was the beginning of a long friendship. Joe talked about his herbal medicine practice and his developing business of tincture preparation, and I talked about my cultivation of beautiful herbs. Neither of us knew too much about the other's topic of conversation. It seemed a very good match.

Also during the year, I had made other very useful connections. The first one was via the Physic Garden, where I met Peter Wilde, who had developed a prototype for extracting plant aromas that he demonstrated to us at the Physic Garden. His 'Rose Extract' was superb and his hope was to be able to extract rose essence on a large scale to compete with the processes of 'Rose Absolute' extraction and 'Rose Attar' production. In conversation he mentioned to me that he also wanted to work on holy basil (*Ocimum sanctum* – an important Ayurvedic herb) but couldn't get enough seeds to plant on his land in Yorkshire. I told him of our growing conditions, so he gave me a small container of seeds to bulk up. I resolved to plant them in Chevenoz the next spring.

The following May, I had to clear a small patch of the overgrown vegetable garden to sow the *Ocimum sanctum* seeds, which I planted during a short trip from London and left to their fate. The next trip, in June, revealed a large number of overcrowded seedlings, so I then cleared an even larger patch of soil and transplanted them – again leaving them to their fate. On returning for our summer holidays in July, I was amazed to find a bumper crop of seeds ready for harvesting and cleaning – which I did. There was an amazing 1.5kg of fine seeds to return to Peter. In no way do I advocate this as a gardening method, but it demonstrated to me yet again the wonderful growing conditions I had to work with – the abundance of this blessed valley. I spent time that summer wild-crafting seeds of useful plants from the valley – among others, vervain, chickweed, red clover and St John's wort.

So my plant base was taking form. I had some fine seeds and was bulking them up and had started to grow perennial plants that needed to reach maturity. I had amassed a long list of plants from the Herbal Medicine course and from tinctures I had dispensed while working with Antoine, along with ideas from the Aromatherapy course. There were lots of ideas going on in my head, so I sourced seeds and then set about designing a planting scheme. As the land around the house wasn't suitable, it was time to dig up more of the meadow. Again, with my small gardening plough I set about creating an area that would divide into around forty plots, arranging them to protect the seedlings from the encroaching and surrounding meadow plants and to make sure they had enough light. This area of the garden became known as 'the plots' – and in later years increased hugely in size, beauty and importance. Germination rates were so quick and so high that very soon I needed to plough up an even bigger area for transplanting. Again, the success of this venture surpassed anything witnessed at the Physic Garden and took me completely by surprise.

Cultivation of the herb garden

So now I was ready for scale-up mark III, and it was at this stage that I decided to clearly define my ethos and have a concept for the garden. I had had so many experiences, researched a lot and met so many useful and knowledgeable contacts and friends that now was the time to pull all these together. In particular I found it interesting to try to knit together the diverse practices of the Physic Garden and Kew Gardens, on the one hand, with the practices of Jeanne and our Chevenoz neighbours on the other – one highly theoretical, evolving and with a scientific base, and the other long-standing traditional knowledge of techniques and the vagaries of the climate and landscape.

The ideas started coming together. Above all, I hoped that this garden, more than other gardens, would be a garden of wellbeing, for the plants and myself, containing power, symbolism and beauty that would give it harmony and balance – both within the garden itself and with the magnificent surrounding environment. It was also going to be a wild and a connected garden where I would try to preserve the continuity between the garden and its surroundings with minimum fencing and boundaries. This was an important consideration as I wanted to welcome the plants from the surrounding meadows which drifted in on the wind or attached to the coats of visiting animals (who were usually also welcome). Many of these plants were very beautiful and had interesting medicinal properties (e.g. the mulleins, geraniums, vervain, meadow sage, valerian, and the sweetest smelling sweet vernal grass).

Also, connection was an important aspect of healing, as shown by the unorthodox work on psycho-social oncology of the Simonton Cancer Center[3] which corresponded with my experience with the Breuss Diet. I needed to be deeply connected with the garden for the health of both the plants and myself.

From this beautiful garden I would grow carefully sourced plants in the right quantities for tincture making, for infused oils, for tisanes and dried herbs, and eventually for distillation of essential oils. Working with Antoine and the herbalists at the clinic where I had observed treatments had given me a good idea of the tinctures that were most useful to them. After my trip to La Drome and the Dutch growers, I knew that *Hypericum* (St John's wort) and *Calendula* (marigold) were 'must-haves' for infused oils. I would need these plants in much larger quantities. There were also seeds from annual plants like chickweed, skullcap, clary sage and German chamomile to be sown – for use in the current year and to keep viable seed for future years – and the perennials that would take a few years to establish: the beautiful and ancient hyssop, and fragrant *Melissa*, lavender and rosemary.

To enhance its beauty and healing nature further, I would also select single plants from other sources – as in a garden. These plants would always be beautiful and often significant healing plants, although I wouldn't necessarily use them to make products.

Finally, cultivation methods would be based on ideas and practices that I regarded as holistic: these included aligning my practices to the seasons, following the sun's cycle and handling plants accordingly, and harmonising with the moon cycles and the constellations using biodynamic principles. So with these parameters decided on, the garden could come into being. On this scale, I needed help.

****

On a beautiful spring morning, our local farmer Stéphane arrived in the meadow with his tractor and plough and was ready to start. I had pegged out an area of approximately 50m across by 40m deep that I thought would be sufficient for my current needs. Alighting from his tractor, Stéphane carefully surveyed the land and walked over it, feeling large grass tussocks with his boot, kicking any rocks or flint stones, looking at what was growing there. Then, with gentle precision and deep concentration, he lined up his tractor and plough, revved up the engine and dropped the shining plough blades into the earth. I watched, awestruck, as the action of the deep blade cut into and turned the turf over cleanly to expose an exquisite sparkling black earth, writhing with worms, centipedes, beetles, ants, grubs: a myriad of life forms, movements and energy. The sunlight glistened and reflected on drops of moisture, flint stones and gravel. This ancient meadowland had probably never been disturbed before. Its vitality was astounding and I felt it was an intrusion, almost a sacrilege, to have scarred it in this way. I was breaking into another world that had existed there harmoniously for centuries. It was at this moment that I realised my responsibility for and my deep gratitude to our bountiful Mother Earth.

I now had a large area of beautiful freshly ploughed earth for a garden – to be made up of 'order beds' as at the Chelsea Physic Garden and Kew Gardens, with carefully arranged clumps of meticulously labelled plants where I would note their names, their provenance and some reference number. This has always been the tradition in botanic gardens, where the importance of correct identification of plants overrides all other aesthetic considerations. Since I was preparing to make tinctures and other preparations of these plants for human consumption, I needed to do likewise.

As before, it took days of breaking down the sods, treading them down, then hoeing and raking that beautiful black earth until it resembled the finest of seed beds. By the time it was finished it had carefully spaded edges, and I ceremonially planted a species rose bush in each corner. At the far end I planted seven small may (hawthorn) bushes. But despite the order of order beds, from the start the charm of a French '*potager*' and the concept of companion planting were creeping into the grand plan.

On the first day of May, twelve years after we had seen the place for the first time, I marked out the land, designed a cursory planting scheme and set to work. On that beautiful May morning, I entered another world. It was a '*joli jour*', as Jeanne called such days. The sun was bright and strong, warming the soil that steamed in will-o'-the-wisp strands into the clear air. A few high clouds swept across the valley, but the air was soft and still. Strangely, somehow in that peace and solitude it was noisy – but not with the cacophony of London traffic and noise. Here, each sound was separate – a distant chainsaw felling a pine tree, perhaps; a lorry deep in the valley road changing down a gear for the next bend; the cows with their bells, moving their heads slowly to graze the lush, flower-filled meadow grass. And then there were the birds – the two crows crossing from one side of the valley to the other, a distance of several kilometres, and communing with each other as they did so; the green woodpecker, swooping and screeching as it flew from one orchard tree to one further afield – perhaps seeing some other bird off its patch; the smaller spotted woodpeckers tapping incessantly in the old pear tree; the goldfinches chattering together; the magpies with their raucous noise; the jays – even noisier, and the clicking redstart commenting incessantly on its changed territory. Sitting back on my heels on my garden kneeling mat, I could be immersed in a single sound and connected to its source. The valley was so alive and vibrant.

In periods of intense hard work, I divided up parcels of land and planted out *Alchemilla*, yarrow, agrimony, wood sage and *Hypericum*. These were all plants I had wild-crafted or grown from seed the previous year. I was loath to plant them as far apart as seed packets advised (a big mistake) as single meadow plants looked lost in so much space. But that was something I had to learn – just how much those plants grew.

I interspersed plots containing plantlets with plots where I was going to plant seeds – trying to be mindful of eventual heights and forms, the shelter and protection they could give each other, and also the shading effects that the grown plants would create. I solved this problem by creating a grid of half-metre wide paths between the plots. At this stage I was working with small quantities of seeds, so made small seed beds within the designated plots and then later transplanted the seedlings. In later years I had enough seed to sow *in situ* and thin out as required. This latter method produced stronger plants and earlier maturation and flowering by at least two weeks.

As the daily ritual, at ten minutes to midday the Angelus rang out over the valley – the melodic three times three beats and then the long rhythmical chimes of the church bell. In this Vallée d'Abondance, it was as if golden grace was pouring down over the land, blessing it and everything in it. In French Catholic tradition it was time to stop work, to eat and to rest.

Within a few days I had planted thirteen main crops: *Hypericum, Melissa, Lavendula* (Hidcote), *Hyssopus, Echinacea, Calendula, Achillea, Scutellaria, Marrubium, Artemesia absinthium, Matricaria, Salvia sclarea,* and *Agrimonia;*

and smaller quantities of others: *Stachys, Levisticum, Silybum marianum, Arnica, Staphisagria.*

But even at this stage, I recognised that I was working with something precious. The newly tilled black earth was so alive and vital and other conditions of climate were so perfect for growth that I knew I had to create something truly beautiful. I was also aware that many of the 'rogue' invaders from the surrounding meadows also had healing properties and I was loath to eject them. So I planted these in the corners of each individual plot. I used structural plants – tall and handsome mulleins, meadow geraniums, sainfoin – and later added smaller bugles, delicate hairbells, my friend from the Breuss Diet: herb robert, primroses and cowslips, and then beautiful Physic Garden plants – *Staphisagria, Iris sibirica*, evening primroses, and the Alpine white asphodels that we had seen in the high mountains. I had plenty of space at this stage and the paths were wide. I could be welcoming and generous.

I then did something spontaneously and boldly! I wanted to commit to this project in a very special way. I still felt guilty at having dug into this pristine valley earth. It was an intrusion into virgin territory and for that I needed to give something in return. In the very centre of the plots, at a crossroads of the main paths, I dug a hole – a deep one, and then carefully removed my mother's wedding ring from my finger and placed it in the black earth. Over it I said, as Mrs Zealstra had done before: '*Donné c'est donné!*'. I would never retrieve it. I thus became 'married' to this garden. I bade the ring '*adieu*', filled the hole, covered the spot with a beautiful oval stone and then planted significant plants around it. This was my first act of shamanic giving and receiving.

The plots

As years passed and more ideas formulated and needs changed, these plots developed and increased in size. Research at the Wellcome Library provided me with invaluable information and I adapted my planting schemes. Monographs on the essential oils[4] supplied details on every aspect of production: cultivation parameters, choice cultivars and optimal planting distances; the effect of drying and storage of herbs; peak oil production time; optimum yields. This treasure trove, based on research from many authors over decades, made me realise that with precision and care, I could produce the finest oils.

With this information, I found the best spots for permanent beds of lavenders, *Melissa*, hyssop, *Scutellaria* and St John's wort (the perennials), which

The plots in early summer

I interspersed with the annual plantings of clary sage, chamomile, marigold, *Pelargonium graveolens* and chickweed. I also learned which cultivars of lavender produced essential oils of highest quality and yield in which conditions, but I knew the unique growing conditions of Chevenoz were a given and would greatly influence the quality of the oil produced. It would be Chevenoz lavender oil.

Contacts with seed producers also helped me to build up a collection of fine plant varieties and cultivars that bred true over generations and made high-quality products. To preserve the purity of these lines, after establishing the perennials (e.g. lavender, rosemary, *Pelargonium* and *Melissa*), I took cuttings or divided root stocks to propagate them. The *Calendula* from Chelsea Physic Garden bred true for years to come, as also did the wild crafted plants. In all cases I recorded the provenance of seeds and plants. (See Appendix II, Note I.)

The rose plantings

It had always been my intention to grow beautiful roses in Chevenoz. Every house or *potager* in the *commune* had a much loved and cared for rose bush against the house or rambling along the perimeter fence. They thrived in these conditions and some of the old French varieties were superb.

I received my first order of species roses from the U.K. company Peter Beales. My particular interest was to grow Damask roses, suitable for rose water distillation, and he sold the varieties Ispahan, Kazanlik and Quatre Saisons. These were all rose varieties renowned for their perfume and oil quality. This was definitely forward planning as I knew that it would be several years before I would have enough flowers to work with. My previous experience with roses was that they have distinct preferences for different soil types, quite regardless of what catalogues tell you. Once I knew that these roses were suitable, I repeated the orders each year and extended the list of varieties to include many other highly scented roses and some old French rambling and climbing roses too.

My roses became the loves of my life! They thrived wonderfully. Besides the species roses I bought, I was attracted to a little bush rose spreading across the fence between a neighbouring and neglected garden and ours. On investigation, I realised it was *Rosa gallica* – the Apothecary's Rose, growing here in Chevenoz! So I took several root cuttings and created my own little Apothecary's Rose garden. The cuttings took quickly and the many flowers were of wonderful colour, form and perfume. I realised that I could dry the petals in two or three days and they retained their colour and perfume, and could be used in a number of herbal preparations.

Over the years I had started to draw again and I became very attracted to certain features in drawings by Edward Burne-Jones. In family memorabilia, I had found an invitation to my great uncle to a preview in London of Burne-Jones's painting entitled 'Psyche's wedding', which was painted in honour of his daughter's wedding in the parish church in Rottingdean (where we later moved to…). Our daughter Clare was getting married that summer and I loved the idea of strewing rose petals around the bride, so dried my petals for the occasion. They were soft, perfumed, deeply coloured and exquisitely beautiful.

Eventually the rose collection consisted of over sixty large and magnificent bushes for rose distillation and dried petals. They were all selected for their perfumes, giving a range from sweet to 'nutmeg-y', that made the most beautiful floral water. But sadly, unlike the huge Bulgarian rose fields, my collection was never going to be sufficient to produce rose oil.

(See Appendix II, Note II.)

Garden practices

I was at the stage now to select the practices I would use to care for my healing garden, to produce the herbal products and to satisfy my personal ethos as well. My gardening experiences in temperate southern England, and the even more temperate Chelsea Physic Garden, advised me for a lot of things, but there were some aspects of gardening where I was going to need to make some quite significant adjustments.

Our neighbour Jeanne became my teacher. She had lived in the same house all her life and learned to garden from her mother. Her tidy rows of salad vegetables, potatoes, beans, leeks, onions and cabbages were interspersed with gaudy orange African marigolds, bright green spurges, orange nasturtiums, red roses, sparkling white marguerites with their golden centres, and, in the corner of the plot, a hidden cache of lily-of-the-valley and Christmas roses. Some of these plants were useful companion plants to support and strengthen her vegetables and to deter pests and diseases. There were also others that could have been weeds: the earliest pale yellow flowers of the year (coltsfoot), which Jeanne's mother collected and dried to treat children's coughs, salad burnet, wild cress and many others. These plants crossed the divide between plants to forage from the surrounding meadows and those which were very useful to have 'on hand' in the garden. But although her mother had loved her flowers and Jeanne did too, to have a specific flower garden was a luxury and not considered part of the women's tradition of providing a livelihood alongside subsistence farming. Following family tradition, Jeanne had a strict regime in her gardening year, starting at the beginning of May. Despite any good weather at the end of April, no planting would ever take place before May 1. By this time, she considered that the soil had warmed up sufficiently to sow seed. She was always mindful of the three days in May – the 11, 12 and 13 – called *Les Saints de Glace* (the Ice Saints), when weather could turn cold again and emerging young seedlings needed protecting. There was also a period she called '*La Lune rousse*' – the first moon in May, when cold winds and night-time temperatures could turn delicate green leaves red. So with these provisos, she brought her vegetable garden to life.

Watching and talking to neighbours, it was quite apparent that so many of these rhythms and customs were still deeply embedded within them. I was surrounded by people who understood their environment and their climate in a way that I didn't, and never had: Jeanne as a talented gardener; carpenter

Roger, who knew when to cut wood for timbers, for fire wood, for fine cabinet making; Stéphane, who watched the sky for approaching weather, noted the winds and had names for them, and watched and reacted to his cows' rhythms. So many of the older generation also had intimate knowledge of their native flora and where to forage – for sorrel, dandelions, nettles, horsetails and many others. Especially important was knowledge of local mushrooms: which were edible, which toxic to the death; under which trees to find the *chanterelles, bolets, russules, coprins*; in which season and weather conditions. These close-guarded secrets were traditional knowledge based on observations over generations and handed down with little input from foreigner interlopers with different ideas. It was so embedded in their Consciousness, it could have been almost innate. Through continuity and deep familiarity with their environment and climate, these people were still living close to the Earth and its bounty, and in harmony with its rhythms.

By this time, we were living in Chevenoz almost all the time as I found it was easier to devote myself to the work rather than trying to juggle and fit in lots of other activities. I became a peasant. Each morning I would set off down the garden with my tools and wheelbarrow and start to work. There was something deeply satisfying in doing this. The morning air and sunshine and the excitement around me – the birds, the black squirrels, distant dogs and cow bells – became my world. After quite a short period of time I found that I too worked with these rhythms. The daily inspirations and expirations blended into the increasing day-lengths, the moon changed her course across the night sky and changed from a delicate crescent to a brilliant full moon. These rhythms became part of me – or rather, I of them. Day after day and then week after week, my plants grew, the plots burst into colour and fragrance, the bees and insects arrived. The energy and life force were amazing. I had never witnessed such power.

Organic cultivation

The concept of 'organic' cultivation wasn't even considered in our little *commune* (nor was it at that time at the Physic Garden). Pesticides and herbicides were not used by the farmer nor by gardeners – other than a drenching with Bordeaux mixture on the occasional vine surviving this altitude; fertilisers were garden compost and farmyard manure; and the long hard winters killed off so many soil-borne plant pests and diseases, giving young plants a good chance to grow strongly in the spring months. But because I knew some sort of organic certification would be required of my products, I decided to adhere to those practices as far as was applicable. Discussions with Stéphane about his agricultural practices in the surrounding meadows ascertained that he had never used pesticides on them, and I knew that the land I was cultivating had been in the hands of the Morel family and then us for decades. The land I was using was pesticide residue-free, undoubtedly. I thus resolved to follow all organic practices to the letter – not because I thought they had the definitive answer to all problems, but because I thought they were headed in the right direction and had a system of monitoring their practices! In later years I investigated biodynamic regimes and Demeter certification and realised these regulations were also not possible. On the small scale I was working, any outside certification and monitoring would be prohibitively expensive. The system of certification was designed for much larger-scale production methods. But as a responsibility to my customers, I needed to choose criteria for growing the most healthy and vital plants I possibly could and at the same time conserve the soil's structure, fertility and innate beauty. I decided to use certain well-defined strategies – again aimed to maintain purity, harmony and balance. I considered the health of the soil to be of prime importance in the activities of the garden and so the garden practices tried to reflect this. My water management would be one of minimum intervention so that the plants could reflect the general levels of humidity in the atmosphere and respond to it and the moon's rhythms. I would also consider the light intensity of different parts of the garden. The intensity and quality of light is crucially important in several of the processes that I was going to use. In particular, they affect flower colour/pigmentation, rapid plant growth and, I suspect, 'photo-energy' or vibrational energy of the essential oils.

Minimum intervention

Besides following my own-styled organic practices, on a more practical level, I became aware that I needed to let my plants be. Given the right parameters for growth, they thrived with minimum intervention and loved being 'wild'. Reading about quality of essential oils – of lavender for instance – growers in Provence advocate planting in the poorest soil for high-quality oil production. In effect, this means growing the plants 'under stress'. This has often been stated and went against all my aspirations for my garden. I understand that lavender plants can survive in those conditions whereas lots of other plants can't. But I've adopted a strategy where my lavender plants grow in Chevenoz soil that by nature is alluvial and full of nutrients. Over the years, I have witnessed the build-up of heat in early July, sometimes to heat wave (*Canicule*) temperatures. The soft mountain air becomes dry and still and there is a temptation to irrigate the precious crops. Surely the plants are under stress then? But after a few days, the storms arrive and the wilted plants become drenched by sheets of torrential rain, or even battered by hailstones. This is Nature's rhythm and I succumbed to working with it. Likewise with soil quality: in the early days I used to spread farmyard manure from Stéphane's cows (fed exclusively on local meadow grass) onto the plots. But later I decided to only use our own beautiful matured compost to put back into the soil what had been taken out of it. Over the years I have never noticed a reduction in fertility and vigour in the plants – quite the contrary.

As things developed and I observed closely what was happening, I decided that the plants that grew best were the ones that had least interventions. Those plants I grew from seed and then thinned out were always stronger than those I transplanted. The well-established perennials like *Melissa* went from strength to strength for quite a few years before I needed to divide up the clumps. But two plants very dear to my heart, which both produced beautiful essential oils, couldn't survive the harsh winter conditions of Chevenoz. These were rose geranium and rosemary. I had sourced fine cultivars of both so endeavoured to keep them going for as long as possible. I took numerous cuttings and either left them with Jeanne to overwinter indoors or later took them back to England with me. These interventions were not sustainable, so I stopped growing these plants. The rest – my lavender, *Melissa*, hyssop, *Hypericum*, and many others – all survived Chevenoz climate and also thrived. They were well connected.

As my relationship with the garden strengthened over the years, I used minimum intervention to also preserve soil quality. I was always mindful of that freshly tilled beautiful earth and wanted to protect it. So I did the minimum of tilling and digging. Because of the hard winters, most weeds were killed off by the time the snow melted. The direct March sunshine on the south-facing slope warmed and dried the soil quickly, and that was the time to rake over the surface lightly and remove any early seedlings, leaving the earth ready for new sowings. This was the time when I spread the compost.

Rotation of crops

Another important cultivation technique that I used was to rotate my crops. Each year I would move the patches of annual plants around the plots. These were the *Calendula* beds, *Scutellarias*, German chamomiles and, in the early days, my beautiful rose geraniums from Kirstenbosch Botanic Garden in Cape Town. I did this as a considered 'good practice', even though my only plant pest/disease was an insect/fly that attacked young *Hypericum* buds. They laid their eggs singly on a young flowering shoot and a grub emerged that ate the developing apical flower buds. My early reaction was to pick these grubs off by hand, but I later found that I could leave them there and the plants survived. This was an aspect of 'sharing' that I later adopted. I did take note that monocultures encouraged the spread of these grubs, so made my *Hypericum* plots as small as possible or planted in groups of two or three around the garden. Apart from this, my garden was disease-free.

I'm very happy that I adopted such cultivation methods, as during the last decade agricultural practices within the valley have changed considerably. Whether because of a new and younger farmer in the *commune* – who has recently passed his exams and has ambitions – or because of the changes in EU farm tariffs over time, smaller farms have merged into larger ones; our new farmer Fredo doubled the size of his herd. His methods are more intense. He rents, grazes and mows more land, and even buys in hay for the cattle. More antibiotics are now used in the milking parlour, and disinfectants to ensure milk hygiene. Also, the farm run-off and all manure is sprayed back on the land. Perhaps the most significant change has been in hay-making regimes. The old practice of main harvest in June/July followed by the second 'regain' of slower-growing late summer grass has now become three mowings. This is due to a huge increase in farm machinery – tractors, bailers, winnowers – and perhaps a change in the price of hay. Fuel prices don't seem to have had any inhibitory effect on tractor use. Small parcels of land that had previously been cut by scythe and hand-raked are now skimmed over and bailed in no time at all. This has had a profound effect on the meadow flora and seed production. Many Alpine plants like geraniums and cransbills, globeflowers, yellow rattle, scabious, clovers and fine grasses like quaking grass have disappeared and have been replaced by coarser *Compositae* – dandelions, hawkweeds, coarse grasses and sorrel. We now have to go up to the higher *alpages* where the terrain is too steep and rocky to mow to find these Earthly treasures. The effect on my weed populations has been marked. These new interlopers are no longer so welcome.

Composting

So often reams are written about composting: the 'Dos', the 'Dont's', the necessary manoeuvres. Our method was very simple and was influenced by practice at the Physic Garden. It had minimum intervention but good preparation and practice. We constructed three large wooden slatted cages, allowing plenty of air circulation, and using one cage per year introduced plant material. The rules were that woody stems were kept out and relegated to the bonfire; general weeds with soil attached to the roots went in; larger plants and leaves were mulched with the garden shredder and then added. This third action was crucially important to the future activity within the compost pile. Grass cuttings were added in the early days, but later were always left on the lawns (except on those special occasions in the summer holiday when the 'croquet lawn' was quickly reconstructed). I also added plants like nettles and comfrey – both high in nutrients – to the plant mass. In the high growing season of May, June and July, the volume of plant material composted was considerable, as it also was in autumn when the garden was put to bed and everything was razed to the ground and then shredded. At the end of the year the plant mass was soaked with water and covered with a tarpaulin. Very soon – within a couple of days even – the temperature of the top layers raised to around 50°C. This continued for several days and then gradually cooled down. Then the worms rose up, thousands of small, red, writhing and active creatures. In our case, they were aided by woodlice, beetles, grass snakes, mice, and anything else that could take advantage of this warm food store. They stayed there until their work was done. In the spring of the following year, we used up the oldest compost (18+ months old) from the third cage. We then turned the previous year's partially composted plant material over into the now empty compartment, soaked it again and covered it for the year, and started a new cage for the current year's needs. The prepared compost had turned light, friable, sweet-smelling and even-textured. We used it to spread over the plots and the vegetable garden. On occasions I prepared a plant 'purin' of comfrey (*Symphytum officinale*) or of nettle (*Urtica dioica*) and doused it over leaves to strengthen the plants or the colour of the flowers. This was a 'giving back' and a system that worked well.

For the rest, interventions were Nature's and not mine. The hard winters have certainly influenced my practices in the garden by limiting my choice of plants, but they also have a very beneficial effect. Certainly, autumn brings with it the usual mildews and rusts, to aid the seasonal decay and breakdown of plant materials to go back into the earth to be recycled, but afterwards these

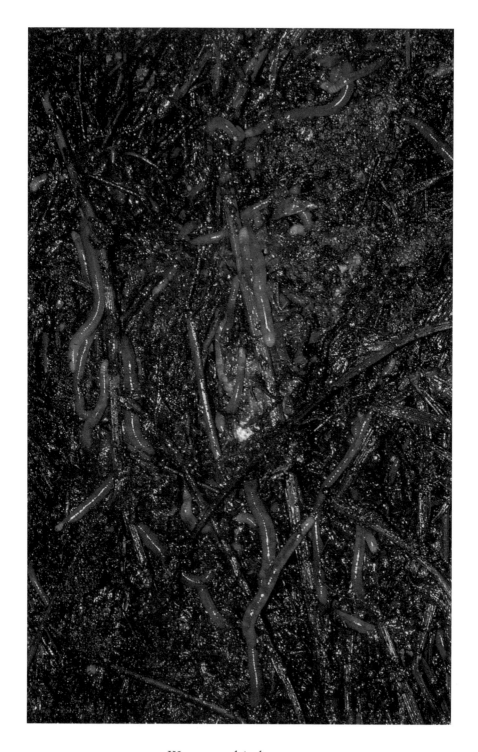

Worms at work in the compost

populations are killed off by frosts and long periods of sub-zero temperatures. So many garden 'pests' and diseases don't survive these Alpine winters.

I have also realised that growth and conditions vary from year to year. Like vintners, I had to accept that there were good years and there were not-so-good years. Plants are not commodities, yields can't be depended on, quantity and quality are different dimensions. This was a partnership and I was the half of it. What I received for my toils and endeavours was a precious gift.

Cosmic influences on planet Earth

My neighbours all read 'L'Almanach Savoyard'[5]. This little booklet, for sale by the till of our local shop, was first published in its current form in 1946 – a post-war effort to re-kindle enthusiasms for traditional farming methods and practices and to keep rural traditions, knowledge and customs alive. Its table of contents includes details of astronomical phenomena throughout the year – eclipses, the appearances and positions of the planets in relation to the sun and the Earth, times of sunrises and sunsets throughout the year, the phases of the moon with its waxing, waning, ascending and descending rhythms and influences, and the effects of the constellations on weather forecasts and plant growth. In it is space to note, year in, year out, when the first primrose is seen in the meadows, when the first cuckoo is heard in the valley, when the first swallow arrives and the last one departs. Thus, it gives the opportunity for everyone to augment traditional knowledge with personal observations gathered through closeness to the natural world, and thus for the knowledge to be kept alive and handed down over generations.

My first perusal of the almanach surprised me. This wasn't an obscure publication. It was a highly anticipated, accepted and welcome reference book to lead one's life by and to be referred to and discussed by all. Each month described tasks for a traditional subsistence smallholding or garden and detailed planting, cultivation and harvesting times throughout the year, with possible weather conditions influenced by phases of the moon and its relationship to the zodiacal constellations.

All this led me back to mediaeval herbals, which show that from those times onwards, there has always been a hierarchy of influences: the basic forces being the Elements – of Earth, Water, Fire and Air, i.e. those factors surrounding us here on the planet. Further away is the sun – the source of our energy, of fire, giving us light and warmth. Its daily passage from east to west across the sky in

*My Shamanic quilt – the Iris from Knossos connected
to the heavens, the Earth and everything else, with a
backcloth of the Chevenoz skyline*

larger or smaller arcs gives us the seasons of summer and winter. Closer is our satellite the moon, with its characteristic attraction and gravitational pull and its phases and rhythms.

So the mediaeval mind (like the later biodynamic movement adherents) saw all things as interconnected – the cosmos with its luminaries: the sun, stars, moon and planets; and the Earth with its immediate influences of the Elements and everything on the Earth – both animate and inanimate. This was the belief system I decided to adopt and try to live by.

For more in-depth information on these topics, see later descriptions in Chapter VII and related appendices.

Chapter notes

1. Squire, Sir John: Grass of Parnassus – an Anthology of Poetry for Schools. 1947. Hardback edition. London Edward Arnold publisher

2. *Chatelaine Claude et Baud George: Habundantia: La vie au Val d'Abondance à travers le temps.* Editeur : Impr. Sopizet (1983) ASIN: B0014MWQE6

3. Simonton, O. Carl. www.simontoncenter.com

4. Günther, Ernest: The Essential Oils. 1948. NY Volumes I to VI Van Nostrand Co

5. *L'Almanach Savoyard.* www.almanach-savoyard.fr/

The stone table in snow

VII

Ideas and influences: the theories and the practice

'Reason sets the boundaries far too narrowly for us and would have us accept only the known – and that too with limitations; and live in a known framework, just as if we are sure how far life actually extends...'

C.G. Jung, 'Memories, Dreams, Reflections'

Throughout the winter months while I have been developing my garden, I have had the luxury of time to research, to read, to contemplate and to be creative. This is a gardener's life – and especially in such a climate of long and frozen winters. My cancer and the death of my sister made me determined to find a deeper understanding and meaning for my own life experiences and for what I was attempting to do: in essence, to find an explanation for the feeling of supreme wellbeing that I had experienced during the Breuss Diet, and to devise a way of growing the highest quality healing herbs that I could on our land in Chevenoz. Also, the Jungian analysis in which my dreams and personal symbolism featured so strongly gave me the challenge – and eventually the breakthrough – to encourage me to look at, and in many instances to embrace, ideas that were quite foreign to a scientific perspective and my previously held worldview. It also gave me a deeper understanding of connection and relationship. This was a weaving process. Many of the ideas took years to assimilate and to accept intellectually and emotionally: the capabilities of a human being, our relationship to plants and our environment, and the process of healing (an ongoing pursuit, of course).

These ideas and influences have stemmed from very diverse places. On occasions an experience questioned my worldview and I took steps to try to understand a new idea. On others, I had the opportunity to explore and follow my enthusiasms – with no idea where it would lead. I had time to delve and to experience. My researches were basically in two directions: the 'why' – an understanding of the energy I had during the Breuss Diet, which was leading me to another dimension of the healing process, which led me quickly to the influential players: Goethe, Steiner, Humboldt and Bach. The second direction was the 'how' – to be able to appreciate and follow, both practically and intellectually, biodynamic and other cultivation techniques that worked with an energetic or spiritual dimension.

The theories from the polymaths (those who have 'learned much')

On one occasion I was having lunch at the Physic Garden and was curious to watch a colleague, obviously distressed, sit down in silence and take a small bottle out of her bag. She opened her mouth, squirted a few drops of tincture under her tongue and then a few seconds later swallowed, took a deep breath and visibly relaxed, and joined our company. This was such a simple task with a seemingly profound and instant effect. In later conversations with this person, whom I had great respect for, I learned that she had been deeply stressed that morning and so used a Bach Rescue Remedy to calm herself before eating lunch. I was impressed and vowed to find out about this – and experiment myself.

My starting point was the work of Edward Bach – a successful medical doctor who became a homoeopathist and finally an overt 'sensitive'. He had two great interests in his life: an overwhelming compassion for all those who suffered and a deep love of Nature. As a medical student in the 1920s he observed that treatment of disease was often a very painful process and he considered that the patient's personality (their outlook on life, feelings and emotions) was of even greater importance than the body in the treatment of disease. His thesis was that true healing should be painless, gentle and benign, and his guiding principle was: 'Take no notice of the disease, think only of the outlook on life of the one in distress'. Added to this, his deep Christian beliefs gave him a certainty of a beneficent God and the existence of a Soul, and this gave him a conviction that: 'Final and complete healing will come from within, from the Soul itself, which by His beneficence radiates harmony throughout the personality when allowed to do so'[1].

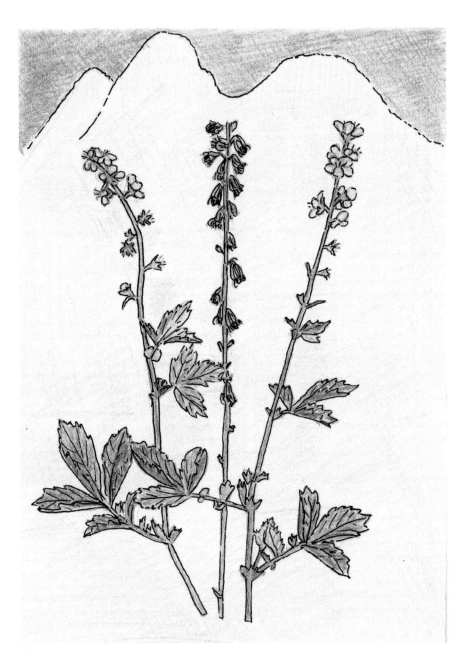

Agrimony (Agrimonia eupatoria) – a Bach Flower Remedy

While contemplating this idea of dis-ease in a patient's personality, Bach found that by using his intuition and adopting the emotions of a sick person – be it fear, anger, despondency, etc – he could enter a state of deep contemplation and go into Nature to commune with the plants in his garden and the local countryside. In this state, he found that eventually a plant with the capacity to heal this particular dis-ease would 'speak' to him (i.e. he was receptive to the healing power of the plant). Through this work, he discovered twelve plants to heal those emotions which he saw to be the causes of many physical diseases. He called these plants the 'Twelve Healers'. In time he added to this group, creating a list of thirty-eight plants[2,3].

From these he created the Bach Flower Remedies. His preparation methods of these essences were more akin to alchemy than modern chemistry. They were based on Hahnemann's homoeopathic tincture preparations and entailed shaking the alcoholic extract of the plant vigorously in a prescribed manner and then diluting it serially with water (each solution being ten times more dilute than the previous one) until, theoretically, none of the original substance was left in the final solution. This technique has been adopted by e.g. the Australian Bush Remedies, Perelandra Essences in the USA, Avalon, and Findhorn Essences. In all cases, the premise is that plant extracts prepared in this way can heal human emotional dis-ease. From their popularity over a long period of time, this appears to be true.

So my question was (and continued to be for some long time): how did Bach get into this different 'frame of mind' to be 'perceptive' to the healing power of plants? This innate ability can be seen in sick animals and in many traditional cultures where wild plants are the sole source of food and medicine. But Western culture has emphasised materialism, the body physical, synthetic drugs and surgery as a means of curing disease. The scientific method of separating/classifying/dividing into smaller and smaller entities, to measure and describe, has yielded spectacular results of curing the physical body, prolonging life and of eradicating infectious disease, etc. But it has also separated us from the natural world and led us to distrust our own immediate experience of Nature, our capacity to relate to her and initiate our own healing.

My quest then led on to Johann Wolfgang von Goethe: writer, natural philosopher, artist and renowned polymath (1749–1832). Goethe lived in a time when this separation was becoming the scientific paradigm and objectivity and measurement were seen as crucial to scientific observation. But Goethe saw a human being as a 'most exact instrument' for bringing scientific observations

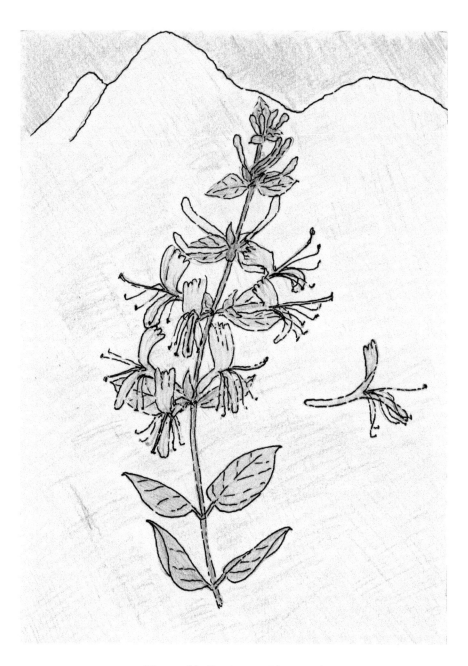

Honeysuckle (Lonicera periclymenum)

A Chevenoz Bach Remedy preparation: honeysuckle.
For 'those who live much in the past, perhaps a time of great happiness, or memories of a lost friend, or ambitions which have not come true. They do not expect further happiness such as they have had'.

into the world of lived human relationship with Nature. Thus he was advocating a form of subjectivity that used intelligence alongside many of our other sensitivities to give a balanced view of the natural world and our relationship to it[4].

For the last twenty years, Schumacher College in Devon has run post-graduate courses in Holistic Science based on Goethe's ideas. They describe the course as an expanded science that 'includes feeling, sensing, thinking and intuition as powerful research tools... which we can use to solve the many urgent problems of our time' and 'a transformative learning journey that brings soul into the very core of science.'[5] These ideas from Goethe, using 'man as a precise instrument for measurement' through observation, through imagination and through creativity, have been practised by poets, artists and shamans for aeons. Some scientists would say that it is also their method. But it is certainly not the classical scientific method based on separation and objective observation as described by Karl Popper. Interestingly, as science has progressed from study at the molecular to the particle level, objectivity is no longer a requirement or even a possibility (e.g. in quantum physics research).

It was during a course at Schumacher College that I first saw the results of many students studying plants by this method of scientific observation. I was deeply impressed by the precision, sensitivity and artistry involved in their presentations and details of plant anatomy and development that I had never come across in my study of botany. This was a different way of looking at plants. On the course I met Evelyn Roe, who had been working in Africa as an ethnobotanist. She had come to Schumacher College to do the master's degree in Holistic Science and for her research had returned to Africa to study the East African water lily. In her beautiful M.Sc. dissertation entitled 'The Way of the Water Lily. Reflections on the Influence of Goethe's Way of Science on my Botanical Work',[6] she described the four stages which make up the Goethean method as:

'Stage I: Exact Sensorial Perception – to accurately observe details of outward form, making notes and drawings; use sight, feel textures, smell. Describe your sensory experiences and observations. Put the plant at the centre of your attention.

Stage II: Exact Sensorial Imagination – to move into your thoughts. Remember the plant precisely. Imagine looking fluidly from one part of the plant to the next. Try to draw or paint from memory. Perceive the dynamic processes as the plant 'comes in to being' in your mind.

Stage III: Seeing into Beholding: to still your imaginative thinking and create a space in which the plant presents itself. This is equivalent to the plant 'speaking to us'. Explore the gestures.

Stage IV: Being one with the plant. This final stage of recognition needs a change in one's mode of Consciousness to allow a direct experience of inner unity with the plant – to catch a glimpse of the true nature of the plant.'

So this described in detail how to make a mind shift as Bach did, to take in information from the senses, to use imagination to imprint them on your

Consciousness, and then to receive the plant in a gesture of open relationship. In Evelyn's case this process had a profound effect on her and on her later ethnobotanical work:

> 'My personal experience of increased mindfulness came during my Goethean study, after sitting with the water lily for many hours. I became aware of a shift in my focus, of an experience of heart and mind opening, and a deep sense of gratitude for being able to know this plant. My attitude towards the water lily was grounded in respect and care for its well- being.'

Goethe's work was an important influence on Rudolf Steiner (1861–1925). Like Goethe, Steiner was a polymath: a philosopher, doctor, social reformer, architect, educator and, later, the founder of the esoteric and spiritual Anthroposophy movement. His influence spread into distinct movements in education, biodynamic cultivation and architecture. Steiner regarded the whole person as extending beyond the physical body to the Etheric body, the Astral body and the Ego. He considered that the modern scientific approach was insufficient on its own for gaining insights into the deeper aspects of a human being. Like Goethe and later Bach, he saw that these insights could be gained by changing perception, i.e. developing enhanced powers of mind activity to extend into a non-physical reality. He called this ability the power of imaginative (as made up of images) perception. His view was that to maintain health, there needed to be a balance between the sensory perception of the material world and the imaginative perception of the etheric world, and also with the Astral body and the Ego. In sickness, the balance was upset. He also considered that plants had an Etheric body that could connect with that of the sick person – so the plant could provide the healing necessary to bring the individual back into balance.

As an example of how this could work, Steiner chose the plant mistletoe for its capacity to heal an individual with cancer. He described the patient as being 'conformist, not knowing what she wants out of life' and mistletoe as 'aristocratic, Bohemian and contrary – a maverick', and described how the plant could restore balance by providing what was insufficiently strong in the individual. Incidentally, mistletoe has since been found to be an effective drug in Western medicine used in cancer therapy.

Again, this very simple account of Steiner's work on healing is selected to describe his ideas on connection and balance, and ways of perceiving Nature other than by objective and sensory observation[7].

Alexander von Humboldt
(1769–1859) – the man who saw connections

It was considerably later that I came across the work of Alexander von Humboldt. In many ways, he was the forerunner of the Ecology Movement, but perhaps 150 years before his time. Why had he not figured in ecology lectures so long ago when I was studying botany?

In her book 'The Invention of Nature',[8] Andrea Wulf researched his travels and his work over the period of his long life. Here was a German explorer, a natural philosopher, a botanist and a thinker. He was a close friend and colleague of Goethe and was working in a contrary way to the current scientific paradigm. His passionate desire was to have a better understanding of the natural world and to travel extensively to survey it. As Goethe's Faust, he was driven to 'detect the inmost force which binds the world and guides its course'. The real purpose of his first trip to Tenerife was to 'discover how all the forces of Nature are interlaced and interwoven'.

At this time, there were many natural philosophers, poets, writers and artists who were railing against industrialisation and the separations of science, but von Humboldt wanted to see Nature with both his head and his heart. His head had a formidable memory, with the ability to make connections between everything he saw, and he was aware of Goethe's idea that man and his senses were 'a most precise instrument' for such work.

His next trip to South America amazed him, and especially the first impression that he had that 'everything seemed somehow connected'. This idea would shape his thinking for the rest of his life. And of course, his mind was especially suited to such an idea as he had the capacity to absorb what lay in front of him and reach back in his memory to what he had seen in other landscapes. After a while, everything he had ever seen fell into place and he then described Nature as 'a web of life and a global force'. From this idea stemmed the most beautiful, original and intricate maps and drawings showing the connections between plant communities and climatic zones across continents. Being an artist as well as a precise biologist, he described this web as 'Ein Naturgemälde' – a sort of landscape painting. In 1806 in Berlin, he published his 'Essay on the Geography of Plants', which was the first real description of ecology – most other books of the time were on classification. The basis of his thinking was connection.

Wulf also cites other natural philosophers like Friedrich Schelling and the chemist Humphrey Davy, who rejected the chasm between the subjective world of the Self and the objective empiricism of scientific method. Shelling emphasised the 'vital force which connects Nature and Man' and Humboldt agreed, stating that 'Nature was in communication with our inner feelings'. As science was insisting that Nature was stripped of its magic, Humboldt was doing the opposite. He wanted to make sense of the natural world intellectually and also to experience it viscerally – and that meant to combine scientific research with a warmth of feeling and a force of imagination. He also came back from his travels with a high respect for the knowledge of the native people that he had met – he understood their connection with their environment.

This fitted in so well with Goethe's method of observation and also with many scientists in the coming decades. These ideas influenced the Romantic Movement in the latter part of the 19th century and gave rise to a wonderful synergy with the Arts & Crafts artisans and the Nature Poets. It also encouraged a closer personal relationship with Nature. This is seen in the lives of Henry David Thoreau, who lived a solitary existence in Walden Woods in upstate New York, and John Muir who walked across the states to California and was instrumental in the development of the American National Parks. Muir's view was that in order to understand Nature, one's feelings were as important as scientific data. Hence he unashamedly talked to violets. After an earthquake of considerable magnitude, he asked a violet 'her' opinion: 'it's all love!' was the reply.

Thus all this work brings science, imagination and art together in a way to give a sense of wonder for Nature. And this is the legacy for plants and for the environment – as we only really protect what we love.

...and the practice

This second strand of research was to enable me to understand and embrace the practices that I planned to adopt in developing my garden and growing the plants. My gut feeling was undoubtedly to follow the well-tried methods of my neighbours, and these methods were strongly influenced by the *Almanach Savoyard* and traditional knowledge of the region. But I had also come to these ideas from a theoretical standpoint, in particular from the ideas of Rudolf Steiner. His lectures to farmers in his native Germany in 1924 led to the development of the biodynamic movement and, later, Demeter cultivation – both methodologies that can be used in organic cultivation and also integrate scientific understanding with a recognition of Spirit in Nature.

Reading about these ideas, I alighted on the work of Maria Thun[9]. This dedicated and meticulous Austrian woman, a follower of Rudolf Steiner and an authority on biodynamic methods, has recorded decades of results of her experiments on the effects of cosmic rhythms on plant growth. Essentially, she describes when to intervene in the plant's life in order to produce the most perfect and effective food, plant medicine or product suited for a particular purpose. This 'art of timing' is further described in the work of Johanna Paungger and Thomas Poppe[10].

Biodynamic principles

The first principle of this discipline is that everything in the cosmos is in balance. Huge cosmic forces hold the elements of the solar system together – neither too far nor too near – and keep its heavenly bodies spinning and moving in regular orbits and in relationship to each other. This creates the rhythms of Nature.

The most significant of these rhythms is the rhythm of the central player of our solar system, the sun. Over the course of a year, each day the sun rises daily in the eastern sky, and arches across the southern sky and sets in the west. During the first six months, each day becomes longer, with the sun's arc becoming higher and higher in the sky and the angle of the sun's rays upon the Earth getting greater and greater. During this period, the rising and setting points of the sun veer northwards. Then after the summer solstice, when days are longest, the process reverses until the winter solstice. During this time, the sun is positioned against a backcloth of the fixed stars – appearing to move gradually from one zodiac constellation to the next until, after a year, it is back in its original place in the heavens. As spring turns to summer, heat and light reaching the Earth from the sun increase and plants grow greener, larger and faster. Then, after this pivotal mid-point, the processes reverse.

And the moon has a similar rhythm but within its own time frame of around twenty-eight days. Each day the moon orbits the Earth, and during the course of the month it appears to change form. At times it doesn't appear to be there at all, and then on fourteen subsequent nights it appears firstly as the most delicate crescent, then as a half moon, and then ultimately to the glorious complete orb of silver reflected light – full moon. Then, again over the course of around fourteen days/nights, the process reverses until the moon is no longer apparent – this is the moon's waxing and waning. During the waxing moon, the plant absorbs, builds up, stores energy and gathers strength. It becomes more resistant to disease and generally its vitality increases. At full moon, a clearly perceptible force can be felt on the surface of the Earth (by humans, by animals and by plants), and these processes have reached their maximum capacity. During the waning moon, each night the illuminated surface facing the Earth decreases until it disappears. During this time, the vitality of the plant decreases – including its colour, odour, flavour and medicinal properties. The plant expends energy in consolidating and storing. These processes reach their maximum towards the new moon. So this is a time to harvest plants for storage and to sow and plant root vegetables.

During these fourteen days there is also another fluctuation (as with the sun during a period of a year): over approximately the same two-week period, the arc of the moon's orbit rises from its lowest point in the sky to its highest, and then the rhythm is reversed. This is the moon's ascending and descending. Again, during this period, the moon is seen in front of the fixed zodiac stars, moving from one constellation to the next every two to four nights and returning to the original position after twenty-eight days. During the ascending moon, plant sap rises more strongly and the upper parts of the plant become filled with sap and vitality. As the moon starts its descent, the processes reverse. A plant is around 90% water by mass so is influenced strongly by the moon in this way. When the moon is close to the Earth (at its zenith), water is pulled up from the roots to the aerial shoots in plants. As the moon retreats, water falls back towards the roots.

The moon is attracted to both the sun and the Earth and thus has an elliptical orbit around the Earth. As the moon ascends in the sky, it is coming closer and closer to the Earth (its perigee) – exerting a huge force and attracting/pulling the water mass towards it. The sun also exerts a force but because of its much greater distance from the Earth, this is thought to be about half that of the attraction of the moon. At full moon and new moon, the Earth, the moon and the sun are in alignment and the forces are additive – they are all pulling in the same direction. When the moon moves further away from the Earth (its apogee), the force decreases, so the pull on the water body is less. At first and last quarters, these three bodies are not aligned, and the forces are opposing and the net force is less.

And then there are the Planets – those huge and bright 'wanderers' with seemingly irregular paths across the sky. Sometimes they appear to move from east to west and then zigzag back in their retrograde motion. Since ancient times, observers and stargazers have known them to be different from the fixed stars in the firmament that make up their backcloth. These enormous bodies all have their gravitational pull on the Earth, to a greater or lesser extent according to their distance, and also they work in conjunction with each other, exerting positive or negative effects on living things. Millennia of observations have brought about an understanding that when a certain planet is in a certain position in the sky (against the background of the fixed stars) there are specific influences on growth and behaviour. And when there are combinations of more than one planet's position relative to the sun in the sky, things are more complicated, but nevertheless sometimes predictable. This understanding gave rise to astrology – the sometime art and sometime science of prediction of events, and even human behaviour, according to cosmic influences. Thus the planets have fluctuating forces that they exert separately or together on the stratosphere and the surface of the Earth. These also establish weather patterns, bringing storms, drought, winds and heat to the Earth's surface.

Lastly, the zodiac signs: the broad arcs of the planets' orbits pass in front of these 'fixed stars' – so called because they hold their positions relative to each other in the night sky. Human imagination has created characters/animals of archetypal significance to describe groups of fixed stars. These are the twelve signs of the zodiac: Sagittarius (the Archer), Virgo, Aquarius (the Water Carrier), Leo, Scorpio, Libra (the Scales of balance), Gemini (the Twins), the Bull, the Ram and the Goat, Cancer (the Crab) and Pisces (the Fish). In one year, the sun passes in front of each of these areas – taking about twenty-eight days to pass across each sign. The moon takes around twenty-eight days to pass in front of them all – taking from two to four days to pass from one sign to the next. It is the effect of this passage of the moon across those parts of the sky containing the constellations that is the most difficult to understand, but since ancient times the specific influences of these regions of the sky on plants (and humans) has been studied and recorded.

Le Calendrier Lunaire, *L'Almanach Savoyard* and Maria Thun's work are all important contributions to the biodynamic movement, which uses these rhythms. Although small-scaled, this movement has spanned decades. Their aim has been to document their results in cultivating plants using these cosmic rhythms. And it is these meticulously documented results that show clearly that the correspondences (relationships) between the Elements, the planets, the constellations of the zodiac and cultivation techniques are effective.

(For details of Maria Thun's correspondences and how she identified them, see Appendix III.)

Le Calendrier Lunaire

The author and editor Michel Gros cultivated vegetables, adopting biodynamic principles, and first published this little booklet in 1980 as a calendar/manual for gardening using the rhythms of the moon for best advantage for plant growth. Besides the moon, it places special importance on the influences of the planets and the constellations on plant growth and development. For completeness, it also includes the effects at the nodes when the orbit of the moon is in the same plane as the sun's orbit, the planetary aspects, and their effects on plants. Thus it is a synthesis of astrological and astronomical knowledge – both ancient and modern.

Its carefully designed charts plot the rhythms, sequences and magnitude of effects on plant growth as the moon passes through its courses throughout the year. The charts are impressive, complex and beautiful. And with them comes highly practical advice: the optimal times to do interventions, times to harvest particular parts of the plant, and times when the forces are too strong to intervene in any way at all!

And of course, a plant in its natural environment, rooted to the spot and influenced by all these cosmic forces and rhythms, grows in harmony with them. This is the health and vitality of the plants in the Alpine meadows of Chevenoz. To a plant, all things are connected.

The moon over Chevenoz

Gardening with the spirits of Nature

These ideas, which have introduced another energetic or spiritual component into the equation, have been taken up by others – notably Eileen and Peter Caddy in their Findhorn Garden in northern Scotland. Here they worked with 'Nature spirits' to produce a wonderful garden in inhospitable conditions. Although their spiritual beliefs were regarded as unacceptable by many fifty years ago, their ideas on sustainability and working with the forces of Nature are now highly accepted.

> 'It had much to do with people getting in touch with the
> non-tangible world, the spirit world, if you like. It's to do
> with people's connection with Nature, whether that be a
> 40lb cabbage or the Eco Village that is here.'[11]

JONATHAN CADDY, SON OF THE FINDHORN FOUNDERS

With a similar philosophy, Machaelle Small Wright has created and worked with her garden Perelandra in Virginia, USA, since 1977. She has devised a method of working with 'Nature Intelligence' in a conscious and coordinated way and has created an environment based on the principle of balance between the laws of Nature and form. She calls this 'Co-creative Science', which is studying reality and how it works from Nature's perspective so that humans and Nature can work together in peer, balanced partnership. Over the years, with trials, tribulations and dedication, Machaelle has learned to perfect the technique of communicating with her plant spirits (or Devas – a term used by the Findhorn community) and working with them. From this came the development of a research centre, where her garden is the laboratory and where Nature Intelligence has a place to work out the laws of Nature – balance – in new ways that better address our current environmental and health issues. She has also developed a range of healing flower essences of highest quality and energy that she learned to measure using kinesiology techniques, which she describes[12].

These pioneers have lasting legacies in our current world of spiritual alienation, chronic illnesses and environmental catastrophe. They all make connection between a Consciousness in Nature – be it a vitality, energy or Spirit – and our spiritual selves.

Networking with the Network!

In the context mentioned above, I was drawn to the ideas of John Heron[13] describing the concept of Participation. This fitted in well with the final stage of Goethean science. From these ideas, I realised I was not alone in wanting to develop my own spiritual enquiry and seek discussion. Heron's description of participation is akin to:

> *'Music heard so deeply that it is not heard at all, but you*
> *are the music while the music lasts.'*
> FROM T.S. ELIOT, 'FOUR QUARTETS'

In 1996, I was invited to give a presentation on my garden and herbal products at a French meeting of the Scientific and Medical Network in Les Courmettes, near Cannes in southern France. For this meeting I produced a small brochure entitled 'Vital Plants' describing my then-current philosophy and influences. Already I was bold enough to speak of:

> *'Harmony and Balance in all things… it is my learning process to participate*
> *Body, Soul and Spirit with the daily processes that I engage in. It is an*
> *integral part of my premise that the vitality of the plant can be transferred to*
> *the product by careful, loving and precisely timed interventions. My intention*
> *and my participation are of value.'*

It was at this meeting that I met two people who were able to feel this 'vitality', as I then called it. Holding a small bottle of lavender oil in the palm of her hand, one woman was deeply impressed by the energy she could perceive. This was supported by her colleague, who was also a practising dowser and water diviner.

Flames in a Chevenoz fire

The concept of Qi

In times during the winter months sitting in front of a roaring log fire, I was able to prepare myself for Gabriel Mojay's Diploma in Traditional Herbal Medicine and Aromatherapy course in London. This course was going to give a new perspective to herbs and the human body. Originally trained as a Shiatsu teacher, Gabriel based his ideas on the Chinese model, where health of the body is governed by balance of a basic life energy – Qi – that is transmitted throughout the body in channels or meridians. In this model, Qi balances the governing principles of Yin and Yang, of Excess and Deficiency, of Hot and Cold.

Preparatory reading for the course was 'The Web that has no Weaver' by Ted Kapchuk[14]. A seminal understanding came to me when I read this and realised that a human being can be described in very different ways (the Chinese description being very much more ancient than the modern Western one). Both models are effective, but can seldom be super-imposed – even though on occasions, Kapchuk attempted to do so. His example of a sample of people who by diagnosis in Western medicine all had coronary heart disease, but in Chinese medicine had a variety of different diagnoses, was challenging. Both systems had effective, but very different, ways of treating these patients.

Gabriel's course studied essential oils from both perspectives – a Western one, treating the physical body with chemical active ingredients according to Western physiology and medicine, and also an Oriental perspective, based on the balance of Yin and Yang states and Qi energy, which mediates that balance[15]. It was Qi energy that I thought might be an explanation of the vitality I was trying to conserve in my plants.

As described previously, the holistic Chinese model treats the whole person through the connections of the five Elements (Fire, Earth, Metal, Water and Wind), the Seasons of the year, the Organs of the body, the Emotions and the Spirit. Although much more ancient, this model is similar to the one used by mediaeval European herbalists. So to make the link between Western herbs (which were documented in Mediaeval Herbals) and an Oriental system, Gabriel went back to the Western model of correspondences that existed from the time of Galen (ancient Greece AD 130–210) up to mediaeval times. Galen described the four Humours (a person's basic physical or mental qualities or disposition) as Sanguine (Corresponding to the Element Fire) – an optimistic and happy person; melancholic (Earth) – depressed and anxious; choleric (Air) – irritable and impulsive; and phlegmatic (Water) – listless and not easily moved. The combinations of the Humours in an individual gave the temperament – which ideally was balanced. Interestingly, C.G. Jung also used these four Humours as the basis for his main human personality types of Thinking (Air), Intuition (Fire), Feeling (Water), and Sensation (Earth), and these are the basic personality types used in the Myers-Briggs test for psychological preferences that shape a person's worldview (and have been frequently used in interview techniques).

On this course I had the opportunity to study on two levels – the theoretical, and then direct practice. This course has been extremely successful and continues to this day (2020). I bless my good fortune that my Japanese friend Ayako was my massage partner. Her innate understanding and acceptance of Qi was educational, inspiring, informative and totally convincing. I'll be eternally grateful to her and her deep spirituality, experience and grace. Added to that, the thorough teaching of the chemistry and properties of essential oils set me on course for distilling them.

Auras and Power

During the theoretical course and the intensive massage practice, we were also introduced to wider aspects of energy work. Gabriel talked about chakras in his lectures, and on occasions of relaxation and peace in the beautiful Regent's College gardens, where the course took place, I witnessed individuals practising qi gong and tai chi. We practised the technique of 'Rolfing' and of running our hands over the body in aura diagnostic work. It soon became apparent to me that Qi extends beyond the body and with careful attention can easily be perceived. And herein opened up a huge new world of subtle energy and of study of psycho-spiritual constituents of living beings, according to various esoteric, occult and mystical teachings. At the practical level, I was interested in any way I could measure – or at least recognise – this force in my 'vital' plants.

Via SMN, I also made contact with a very old university friend. John F. Caddy was a marine biologist of considerable influence and reputation. Aside from his biological career, he had become interested in Qi and shamanism and had done considerable practical work with Qi and dowsing. His book, 'A Return to Subjectivity',[16] outlines the huge gulf that exists between objectivity (as in science) and subjectivity (as in personal experience), and the importance of both. From him I learned the technique of sensing Qi with the palms of my hands. This work requires a high degree of subjectivity on the part of the perceiver and thus is received skeptically by those wanting objective 'proof'. As a technique, was it pushing the current paradigm of measurable phenomena too far? Thomas Kuhn (American physicist, historian and philosopher) in his book 'The Structure of Scientific Revolutions',[17] describes the way in which currently held ideas in science change, opening up new approaches to understanding. He called these paradigm shifts. Perhaps we in the West are not yet at a stage where such a paradigm shift is possible regarding the phenomenon of Qi? Although mainstream in Oriental medicine, there is still no point of connection with Western medicine and its understanding of the human body. However, Qi was a phenomenon I needed to pursue in my own understanding and in my explanation of what I was trying to do with my garden, plants and plant products.

Shamanic practices II

'Only those who will risk going too far can possibly find out how far one can go.'
T.S. ELIOT

Indigenous medicine men and women often choose their healing plants by a form of intuition or clairvoyance, or by finding their answers in a shamanic Journey to the spirits of the plants. These other ways of knowing of and understanding connections between individuals and Nature, although innate, have mostly been lost by modern cultures. But they can be cultivated or re-learned by practice and guidance.

The anthropologist Michael Harner worked closely with indigenous tribes in the Ecuadorian Andes and the Peruvian Amazon of South America. Like many at this time, with guidance from these tribesmen, he experimented with the shamans' sacred drink prepared from the 'Soul Vine' – also known as *Ayahuasca (Banisteriopsis caapi)*. After this initiation, in his words, 'his serious study of shamanism began', and he lived with the Jivaro people and learned their ways. Working with other tribes, he later learned how shamanism can be practised without using *Ayahuasca* or other psychotropic plants. From these collaborations came his practical guide 'The Way of the Shaman'[18]. This brought about a shamanic revival in modern Western society. Other authorities at that time were Joan Halifax, whose research with shamans in Western and Eastern cultures resulted in her book 'Shamanic Voices', which details many diverse shamanic narratives. She describes shamanism as 'a lifeway that spans millennia and the entire planet'[19]. Further seminal work was done by Sandra Ingermann, whose book 'Soul Retrieval – Mending the Fragmented Self'[20] took this work into the realms of healing and psychotherapy.

From these ideas come the 'core shamanic practices' used by Jonathan Horwitz (a long-term collaborator with Michael Harner) and the foundation of his work at the Scandinavian Center for Shamanic Studies[21] that he founded with Annette Høst. He thus brought this traditional knowledge to Europe, and Annette added a distinctly Scandinavian emphasis by linking it into ancient Seidr practices of 'wise women' or 'seers'. Later, Zara Waldebäck joined the group and again brought her own emphasis of making the work relevant to modern Western culture by weaving in the power of storytelling and myth with environment.

Modern shamanism, as taught by them, gives a rigorous framework in which to practice and emphasises the concepts of:

Spirit: We can access a 'spirit world' using other parts of our minds/ Consciousness, which we in the West seem to have forgotten, but which indigenous tribespeople still use frequently. It entails going into a trance state and making sense of subtle 'prompts' from another 'reality', using our imagination, creativity and intuition. It is the long-term work of the shaman to interpret her/ his own 'Non-Ordinary Reality' and the spirits within it. Jonathan's description of spirits as 'bundles of Energy in forms we can recognise' gives an insight into the link between human imagination and another 'reality' (interpretation of our existence). Owen Barfield, in his book 'Saving the Appearances',[22] describes in detail how the primitive mind uses a blend of the archetypal symbols that make up the collective unconscious and the individual's own conscious and personal symbolism and experience to make sense of her/his environment. Jungian psychology also gives insight into how an individual (the Subject) can connect with the 'Other' (the Object) using powers different from rational and logical thought. The shaman calls the other reality a 'spirit world' and through belief, practice and connection learns to communicate and interact with it. It is when in an altered state of Consciousness that the constraints of the Ego are released and connection with the 'Other' can occur.

Power: Shamanism works with Power – in the sense of the German word '*Kraft*'. This is a force or energy which permeates the universe. Through Journeying, a Shaman learns to access this force and how to use it in healing.

Connection: In the shaman's world, everything is connected. In an altered state of Consciousness, the shaman is able to travel between the three Worlds (the Upper World, which is the source of wisdom and teachings; the Middle World, which is the spirit world of our Ordinary Reality; and the Lower World, which is the source of Power and healing).

Healing: Sickness in shamanic terms is due to 'Intrusions' (of evil) or 'Soul loss' (in psychological terms, 'fragmentation') – where an important part of the individual is split off or 'stolen' in hostile circumstances. These very simple ideas, expressed in archaic language, point to a significant lack of balance and harmony in the individual.

So there are definite similarities between shamanism and aspects of mediaeval herbalism viz. the connections, an energetic basis, the need for harmony and balance. The results of this work can be astounding – in some instances, far more effective than depth psychology – and can reach beyond the psychological blocks and resistances that cry out for treatment. But to try to describe how it happens is futile. As with magic and miracles, there are things that are not describable and can only be judged by results. In my experience over twenty-four years, shamanism definitely works.

Chapter notes

1. Weeks, Nora. The Medical Discoveries of Edward Bach. 1940. C.W. Daniel Co Ltd, Saffron Walden. Copyright The Dr Edward Bach Healing Centre 1973. ISBN 85207 001 2

2. Bach, E. Heal Thyself. 1931. C.W. Daniel Co Ltd. Saffron Walden. ISBN 0 85207 040. Reprinted 1993

3. Bach, E. The Twelve Healers. 1933. C.W. Daniel Co Ltd. Saffron Walden. ISBN 0 85207 041 1. Reprinted 1993

4. Naydler, Jeremy. (excerpts selected by) Goethe on Science. 1996. Floris Books English edition ISBN 0-86315-237-6

5. Schumacher College www.schumachercollege.org.uk/courses/postgraduate-courses/

6. Roe, Evelyn. Dissertation submitted -086315-797-4 for the M.Sc. Holistic Science, Schumacher College and Plymouth University. August 2013

7. Maendl, Andrew. Rudolf Steiner Medicine. 2003 Sophia Books. An imprint of Rudolf Steiner Books. ISBN 1-85584-133-9

8. Wulf, Andrea. The Invention of Nature: the Adventures of Alexander von Humboldt, the lost Hero of Science. 2016 John Murray publishers ISBN 978-1-84854-900-5

9. Thun, Maria. Gardening for Life. The Biodynamic Way. English edition. 1999. Hawthorn Press. ISBN 1 869 890 32 9

10. Paungger, Johanna and Poppe, Thomas. The Art of Timing. 2000. C.W. Daniel Co Ltd. ISBN 0-85207-334-8

11. www.findhorn.org and 'Findhorn Garden' written by the Findhorn Community with foreword by Sir George Trevelyan. 3rd edition, 2003 (1st edition 1976). Findhorn Press. ISBN 1-84409-018-3

12. Small Wright, Machaelle. Co-creative Science. 1997 Published by Perelandra Ltd. VA 20188 USA. ISBN 0-927978-25-3

13. Heron, John. Sacred Science. 1998. PCCS Books. ISBN 1 898059 21 7

14. Kaptchuk, Ted. The Web that has no Weaver – Understanding Chinese Medicine. 2000. Contemporary Books/McGraw-Hill. ISBN 0-8092-2840-8

15. Mojay, Gabriel. Aromatherapy for Healing the Spirit. 1997. Gaia Books Ltd. London. ISBN 978 0 89281 887 8

16. Caddy, John. A Return to Subjectivity. 2006. Trafford Publishing. ISBN 1-4120-8366-4

17. Kuhn, Thomas. The Structure of Scientific Revolutions. 2012. (50th anniversary edition.) University of Chicago Press. ISBN 978-0-226-45811-3

18. Harner, Michael. The Way of the Shaman. 3rd edition. 1990. Harper & Row. ISBN 0-06-250373-1

19. Halifax, Joan. Shamanic Voices – the Shaman as Seer, Poet and Healer. 1979. Penguin Books ISBN 0 14 02.22.73

20. Ingermann, Sandra. Soul Retrieval. 1991. Harper, San Francisco. ISBN 006250406

21. Scandinavian Center for Shamanic Studies. www.shamanism.dk and http://www.shamanism.dk/who.htm. Jonathan Horwitz, Annette Høst and Zara Waldebäck.

22. Barfield, Owen. Saving the Appearances. Second edition. 1988. Wesleyan University Press. ISBN 0-8195-6205-x (paperback)

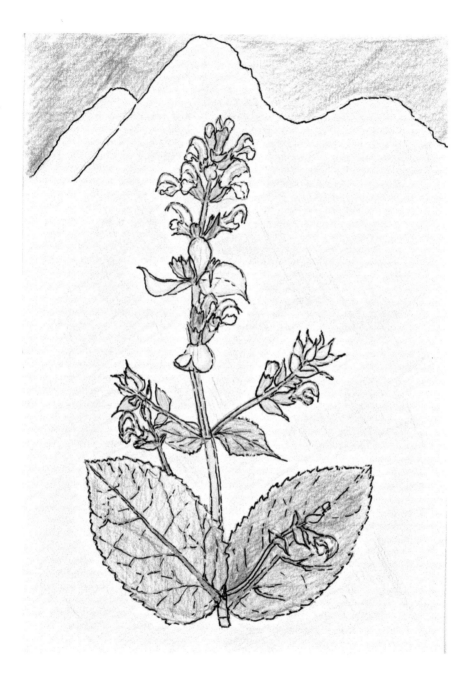

Clary sage (Salvia sclarea).
Another sage and an important and handsome plant in the garden

VIII

A place to work

The winter months were also the time to plan and to prepare the space where my plant propagation and plant preparations could take place. Alongside the house to the west we had an ancient barn. This was a relic from the old farmhouse, which had escaped the fire and remained, albeit in a very dilapidated state, as outhouse, garage and smoking cabinet for the Morels' sausages. It was of traditional Savoyard design with a basic stone-walled inner chamber and then a wooden barn construction around it with a beautiful local slate roof (in a dreadful state of repair).

Even though we had asked them to clear it, when we arrived it was packed to the rafters with the remains of the old family existence – generations of old farm machinery and tools, furniture, frames of old walnut chairs that had lost their straw seats, old mattresses and a lot of things that could hardly be described. We cleared the ground floor gradually, taking Land Rover-fuls of rubbish to the local tip, and thus had made space as a garage. The wooden steps/ladder to the upper floor were at a precarious angle and loosely attached to the front wall. The upstairs beams were in various stages of putrefaction and decay.

So by 1997, we had decided we should start to plan for the barn's renovation. Our daughter Clare and her husband Carlos were both architects and had visited Chevenoz frequently and loved the place. They volunteered to design our new barn. A difficulty was that they lived in Manhattan, so they wouldn't be available to oversee the construction.

Over a period of a year, with the help of Jeanne's son, we dismantled the old barn. Conserving the old roof tiles was the main task and we spent many a long day removing them, tile by tile, and then – with the aid of Stéphane's hay elevator – working in reverse, transporting them to the ground and sorting them into those we could re-use, and those we couldn't. We managed to save

The old barn

around 60% of them so needed to source some new ones. In earlier times there were several slate mines in the region, but as the beautiful tiled roofs of traditional farmhouses were being replaced by cheaper corrugated iron sheets, these mines closed down. There was one remaining working mine in the region, so we went to visit it. We were met on site by a cheery New Zealander who was trying to revive the business. He had a few of the old style and sized tiles that we needed and we happily made a transaction. He then suggested we had a tour and led us to the entrance of the mine. This was less than two metres high with rickety wooden props and rails for a cart – hand-pushed, I seem to imagine, or with a winch and pulley system. These conditions didn't meet with EU Health and Safety regulations in any capacity, and the investment needed to do so was exorbitant. So, having sold off the remaining stock, the mine was closed.

The rest of the barn came down very easily and we were left with a huge pile of old pine beams, some of which were in good enough condition to be chain-sawed into logs; a huge number of corrugated sheets, which were quickly taken away by locals who wanted them to renovate their own roofs or to protect their wood piles; and lastly and most preciously, the rectangular stone-walled inner construction, which had been a stable for cattle.

Then, as these things happen, Clare became pregnant and preferred to spend her later months of pregnancy with us in Chevenoz than in the summer heat and foreign-ness of Manhattan. She and Carlos arranged to come to Chevenoz for the whole of the construction period from May until after the birth in September. We managed to enlist the help of the aforementioned talented and knowledgeable local carpenter (Roger) to work with Carlos and, after many interactions with French bureaucracy, decided on the design and plans and were ready to start. The new design was beautiful and tailor-made for our needs. The front, south-facing wall was completely glass and downstairs comprised the windows of the greenhouse/conservatory. Upstairs it let light into the large studio space that we would use as a preparation area and drying space, with large mesh nets in the rafters for drying herbs out of direct sunlight. It was also for Ben to use as a photographic studio. Since it was such a lovely space, we tucked a little sleeping loft and a very small bathroom under the back rafters. Downstairs, the front area was a glasshouse, behind it garage space, and the stone-walled 'Cave' was to become my distillery and preparation room – part laboratory and part alchemical and magician's cave!

Construction was laborious and each day Carlos and Roger worked away with no common language. Franglais and Carlos's mother tongue, Spanish, somehow sufficed. The two of them had much in common and a shared love of aesthetics and craft. Roger was delighted to meet someone with such creative ideas and not worn down by age-old tradition and the sort of closed mind that can accompany it. Carlos was from the New World and brought with him a refreshing freedom and optimism. Roger had his own ideas, however – of what would survive the climate and conditions of Chevenoz, the Earth tremors, the slipping clay schists and subsidence, the shrinkage of the Alpine wood. It was a good combination, and the outcome was stunning.

At the beginning of September of that year, the roof was on, the outer shell and inner structure were almost complete, and at full moon on September 6, Clare started her labour. On September 7, 1998, I witnessed the birth of our first grandchild at the Maternity Hospital in Evian. The child was born – she came into this world 'comme une flèche' as the 'sage-femme' (as the French still call their midwives) said. Clare had given birth to a beautiful baby girl, later named Soledad. The barn is called 'Chez Soledad' to this day.

Over the next few years, we kitted out the barn according to our current needs. I started with the greenhouse area – la serre. Beneath the large south-facing windows we installed a wide potting shed-style bench the length of the space. Under this were

The renovated barn

bays to put soil, compost and pots in. On the surface were large rectangular plastic trays in which I could stand the plant pots and irrigate them. We also installed an automatic watering system for those periods when we were away and a couple of incubators in which to germinate seedlings. All this was modelled on the Physic Garden potting shed. I could germinate seeds, prick them out into small pots – five seedlings per pot – and then grow them on before hardening off and planting in the garden. In front of the barn, on the sheltered south-facing slope, we had also constructed a cold frame in which to do the hardening off. The first spring this worked well – we had a coolish and not too sunny spring. The following year, however, I experienced a lot of difficulties. Unlike in the temperate London climate, here in Chevenoz we had lots of early spring sunshine – even though external temperatures, especially at night, were very cold. With the sun so low in the sky, our overhanging roof carefully designed to protect from summer sunshine wasn't adequate. Within *la serre*, daytime temperatures could reach 30°C+ and although the days were short, light intensity was high. So the seedlings grew at a furious rate. I then hardened them off but the external soil temperature was too low and the ground was still hard, even frozen. It was impossible to plant these young plants out. If I started the process later, greenhouse temperatures were too high. The Physic Garden's tried-and-tested method was for temperate English gardens and not for these continental French ones. Over the years I had produced enough seeds and could plant them out directly in the plots and then thin them out to leave plants in their growing positions. There was a lot to learn here in this decidedly foreign environment.

I then used the space for another purpose, which worked well. Because my lavender and rosemary plants were cultivars that wouldn't breed true from seeds, I had to take cuttings. This was a technique I had learned at the Physic Garden and one which I loved doing. I planted twiglets, carefully chosen and torn off the parent plant, and put around twenty in each pot. Placing them round the edge of the pot encouraged root growth. It always amazed me to see how the growth spread around the perimeter of the pot – one cutting influencing the activity of its neighbours. These pots were covered by polythene bags to keep the aerial parts of the stems moist. Once roots were established, the new plantlets were transplanted to individual pots and left until they were ready to plant out. In this way I bulked up my lavenders and rosemaries until I had enough to distill for essential oils. I also took cuttings of the beautiful Cape Town rose geranium plants.

The next area to develop was the *Cave*. This was a wonderful space – very ancient – and must have housed farmyard beasts (relatively few, or at least small ones) for centuries. We rough-plastered the stone walls and paved the floor with slate slabs. I found a stable trough, large and round-bottomed, to use as the sink to wash my large glass bottles and glassware. I would have preferred it to be stone but bought a more serviceable polypropylene one to avoid too many breakages of these precious vessels. Carlos had designed this *Cave* with three small windows in the building aligned. In this way, the morning sunshine arrived through the east-facing windows, and the evening sunshine from the west-facing one. During the day, the *Cave* was cool. This made a beautiful space to work in. Another workbench was installed and a fridge, and in the corner I left space for the still. This was only a prototype to start with while the parameters of the definitive model were being worked out. We painted the doors and windows of the barn a beautiful mid-blue – more Provençal than Savoyard (as Roger had said), but distinctive and to Carlos's liking.

Upstairs in the studio space we hung large netting beds from the rafters. With the windows open, a through-draught circulated so herbs and flowers dried out of direct sunlight in two to three days. This preserved colours and aromas superbly. In the first summer of production, I had planted large beds of *Calendula*. Each day at midday I gathered the mature flowers and laid them to dry. These were then used to make infused *Calendula* oil. Other herbs were used fresh and these were prepared on the studio bench –chopped by a huge guillotine and packed into bottles, either for tincture production or for infused oils.

The Chevenoz Cave

Ayako and Calendula flowers

Calendula flowers drying on the racks

By the following year I was doing small-scale production of tinctures and larger-scale production of infused oils of *Calendula, Hypericum,* meadowsweet and chickweed. I was also drying rose petals, *Calendula* flowers, linden flowers for tisanes, and lavender for bags. I was now ready to develop the still.

Research and design of the still

My year-long course with Gabriel Mojay was comprehensive and thorough. It covered so many aspects of essential oil qualities, provenance and uses. Aromatherapists were being subjected to similar rigours of regulation as medical herbalists. Gabriel's courses were training new aromatherapists who needed to qualify according to these regulations, and he made sure we were given adequate information and training. I certainly came away from that course with a strong impression that there were some beautiful oils on the market, but also that many oils were of dubious quality. The criteria for what made a high-quality oil were well known – the quality of the original plant material, conditions of growth, their chemical constituents and proportions, production methods, additional processes like chemical alteration or addition, absence of adulteration. Storage was important too.

We also studied and used hydrolats or floral waters. Originally these were produced in their own right (e.g. rose water, orange water) and were used as perfumes and in foods. Famous perfumes using hydrolats are Eau de Cologne and Queen of Hungary Water – both now made by Joe Nasr of Avicenna. More recently, distillers have realised that these by-products of steam distillation of essential oils actually have intrinsic value as floral waters, in lotion and cream production. There is certainly a market for them among aromatherapists and beauticians who are producing their own ranges of 'paraben-free' creams, lotions and soaps perfumed with hydrolats and essential oils.

My approach to designing a still was influenced by research and then by example. Textbook diagrams of Avicenna's alembic (circa AD 1000 with his distillation of rose essence) and schematic diagrams of industrial stills all gave me ideas.

I wanted something bigger than a bench-top still as we had used in university chemistry classes, but certainly not as big as the still I had seen in La Drome lavender fields, where the operator got into the still and stamped the plant material down with his feet (shades of wine pressing?). I had also seen Len Price's still in action in La Drome, where we, a group of students on Gabriel's Herbal Study Tour, had hand-gathered hyssop plants for the distillation. But I needed something fit for purpose – to suit the amount of land I had at my

A Simple Alembic

Hood

Copper Still
Containing
Plant Mass &
Water

Air-cooled
Spiral
Condenser

Heat Source

Collection
Vessel

Diagram of a simple alembic

disposal; how much was possible for a single person to grow and harvest in a season; physical considerations of space within the *Cave*; dimensions to work with – height of still, weight of things and plants; what was possible without a three-phase electrical system. There were so many considerations…

Gradually the parameters all came together. Using the excellent laboratory glassware and equipment I bought earlier, I set up a basic laboratory – measuring cylinders, pipettes, flasks, beakers, clamps and stands, thermometers, Quickfit condensers. This was all professional and very expensive equipment, so a wonderful purchase. I could use them for experimenting with the prototype still.

My first distillation was using a still with a design modified from an A level chemistry textbook. The still was a domestic pressure cooker with a modified lid, connected to a water-cooled condenser and a glass collecting vessel. This might sound a trifle hazardous, but I was aware of the risks and what to look out for.

Blue chamomile water

And the flowers the blue chamomile water came from

I harvested beautiful German chamomile flowering tops, packed them on a grill in the pan, put water below the grill and set it going, heating it with a Bunsen burner and gas cylinder. Within a short time, the colourless distillate in the collection vessel started to turn blue and then, gradually, floating on the surface of the liquid was a layer of brilliant blue oil (like cornflowers, like delphiniums). I was amazed – and delighted. To read that the colour is due to azulene has a significance, but to see this brilliant blue colour emerge from the pure white and golden flowers and green leaves is magic! And the smell was wonderful too. I managed to collect 2ml of blue oil using a small pipette, leaving me 2.5l of sweet-smelling, lighter blue floral water or hydrolat, which I left to clear and cool and then decanted into brown glass wine bottles and corked.

This was the beginning, the first distillation. So now I had to decide on the scale of future operations and to refine the process, measure parameters of the equipment, analyse the oils and hydrolats and many other things too. Of one thing I was sure. This ancient process was as alchemical as it was chemical, was a creative process and art form as much as it was science. My aim was to research and then make the most beautiful and therapeutic oils that I possibly could.

From research at the Wellcome Library, I found so many details of essential oils – cultivation techniques of their source materials, preparation of the plant material for distillation, distillation methods, optimal yields and their therapeutic uses[1]. This was in addition to the knowledge obtained in the Aromatherapy course – details of the chemical constituents of the oils and hydrolats from Tisserand and Penoël and other leading aromatherapists. I decided to concentrate studies on one particular essential oil and, since it was one that I had so enjoyed using in aromatherapy massage and knew that the plant thrived in Chevenoz, chose lavender. Others would follow later.

This work all takes a lot of time! It took me five years to research cultivars of lavender suitable for Alpine growing conditions and then grow up sufficient numbers of plants to harvest the flowers in quantity. I planted test beds of accepted good oil-producing cultivars and watched to see which ones thrived best in winter snows, spring thaws, and those conditions peculiar to the Chevenoz climate. I eventually chose four cultivars: a French 'Maillette'; a New Zealand 'No. 9'; a beautiful smelling Lavendula vera cultivar from Basel, which I had grown previously in Chevenoz for five years; and I also took cuttings and propagated them from a pale-coloured, highly scented lavender plant that I found growing high up in the hills overlooking Cannes in southern France. I called this cultivar 'Les Courmettes'. These plants were all cultivars of Lavandula officinalis (vera) and not the hybrids (known as Lavandin).

Design of the still and the scaling-up process

At this stage of my endeavours I knew that production would be small-scale and interventions were going to be done by me and by hand in my *Cave*. This determined the main parameter of scaling up the still, i.e. the amount of plant material I could reasonably grow and thus distill at 10kg plant mass for each distillation. From this came the following parameters:

+ The dimensions of the still
+ The volume of steam generators
+ The electrical power needed

Discussions with Julian Franklin at Rothamsted Experimental Station in Hertfordshire were immensely helpful here as he had researched basic still design, and from these discussions came the excellent link with Tim Denny[2]. Tim had researched and designed field stills for eucalyptus and tea tree oils in New Zealand. His detailed paper on still design, with the parameters and details necessary for producing high-quality oils, was invaluable. His prototype still had many parameters that I could incorporate into my design.

Although I loved the idea of an ancient alembic-style copper still, because of health and safety and chemical considerations, I decided to purchase a non-reactive, food-grade stainless steel container, which I adapted with steam outlet tubes and a perforated platform to support the plant mass. For reasons best explained in Tim Denny's paper, this gave me a good depth of plant material for efficient oil extraction without too much of the steam condensing and draining back down the plant material and needing to be reheated. This process, known as refluxing, alters the chemical constituents of the oils considerably. The top of the container was secured with a strong band seal and a hole was bored in it to form an outlet to which a tube was connected, through which the steam and vaporised oils could leave the still. This was then passed into the copper spiral tube that acted as the condenser. A second system for cooling the distillate consisted of a water-filled cooling trough surrounding the copper spiral and a large reservoir of cold water that circulated round the cooling trough, keeping the ambient temperature as low as possible.

Steam generation was a very important feature in the design – I needed to be able to produce a sufficient volume of steam without interrupting the distillation process in a period of time that would be fast enough to prevent certain adverse

The Chevenoz Still
(All not to scale)

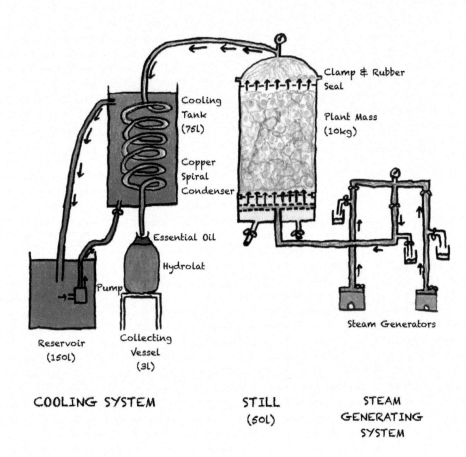

Cooling Tank (75l)

Copper Spiral Condenser

Clamp & Rubber Seal

Plant Mass (10kg)

Essential Oil

Hydrolat

Pump

Reservoir (150l)

Collecting Vessel (3l)

Steam Generators

COOLING SYSTEM

STILL (50l)

STEAM GENERATING SYSTEM

KEY: ∞ – Tap; → – Direction of flow; ø – Pressure Gauge

Diagram of my Still. Based on Tim Denny's model

chemical reactions occurring between the oils and water. The process certainly wasn't simple.

Aesthetics were important in this design, but so were costs. I paid highly for the food-grade stainless steel still and economised on the steam generators and

The still and the steam generation system

reservoirs. The steam generators were wallpaper steamers manufactured by Earlex in Guildford, UK. Two of these connected up to the still could generate steam at the required rate for forty minutes to produce 6l of distillate plus the essential oil. This was collected in 4.5l glass wine decanters and one-litre glass bottles, all with tapering necks so the essential oil rose to the top of the distillate and, as the decanter or bottle became full, a thick layer of oil lay on the top that could be pipetted off at the end of the distillation. The reservoirs were galvanised dustbins. The circulation in this system was powered by a fish tank pump. My pride and joy in this rather Heath Robinson piece of equipment was the complex system of copper tubes and on-off taps that allowed me to drain any condensed water, test for pressure build-up in the system, and shut off either of the two steam generators if a problem arose. To conserve energy and prevent steam condensing where it needed to be in the vapour state, the still and all pipes were lagged.

This still worked wonderfully and over time, I performed over 150 distillations with it. The *Cave* became a very special place where oils were distilled, decanted and aired, and then finally bottled and labelled in 10ml bottles ready for markets. The barn took on the aromas of these oils, which permeated the pine beams and mixed with those of the herbs and flowers on the drying racks. These quintessential oils and perfumes took over the space and infused it with their magic. I could now justly call myself 'La Distillatrice de Chevenoz'.

Charles and Jan Wells of Essentially Oils in Chipping Norton, Oxfordshire, were a great encouragement and help to me. Their enthusiasm for essential oils was heartwarming and their determination to promote high standards and research benefitted the whole industry. I visited them in their converted barns with a few essential oil samples in the hope of finding a future market. Mention of Tim Denny and still designs was a point of contact as Charles and Jan had previously been involved in eucalyptus oil distillation in Australia and knew Tim well. So they knew I had made good connections. Charles arranged analyses of my oils, and later my floral waters, and that autumn came to visit me in my garden in Chevenoz. This was the beginning of my distillation endeavours, which encouraged me to perfect the techniques and eventually produce a range of beautiful oils.

For me, distillation was a continuous learning process that went on for years. I kept laborious records of all the parameters of the distillations and found many ways to refine the process. Although it was possible to find references in pharmacopoeias, the 'secrets' of the trade were learned by direct experience, observation and a 'feel' for the process.

There were so many factors to consider here:

+ The quality of the plant material – e.g. at what stage of maturity should I harvest the lavender flowers?
+ Should the plants be fresh, wilted or dried? Over time I learned which plants gave better oil yields if the plant material was wilted – like the seed heads of carrot, like clary sage. However, wilting should not be done in direct sunlight.
+ How to pack the still so there were no 'rat runs' up which the steam passed without extracting essential oil.
+ Did some plants need special treatment prior to distillation?
+ Was the local spring water that I wanted to use for distillations of sufficient purity for the hydrolats that I knew people wanted to use medicinally?

The interior of the Cave

Some of these questions could be answered quite simply. I took samples of the spring water and sent them off to the French Government Water Analysis Laboratory in Annecy for testing. The results: drinking water standard (*Eau potable*); bacteriologically clean; run-offs of pesticides, nitrates, etc well within stringent limits. And then came the difficulty – we had a beautiful pure water chemically similar to Evian Water – the catchment area of which we were in the uppermost limits of! Of course this aroused the mayor's interest, since at that time a neighbouring *commune* had found a source of chemically identical (to Evian) water that was bought by the factory and yielded a huge income for the *commune*. As it would have had huge implications for the local farming community, this never happened in Chevenoz, and I thus had a supply of wonderful local spring water that I used to collect before each distillation and fill the steam generators with.

To consider the parameters list above in more detail:

1. In the early years with lavender, I harvested the most beautiful newly opened flowers – 10kg of them – and distilled them. Why I did it then, I can't remember – perhaps through enthusiasm or impatience; perhaps I feared storms were on the way and the flowers would be damaged; or perhaps I was leaving Chevenoz for a few days. Whatever the reasons were, I lived to regret my decision. The yield was about a third of what I hoped for, and the perfume was without depth. What a disappointment and such a waste… But once I had decided to follow the *Calendrier Lunaire*, when to harvest was clear. Later I found that with careful observation, I came to know when the right moment was – the bees told me as well. In later years I saw this as working with Nature and as such, it became sacred and surrounded by ritual. The whole process took on another dimension.

2. Whether to use fresh or wilted material depended very much on the plant and, to a certain extent, trial and error. I knew the ideal yields to aspire to and the data I obtained from the reference books at the Wellcome Library were good indicators (e.g. clary sage loses quite a lot of oil after harvesting so needs to be distilled immediately). Carrot seed heads need to wilt for two to three days before distillation for a good yield. The time of day of harvesting is also important for some plants.

3. Lavender packs more densely when wilted in the shade for two to three hours (but also loses some oil). Rose petals need to wilt for a short time (thirty minutes) to pack more effectively, but not for longer as they become so soft that a mat is formed and the steam forms 'rat runs' to burst through.

4. Fresh plants with high water content (e.g. roses) lose much essential oil by air drying – loss by evaporation, oxidation, resinification and other chemical reactions – but these plants don't release their essential oils very readily, so a compromise must be made. Some seeds need to be crushed to release the oil (e.g. juniper berries).

But for all the data and information I could gather regarding other people's distillations, eventually I had to make my own decisions and be satisfied to make the best oils and the optimum quantity that I could from my still and my plants in my Alpine garden. The still parameters were the best I could devise, the timing of interventions was according to the *Calendrier Lunaire*, and the climate and the soil were typical for my garden – and the oils would be as well. I was thus making some fine and unique *Herbes de Chevenoz* essential oils.

Within a few years I was distilling lavender, rosemary, rose geranium, clary sage, juniper, marjoram, *Melissa,* German chamomile, hyssop and carrot seed oils, and hydrolats of all the above plus rose water. Analyses of these oils and floral waters have been published[3] and some can also be found in Appendix IV.

Melissa oil – worth its weight in gold!

Chapter notes

1. Wellcome Library research. So many references here:

    Fölsch, Max. Hartlebens Verlag, Wein und Leipzig. *Die Fabrikation und Verarbeitung von ätherischen Ölen.* 1930

    Charobot and Hébert. Bull.soc.chim. [3] 31 (1904) 402. Climate effects on essential oil production.

    Charobot and Laloue. *Compte rendu.* 147 (1908) 144. Peak oil production time (e.g. for *Pelargonium* and *Lavandula*, maximum oil production is around flowering time).

    Gaponenkov and Aleshin J. Applied Chem. USSR 8 (1935) 1049 The effect of drying/storage on herbs (e.g. Russian sage – there is a decrease of 33% essential oil after three hours storage, so the herb should be collected in the evening and distilled immediately).

    Günther, Ernest. The Essential Oils. 1948. NY. Volumes I to VI. Van Nostrand Co: Vol IV p675. *P. graveolens*: Harvest a few days after beginning of flowering in dry weather in early morning. At this time, the leaves change smell from lemon to rose. Distill immediately after harvest. Yield 0.15%

    ibid. Vol III. p 440. *Lavandula officinalis.* Cut with a sickle. French lavender has a characteristic sweetness due to a high ester content. (50–55% ester). Yield 0.8%. Distill quickly (maximum forty minutes); the bulk of the oil comes over in twenty minutes. The distillate must run cold for best extraction of essential oil.

    ibid. Vol III. p 724. Clary sage. Harvest flowering tops in late flowering period between flowering and seeds ripening. Distill fresh and collect high boiling last runs. Yield 0.15%

    von Rechenberg, C. *Theorie der Gewinnung und Trennung der ätherischen Öle.* Schimmel und Co. Miltitz bei Leipsig. 1910

2. Denny, E.F.K. Field Distillation for Herbaceous Oils. Second edition. 1991. From British Library Document Supply Centre, 2006

3. Price, Len and Shirley. Understanding Hydrolats: the specific Hydrosols for Aromatherapy. 2004. Churchill Livingstone, an imprint of Elsevier Ltd. ISBN 0443 07316 3. This volume has detailed analyses of my hydrolats (Appendices D and E).

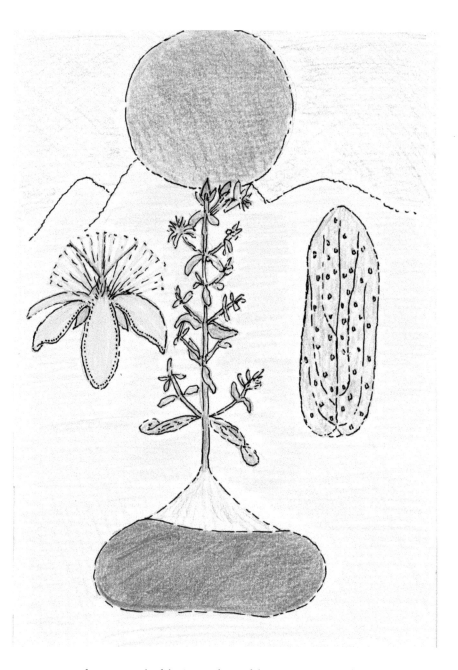

*Hypericum perforatum, Herb of the Sun and one of the most important plants in the garden
(whose yellow flowers and green leaves yield a blood-red oil)*

IX

Herbes de Chevenoz:
the products

Over a period of fifteen years, I developed a range of products that I marketed under the name *'Herbes de Chevenoz'*. Since I was such a small producer and had so quickly found two excellent, knowledgeable and enthusiastic buyers for my products, I never planned to sell under my own label. Both Charles Wells[1] and Joe Nasr[2] were prepared to take what I had produced with occasional pleas for more, whereas other contacts I had made were demanding large and regular quantities, which demanded a scaling-up of production. With my hands-on, labour-intensive methods this wasn't possible – nor, from my point of view, was it desirable. This was a life-changing learning process for me where I interacted with the plants, the process and with Nature. It was an experiment where we were in it together and that's how I wanted it to be.

The tinctures

I had done market research in England to see who was supplying herbalists with tinctures and dried herbs and found that there were very few suppliers – and at that time, even fewer growers and suppliers. But other than Joe Nasr's company, which was pioneering an alchemical distillation process for preparing tinctures, I hadn't found many companies that I felt were producing beautiful and high-quality tinctures. The problem was two-fold: the poor supply of high-quality dried or fresh herbs, and the production methods used. I felt I could solve both these problems in Chevenoz by sourcing the plants locally and choosing the parameters for small-scale production methods. After investigation of the suppliers, I realised that the concentrations of tinctures also varied considerably.

I thus surveyed the alcohol concentrations of tinctures supplied by three main suppliers – Phyto Products Ltd, East West Herbs and The Herbal Apothecary – and compared them to recipes in the British Herbal Compendium.

Also, I had met several herbalists in London and discussed my plans with them to see if they agreed with my strategy and would be willing to try out my products. Links with the Herb Society and leading herb growers via the Chelsea Physic Garden were useful too. Of the twenty plants I selected for tincture making in 1997, thirteen were already growing on my land or in nearby meadows. Tincture making on the scale I envisaged didn't require so much plant material in any case.

My tincture preparation in the first year was using fresh herbs. This was a method supported by the National Institute of Medical Herbalists (NIMH). My first task was to identify and classify the plants and record my findings in an herbarium. This was standard practice of herbalists who supplied their own plant material. Symbolically, the first tincture I made was of mistletoe (*Viscum album*). Since purchasing the orchard, I had been delighted to own trees with mistletoe. Although by tradition we were supposed to prune the mistletoe away each year, these huge and ancient pear and plum trees had been neglected for so many years that they had grown too tall and too infected for us to be able to reach the mistletoe or to save the trees. So for my tincture I selected 200g fresh

Viscum album for tincture preparation

weight of perfect mistletoe – 'leafy shoots, with young berries, from a pear tree' as I recorded. In the tradition of the druids, I caught the bunch as it fell towards the earth. It never touched it!

My recipe book for tincture preparation was a slight volume in traditional green hardcover binding with gold embossed printing on it (as all old botany books were) – the British Herbal Pharmacopoeia[3]. It was the extensive efforts of members of the British Herbal Medicine Association and produced by its Scientific Committee. It contained 233 monographs of separate plants, covering aspects of the plant's nomenclature and synonyms, macroscopical and microscopical descriptions, parts used, therapeutic actions, preparations and dosage. This book referred to dried preparations of herbs, so my method was to assay the water content of my herbs by successive drying and weighing to constant weight. From this I could calculate the amount of fresh plant material needed for equivalent concentration of active ingredients. I also had to adjust the concentration of alcohol used in preparations to produce a tincture of the correct strength.

A companion volume – the British Herbal Compendium[4] – had additional information of a plant's active chemical constituents; published assay methods; therapeutic actions – including pharmacology, indications, other uses and contra-indications; dosage and administration; regulatory status in the UK and other European countries – interestingly, as foods as well; and then literature references. These two volumes represented a vast wealth of information: a veritable herbalist's bible.

A problem at this stage was how to source my alcohol. Since I was making tinctures for the UK market, the alcohol used was subject to UK Customs and Excise regulations and taxes. Qualified herbalists could get dispensations for this, but I wasn't qualified, and in any case, the dispensations were not for use in France. I had prepared myself by acquiring a quantity of *eau de vie* from neighbours who still had licences for distilling their own fruit. I had the pleasure of watching it being distilled from our fermented pears on one cold November morning. Since this was done under legal licence, it was issued with a certificate by the French Customs and Excise authorities. The quasi-bureaucracy of the travelling still and its operation meant that although volumes of alcohol produced were not accurately recorded, the specific gravity and percentage of alcohol were.

I decided from the beginning that I would prepare the tinctures in glass containers. The open plastic vats I had seen in other preparations weren't to my liking. I chopped the herbs with the heavy-duty guillotine, steeped them in the alcohol and then left them for three weeks in cool shade on the stone floor in the *Cave*. I then extracted the maximum volume from the plant macerate using a Vigo fruit press. These tinctures were excellent – aromatic and deeply coloured. At the end of the summer, having sealed them all in polypropylene half-litre and one-litre bottles, labelled carefully, with documentation for transportation, I had prepared quantities of between one and two litres of twenty different tinctures, which we took back to London by car. Here I delivered them to herbalists – who found them impressive.

Because of this distribution and the trust herbalists had in my products, I had measured and recorded all my actions for their safeguard. All details of dilutions, preparation methods and results can be found in Appendix V.

The dried herbs

Flowers grown in Chevenoz often have intense pigmentation and colour. This is a response to the altitude and the high light intensity in the mountain air. Because of the low humidity and high temperatures in the summer months, herbs dried on the shaded drying nets in the barn within a few days. In this rapid process, the vivid colours were preserved along with intense aromas. The products thus made beautiful tisanes and culinary herbs.

For tisanes I collected: *Tilleul* (linden flowers), *Rosa gallica*, lemon verbena (*Melissa*). The culinary herbs were: sage, thyme, summer savory, hyssop, marjoram, *Origano*, basil and various mints.

The infused oils

Two plants with significant therapeutic benefits that do not yield essential oils on distillation are *Calendula* (marigold) and *Hypericum* (St John's wort). However, by steeping the plant material in vegetable oils for a considerable length of time, an oil-based extraction occurs and the active ingredients from the plants infuse the oil, making powerful massage oils. *Calendula* makes a beautiful deep yellow-orange oil, which is soothing for skin irritations, burns, bruises and swellings, sores and rashes; and *Hypericum* is a deep red oil, effective for muscle and joint aches, and for burns, swellings and bruises. Therapeutically, these two oils are excellent.

After experimenting, I found that the best oils were made using dried *Calendula* flowers and freshly picked *Hypericum* florets with leaves. Since these oils would be used for balms and for massage, I steeped the plant materials in high-quality almond oil – a fine and light oil that is easily absorbed by the skin.

Infused oils: Calendula flowers packed into bottles

Calendula bottles on the balcony in the sunshine

Pressing Calendula oil

Recipes and quantities for making infused oils vary considerably. I was guided by Penelope Ody[5] and the British Herbal Pharmacopoeia and over the years adapted the techniques considerably. I came to the conclusion that there were four important parameters to consider:

+ The quality of the plant material
+ The age and quality of the oil used
+ The time of the infusion process
+ The conditions under which the infusion took place

I thus sourced organic almond oil from Spain or Italy and bought the current year's pressings – an important factor as oils can quickly become rancid. This was very fine oil but, of course, expensive. When the cost became more than my markets could bear, I changed to organic sunflower oil of known source.

My *Calendula* seeds were bought from the Chelsea Physic Garden in the first year and I collected my own seeds thereafter. These were relatively small single flowers that over the years bred true, giving dark orange-yellow flowers of uniform colour. The *Hypericum* seed was collected initially from local plants in the Chevenoz meadows and in future years I again collected my own seeds.

Most recipes suggest an infusion time of around three weeks, sometimes suggesting a repeat process known as double-infusion, where a second batch of plant material is introduced after the first pressing. Whether to infuse in the dark or in the light is debatable. Factors to avoid are using conditions that encourage oxidation of the oil, making it rancid, and letting the process go on for so long that the plant material starts to disintegrate, causing the oil to become cloudy. My chosen technique was to infuse once for three weeks using a maximum amount of plant material. For both *Calendula* and *Hypericum* I used 4.2l wide-necked glass jars with screw top lids so I could pack the plant material tightly. I then filled the jar up to the top with oil, pressing down with a wooden spoon to get the air bubbles out (this had to be done again after a couple of days with *Hypericum*). There was thus very little air in the bottles to support oxidation. I then put the bottles in full sunlight on the house balcony and left them for three weeks. This was where I deviated from scientific considerations. Periodically I would turn the jars and stir the contents. Both these plants have such a history and tradition in European herbalism – going back to the times when plants were considered to have connections with the Planets and with the Elements and Humours. So my rationale for infusing in direct sunlight was that both these plants are 'sun plants'. *Hypericum* especially has been used for centuries in summer solstice rituals, and was named after Hyperion, the Greek god who fathered Helios, the sun. Its common name comes from its connection with Saint John, whose special/feast day is June 24 – Midsummer's Day. *Calendula* (another Herb of the Sun) flowers open when the sun shines.

I harvested these plants and infused the oils in the months of July and August only, when days were long and the sun was hot. There were times when the temperature of the oil in the bottles reached 50°C. This aided extraction considerably. After three weeks, I pressed the contents of the jars using a Vigo fruit press and left the resulting oil to settle and clear. Since this oil was going to be used as massage oil or in balms and creams, I then filtered it. Whatever the merits of various methods, my oils were sweet smelling and tasting, with no hint of rancidity, and of a colour intensity and brilliance like no others I have seen. I then stored the oils in the dark and cool and found that they lasted for two to three years in excellent condition. But my advice to customers was always to use within the year of production.

Quote from Joe Nasr of Avicenna (personal communication):

'Dear Hilary,
　　Oh no, marigold oil like yours we will never be able to make. That was a rare handcrafted product suffused with individual attention, care and love. Not that we do not make ours to similar principles, but the problem is that we do not grow our own and cannot source marigold flowers that are anywhere near the colour and quality that you produced.'

On occasions, I made smaller quantities of chickweed (*Stellaria media*) and meadowsweet (*Filipendula ulmaria*) oils, both of which make useful massage oils and creams – chickweed in particular in the treatment of eczema.

(for details see Infused oils records in Appendix V)

The balms and salves

The infused oils made excellent balms and creams. Using a method described by Penelope Ody[5]. I have been making:

Calendula balm: This deeply healing balm is excellent for bruising and swellings, inflammations and skin blemishes, and also encourages healing of wounds and scars. Above all it makes a wonderful, fast-acting remedy for babies' nappy rashes. For the recipe, see Appendix V.

Lavender and rose geranium salve: This is an excellent hand and barrier cream useful for scratched hands and wrists, especially after rose pruning and gardening. The lavender oil reduces soreness and the rose geranium has antiseptic properties. Carrot seed oil heals scratches and cuts. For the recipe, again see Appendix V.

Floral waters

After a few years, these became important products in my range. I was obtaining around 6l of hydrolat as a by-product for each 10kg distillation. But I also developed the technique specifically for the production of rose water. My sixty beautiful Damask rose bushes, some of which became huge and highly productive, were never going to produce rose essential oil – where 10,000 roses are needed to produce 5ml of oil! My aim was thus to make high-quality rose water. During a summer I would do two or three distillations, each time producing around 5l of rose water. These distillations were undoubtedly the highlight of my year – handling exquisite blooms in these quantities was a magical experience.

The highly fragrant Damask roses were delicate and varied. The stars of the show were undoubtedly the Lebanese and Balkan favourites – Kazanlik and Ispahan, with *Quatre Saisons* of equal beauty. And to my collection I added a couple of white Damasks with a richer, slightly nutmeg-y perfume – Madame Hardy and Botzaris, and then the wonderful *Rosa gallica* – the Apothecary's Rose. This mix was aesthetically perfect with an astounding perfume.

Rose is the symbol of love and in many cultures it holds an important and sacred place within society. So too, these distillations became an act of love for me – an experience so intimate, intense and beautiful.

On the prescribed day according to the *Calendrier Lunaire*, (and there were only two or three each year), I woke before 4 a.m., prepared myself for work and went to the garden with my blue cotton cloths. At that time of the morning in June, the cool air is as soft as silk – the faintest remaining breeze coming back down the valley from the night in the high mountains, wafting the heady rose fragrance with it. Working calmly and steadily and completely engrossed, I gathered individual flowers, listening meditatively to the hollow snapping noise as I broke the swollen receptacle at the base of the flower, and amassed them on the cloths – on and on, stripping the bushes of their beautiful flowers and leaving the buds that I knew would open the next day. These times were magical; I was transported to another world. The peace of dawn enfolded me with my beautiful roses and the all-embracing silence. After two hours of bliss, at ten minutes to six, the dawn chorus of birds was at crescendo level and the Angelus rang out across the meadows. The Chevenoz day had started; it was time for me to leave my reveries and for the mortal world to wake up.

Having gathered kilogrammes of roses, at this stage I stopped. The roses rested for a short while on the cool stone floor of the *Cave* to wilt slightly, which made them easier to pack in the still, and I drank coffee and collected the water from the source for the distillation process. Then, slowly and carefully, I packed the flowers in the still – some of them so beautiful that I regretted having to do it. And here I had a dilemma: the flowers needed to be close packed to stop the steam by-passing them in so-called 'rat runs', which passed so quickly through the plant mass that it didn't pick up any essential oil, but the depth of the flowers couldn't be so high that when the petals became damp, they packed to a solid mat. My solution was to only put 50cm depth of petals in the still and to run it for around fifteen minutes. From this first fraction, I got the highest quality and most fragrant floral water, with heady 'high notes' – usually about two litres. Because of the precious nature of these flowers, I then continued the distillation for the second fraction to obtain a further three litres. This second fraction had a deeper perfume than the first one, and later I blended the two together, making two products: *Herbes de Chevenoz* 'Rose Water I' which was the first fraction only and 'Rose Water II', which was a mixture of the two distillations. I think Rose Water I was energetically higher, but many people preferred the deeper fragrance of Rose Water II.

Having worked on perfecting the technique for rose water, I knew which fractions to collect of the other floral waters. For all other distillations I collected essential oils as well, so in these cases, the floral waters/hydrolats were by-products of the process. There were exceptions to this where the floral water had properties and uses slightly different to the essential oil (e.g. rose geranium water, which has a gentler and less pungent odour and makes an excellent body spray; German chamomile water, which again is softer than the oil and makes a good body spray; and juniper water, which is an air cleanser and purifier).

Eventually, my range of floral waters, for which I found enthusiastic markets, consisted of rose, lavender, rose geranium, rosemary, juniper, *Melissa*, German chamomile, clary sage, hyssop and marjoram. Many of them were analysed by Charles Wells and the Government Chemist's laboratory and featured in Len Price's book 'Understanding Hydrolats'[6].

For details of distillations of hydrolats, see Appendix V.

Roses on the Cave floor

The essential oils

From the beginning, I knew I would only be able to prepare small quantities of essential oils. I was completely in agreement with this, as I knew that to scale up would involve bringing in the tractors, renting more land and finding more labour. My project was to develop my garden and myself in the same process. We would evolve together over time. During the years I was working, several dear friends came to observe, participate and help, and were sometimes astounded by the Power and beauty of the garden within its landscape. Others just came to relax and enjoy the healing nature of the garden, and brought me encouragement and fun.

Selecting the plants for these distillations took time, and then the cultivation was a lengthy process. Clary sage and German chamomile were the only plants that I grew annually – all the others were perennials and took several years to establish.

Lavender oil

Lavender became my signature oil and at one time I was producing around 120 little bottles of essential oil each year. The plants seemed so happy in the garden, thriving and growing and being able to completely withstand any adverse weather conditions. We were considerably further north than the Provence lavender fields and our winters were harsher and longer, but the air quality, the soil and the hot summer sun were much appreciated by the plants. Also, the hundreds of insects around – the many different species of bees, butterflies, moths, crickets and grasshoppers, and clouds of small flying insects and those crawling into the florets – all fertilised the flowers and brought vitality to the lavender beds. A local artisan, Alexandre, had fifteen hives in the meadow just below the plots and he supplied me with beeswax for my balms. We used to joke that his wax and honey smelled of lavender and my essential oil smelled of honey. There were deep connections between the products.

Details of these distillations can be found in Chapter XIII and Appendix V.

Lavender

Juniper oil

This oil became very important to me. Juniper bushes grow in the mountains surrounding Chevenoz and most homesteads have their own bushes. The Savoyards use juniper berries for smoking sausages and salamis and in casseroles and game dishes. In particular, I became interested in the protective properties of juniper at many different levels, and used both the essential oil and the hydrolat to purify, preserve and protect.

Details of preparation and distillations can be found in Chapter XIII.

Carrot seed oil

Wild carrot (also known as Queen Anne's Lace) was a plant growing on almost every road verge around the *commune* of Chevenoz. It quickly colonised disturbed land and obviously responded well to mowing. I discovered that it was an excellent oil with antiseptic and carminative properties, used especially for skin disorders. It seemed to be a useful addition to my *Calendula* balm. So I had to source seed heads from unpolluted locations – of which I found many. Results

Carrot seed heads

of distillations varied considerably and I eventually found a way of wilting the seed heads for three to four days before distillation and then distilling them twice to give good yields.

Melissa oil

Lemon balm which 'maketh the heart merry' was also a plant that yielded the most wonderful oil but in *very* small quantities. The plant grew well in the plots and it was worth the effort of finding a good way to distill it. It took me quite a few years to work out how best to get small quantities of oil – sometimes around 10ml from four or five distillations. But this richly perfumed golden oil was actually worth its weight in gold and smelled wonderful. I used it only in ritual and in my *Calendula* balm in minute quantities.

Two other oils that I loved, but after a few years gave up making, were rose geranium and rosemary. Even though the oils and hydrolats were wonderful, neither plant could survive the winters in Chevenoz.

And that is how things rested for several years. I was distilling moderate quantities of lavender oil and much smaller quantities of what I called 'speciality oils' – mostly for my own use as a masseuse and for colleagues and friends. And the hydrolat by-products of the distillations found ready markets with Joe Nasr and Charles Wells, who sold them as floral waters/hydrolats or ingredients for lotions, soaps and creams. Eventually I sold them directly as floral waters at local craft markets – especially at the Michael Hall Markets at the Steiner Waldorf School in Forest Row – and by word-of-mouth developed a loyal and enthusiastic group of supporters. From them, the juniper water also found homes with several psychotherapists and counsellors, who used it for 'cleansing' between treatment sessions.

The incenses

Incenses have been used in ritual and as mind-altering substances for millennia. They are a way of prolonging the experience of inhaling the aroma to induce a change of Consciousness, a trance state. My shamanic training has never used well-known psycho–active substances as an aid to Journeying, but I have often used incenses in ritual and love to return to my Catholic childhood experience of 'dreaming' whilst breathing in clouds of incense billowing from an ornate swung thurible with the drone of a Latin mass as background chant. Over time, using Scott Cunningham[7] as my guide, I have experimented with many dried herb preparations from my garden or surrounding meadows. I would add here that in my opinion, to a greater or lesser extent so many plant essences are mind-altering.

This is obviously a practice to approach carefully and knowledgeably, but at its simplest, burning lavender, hyssop or rosemary branchlets on an open fire is a beautiful experience – lavender encouraging an atmosphere of calm, rosemary of excitement. For smaller quantities of plant material, other techniques can be used – e.g. drying and grinding the herbs and burning small amounts on ready prepared charcoal blocks, or creating cones of plant material mixed with beeswax, giving it a cotton string wick and igniting it as a candle. I also make candles from beeswax by the dipping technique, having added essential oil to the wax. Lavender makes wonderful naturally scented candles.

Another technique is to dry sprigs of aromatic plant material and bind it into smudge sticks, tying it with string – cotton or bass or wool (always a non-synthetic material). The materials need to be woody and tied tightly so the stick doesn't burn too quickly when ignited with a match, but smoulders and releases delicate plumes of smoke into the atmosphere. In all these cases, you need to start with very small quantities and experiment – preferably outside!

Plants I have used for incenses are:

- Agrimony (*Agrimonia eupatoria*)
- Betony (*Betonica officinalis*)
- Marigold (*Calendula officinalis*)
- German chamomile (*Matricaria chamomilla*)
- Fumitory (*Fumaria officinalis*)
- Honeysuckle (*Lonicera caprifolium*)
- Hyssop (*Hyssopus officinalis*)
- Juniper (*Juniperus communis*)
- Lavender (*Lavendula officinalis*)
- Lemon balm (*Melissa officinalis*)
- Meadowsweet (*Filipendula ulmaria*)
- Mugwort (*Artemesia vulgaris*)
- Mullein (*Verbascum thapsus*)
- Orris root (*Iris florentina*)

+ Peony roots (*Paeonia officinalis*)
+ Rose petals (*Rosa damascena*)
+ Rose geranium (*Pelargonium graveolens*)
+ Rosemary (*Rosmarinus officinalis*)
+ Sage (*Salvia officinalis*)
+ Vervain (*Verbena officinalis*)
+ Violet (*Viola odorata*)
+ Sweet woodruff (*Gallium odorata*)
+ Sweet vernal grass (*Anthoxanthum odoratum*)

I dry the leafy shoots, the flowers and the roots like iris and peony (both important constituents of French perfume) and then grind them into powders with a pestle and mortar. These can be used on charcoal blocks or moulded into cones and burned as candles. The woody shoots also need to be dried to prevent mildew and then bound tightly into smudge sticks. In Chevenoz, because the atmosphere is so dry, I can keep these preparations in glass jars for months – in fact, until the next year when I make some more. In more humid conditions they need to be stored with a desiccant (silica gel for instance), and they lose their odours more quickly.

Chapter notes

1. Charles Wells. Essentially Oils. Chipping Norton, Oxon. No longer operational.
2. Joe Nasr, Avicenna Herbs. http://www.avicennaherbs.co.uk/
3. British Herbal Pharmacopoeia. 1983. Published by British Herbal Medicine Association. ISBN 0 903032 07 4
4. British Herbal Compendium. Volume I. Edited by Peter R. Bradley. 1992. Copyright British Herbal Medicine Association. ISBN 0 903032 09 0
5. Ody, Penelope. The Complete Medicinal Herbal: A Practical Guide to the Healing Properties of Herbs, with More Than 250 Remedies for Common Ailments. 1993. Dorling Kindersley Ltd. ISBN 0 7513 0025 X
6. Price, Len and Shirley. Understanding Hydrolats: the specific Hydrosols for Aromatherapy. 2004. Churchill Livingstone, an imprint of Elsevier Ltd. ISBN 0443 07316 3
7. Cunningham, Scott. The Complete Book of Incense, Oils & Brews. 2003. Llewellyn Publications. ISBN 0-87542-128-8

Chevenoz rose (Rosa gallica)

X

Essences for body and psyche

*'My beloved is unto me as a cluster of camphire in the
vineyards of En Gedi...'*
'SONG OF SONGS', THE OLD TESTAMENT

(Camphire is thought to be *Lawsonia inermis* – a shrub that produces clusters of cream yellow flowers with a sweet and powerful scent.)

The use of plant essences is an ancient and diverse art, perhaps as old as history. Attractive and beautiful scents, usually of plant origin, were used to counteract the repulsive and pervading smells of decay and putrefaction and their associated diseases that resulted from the natural course of life's events. Incenses have been used for at least 3000 years. Egyptian records from the 7th century BCE show that they were used in rituals, ceremony and meditation, in divination, to appease the gods and to protect from evil. As civilisation wended its way across the globe, so did the use of plant aromatics. From Egypt and Babylon, the custom travelled to India, to China and then to Japan. The Silk Road was a trading route for precious incenses, and the Incense Route took them to the Mediterranean. Originally incenses were made of local materials: the Indians favoured frankincense and roots, as well as flower essences; Chinese incenses, predominantly used in temples, were made of cinnamon, styrax and sandalwood; considerably later, the Japanese created *Koh* out of *Hinoki* (*Cupressus* species) for use in tea ceremonies, and later still, for recreational and social occasions. Other cultures also had their traditions – e.g. the Native Americans have used cedarwood and sage bush (*Artemisia* species – not to be confused with European sage, which is *Salvia* species) as incense since time immemorial.

In many of these examples, incenses have been used as mind-altering substances to expand Consciousness in religious ceremony. Christian churches use frankincense, myrrh, spices and cedar, with clouds of smoke emanating from the thuribles in Catholic and Orthodox churches. Add flickering candles and chanting to this mix and the mind is truly altered! Rose water is used in Muslim mosques, cedar in Buddhist temples, sandalwood in Indian temples, juniper in Tibetan villages. These practices are all a connection with the divine. Fragrance is associated with holiness – the gods, angels and saints are all sweetly fragrant and the 'odour of sanctity' has been recognised and acknowledged for millennia. Paradise has been described as a 'prairie from which rises at all times an extraordinary perfume'.

From the Old Testament's Song of Songs mention of *Calamus* (a rattan palm), cinnamon and myrrh onwards, there are wonderful examples of uses of plants in sacred moments of all cultures – for anointing, for purifying and for blessing. Anointing with aromatic plant oils and essences has always been a sacred act used at significant times to 'seal in' a divinity or spiritual presence. The biblical description of anointing Jesus's feet with precious spikenard oil by 'the sinner', Mary Magdalene, signified Jesus's position as Son of God. It was an example of loving kindness and comfort offered to another at a time of crisis and suffering. The last rite and sacrament in the Catholic church – extreme unction – anoints the forehead of the dying person, preparing him/her to meet God. It is important that the oil is perfumed, indicating its sanctity. An especially beautiful and sacred oil – made of essential oils of neroli, rose, cinnamon, jasmine, ambergris and musk – was used for the anointing of Queen Elizabeth II at her coronation to recognise the solemnity and sacredness of the event. Another practice of spiritual importance was the burning of incense in ancient Egyptian and then, later, Jewish rituals. Plants, sanctity and the divine have always been connected, and for very good reason. Besides the Power and beauty of plant scents, which have a biological function of attraction, they are also mind-altering. They have the capacity to help an individual communicate with 'the transcendent', to enter another state of mind for meditation, for shamanic Journeying, for prayer[1].

Hindu records from at least 3000 years ago have also shown that perfumes and aromatic products were used therapeutically. These practices are now embedded in Ayurvedic medicine, where aromatic massage uses infused oils from indigenous plants. Aromatic massage was also a feature of ancient Chinese medicine. As their properties became well understood, plant oils and extracts e.g. rosemary, became used in food preservation and cookery, where their use as stimulants made food more easily digested. The ancient Egyptian art of embalming and mummification of their pharaohs also preserved bodies. Oils such as thyme, lavender, cedar, peppermint and rose were used as a mark of deep respect. Through their antibacterial and anti-fungal actions, these oils had the capacity of delaying putrefaction – they were not just masking the smells.

In ancient Greek and Roman culture, it was recognised that herbs and oils influenced emotions by affecting the Humours and thus the Temperaments. Later, Dioscorides, who was a Greek surgeon active in the Roman army in AD 1st century, catalogued oils in his medical encyclopaedia and they were used to stimulate soldiers towards aggression, and as blood staunchers and wound healers after the ensuing battle injuries. Later uses were to protect populations against plagues and pestilence (e.g. with juniper, thyme and lavender).

A way of extracting plant essences in fats, waxes and oils (a process known as *enfleurage*) was practised by ancient Chinese, Egyptian and Persian civilisations, but it wasn't until the 13th century in Persia that an alchemist and physician, now known in the West as Avicenna, perfected a technique of distilling the renowned rose water of Arabia. Rose water from Damask roses (from Damascus) became world famous and was exported to China and the West by the crusaders. Avicenna's distillation technique was used for centuries for floral water production and not for distillation of essential oils. This came considerably later[2].

Essential oils and the modern aromatherapy movement

A French chemist, René-Maurice Gattefossé, was the first to coin the name and write a book on aromatherapy. The Gattefossé family owned a business near Lyon in France, importing exotic essential oils and exporting high-quality synthetic perfumes. Early in his career, working at his laboratory bench, Gattefossé burned his hand badly and immediately plunged it into an available beaker of lavender essential oil. The ensuing relief of pain, calming of inflammation and healing of burned tissue without scarring were so surprising to him that he vowed to research the therapeutic properties of essential oils from then onwards. He did so for the next fifty years. In 1937 he published his research findings, which were translated to English and published in 1993 as 'Gattefossé's Aromatherapy'[3]. This charming little book, in its style and creative outlook, led to more extensive use of essential oils in the perfume industry. It also led to their uses as antiseptics and other physiological applications.

The conclusions at the end of his book, after extensive testing, state that essential oils indeed have remarkable therapeutic value that will position them in future pharmacopoeias. He also concludes that their superior properties relating to their electromagnetic composition give them tremendous potential to act via the nose and olfactory nerve and thence to affect body tissues and bodily fluids. This led the way to therapeutic massage and the modern aromatherapy movement.

Later, French doctors and chemists studied oils further – significantly, Dr Jean Valnet[4], an army surgeon who used oils to treat battlefield wounds. From his work, many essential oils were included in the *Pharmacopée Française* and were taken internally (as they are to this day) as well as externally. Marguerite Maury was one of his students and she brought a more holistic and spiritual dimension to the discipline:

> 'Elixirs contain not only macerated odoriferous plants. These substances have been treated in a special manner in order to extract their "essence". What is understood by essence in the pure sense as used by mediaeval alchemists, for example, is the actual energy, the Soul of the plant.'[5]

She also proposed the idea of 'individual prescription' of blended oils to harmonise the physical, psychological and spiritual nature of the patient, bringing everything into balance.

Besides Maury, a number of important researchers and practitioners looked at all aspects of essential oil chemistry and properties. These included French and Italian chemists Daniel Penoël, Giovanni Gatti and Paolo Rovesti. These last two also examined the effects of oils on emotions. Then the practitioners researched and set to work as aromatherapists and masseurs/masseuses, viz. Robert Tisserand, Shirley Price, Patricia Davis, Valerie Anne Worwood[6]. At this stage it was realised that essential oils were powerful, dynamic, synergistic and had electro-chemical/energetic properties. They were noted for their abilities to improve performance and the capacity to remember, to make a subject relaxed or alert and, especially, to change mood. Aromatherapy had arrived as a holistic and effective complementary therapy, and aromatherapists had come to understand the importance of essential oils in mind and body medicine.

Aromatherapists of the 1980s and 1990s were describing the actions of essential oils at three different levels within the individual, viz: the body physical, the emotions and the Spirit.[7,8, & 9] The actions of oils on the body organs – which they reach via the blood stream – were well understood. The chemical molecules could be analysed and tested in the same way as pharmaceutical drugs. But within the Western medicine model, there was no real basis for the actions at the levels of emotions and psyche. Chinese medicine had the connections of the Emotions and the Elements, and Ayurvedic medicine had Elements and Dhosas, with Qi and Prana dynamically keeping everything in balance. But in modern Western medicine and psychiatry, the concepts of Soul and Spirit or their equivalents had been systematically overlooked.

The holistic nature of essential oils

After these decades of research, we have come to understand (to a considerable extent) the chemical composition of an essential oil and aspects of its electro-magnetic properties. We know how an oil enters the body – via the skin and blood capillaries in massage, and via the nose and olfactory system when breathed in. Practically, we know much about the effects of an oil on the body and the emotions when used in aromatherapy. But for all the analyses and amassing of facts, there are aspects of essential oils that are not describable in these reductionist terms. As Valerie Anne Worwood describes in her book 'The Fragrant Mind', tea tree oil is a powerful antimicrobial agent, but its two main components – terpinen-4-ol (40% by volume) and gamma terpinene (28% by volume) – are considerably less so. She suggests it is the synergistic effect of *all* the components that makes an oil what it is. So much analysis has been done at the chemical level, so much safe handling data produced, and chemical 'tinkering' of oils has been done to make 'chemically identical' oils or 'less toxic' ones, etc. But for all the careful mixing of ingredients in the laboratory, an essential oil is not produced. Nor can chemists describe how an oil works. Something is missing from the equation, whether it be the vast numbers of molecules present in oils that have not been identified or are not considered to be biologically active, or whether it is a 'vitality' hinted at by Paracelsus in mediaeval times when he called the oils *'quinta essentia'* – the quintessence of the plant. This very name hints at another dimension than the physical.

And as a distiller, I know from experience that the oil that I decant from the top of the bottle of hydrolat after a distillation has an energy and Power about it that a synthetic perfume doesn't have. I realise that to say such a thing without concrete evidence is challenging but this is my subjective experience and contribution to the knowledge base. Of course, my rational mind has wanted to test this – and to a certain extent I have. Using kinesiology techniques and measuring Qi or the auras of these oils has shown me that a pure essential oil distilled from plants in full health is not the 'sum of its chemical parts' but a synergistic, dynamic and powerful substance pulsating with a life force. It is alive. And this gives it a holistic nature.

But for my story now, I want to emphasise the deep and lasting connection between plant essences and humans at every level of our existence – from the physical to the emotional to the spiritual at times of birth, solemn ritual, celebration and death – and their effects on the mind's capacity for imagination and a spiritual life. And it is this last point that has helped my rational mind understand the basis of shamanic Journeying.

Aromatherapy and our sense of smell

Not all plants have a smell. Of the estimated half a million plant species on this planet, around 300 different essential oils have been extracted and used in aromatherapy. These all have two important characteristics – as oils, they are insoluble in water (usually being lighter than water, they float) and as perfumes, they vaporise at low temperatures and can be easily inhaled. These two properties are used in aromatherapy treatments, where the oils are mixed with a carrier oil, usually almond or a fine one that can penetrate the skin and reach the blood capillaries just below it. Once the essential oil molecules (the chemical particles that make up the oil) enter the blood system, they are then carried throughout the body to the organs – the heart, liver, kidneys, lungs, intestines and brain – and to the muscles and nerves, where they will have an effect. Shortly after being applied to the skin and absorbed, they can be traced in the body. e.g. After a massage with 2% lavender oil, the main constituents, linalool and linalyl acetate, can be detected in the blood within five minutes, reaching a maximum concentration after twenty minutes. After ninety minutes, most traces have been eliminated from the body, having set off chains of reactions within the organ tissues with longer lasting effects.

Smell is our most primitive sense and one that we do not use to the extent that we once did. Earlier humans relied far more on their sense of smell – for sexual attraction, for hunting, for determining quality and suitability of foods, to avoid disease, putrefaction and toxins. Our sense of smell predominantly has two polarities. Either a smell is attractive or repulsive. This primitive response is our connection with Nature. We are attracted to most of the plants that smell, but for a few exceptions like the giant stinking titan arum (*Amorphophallus titanum*) from Sumatra (which most people find revolting, but pollinating flies adore). We find the scents primitively attractive, vaguely pleasant or even blissful – hence their use in floral notes in perfumes. The scents all have one property in common: at ambient temperatures, they easily turn from oily liquids or resins to gases that freely mix with air.

As a vapour, the essential oil molecules have a fast and very direct pathway via the nose to the mucous membranes in the nasal passages. It is estimated that there are some 5–10 million scent-detecting olfactory cells in the nasal epithelium (membrane) above the nostril in a human. And these cells are sensitive to some 10,000 different chemicals. Although we have lost much of our smelling capability as we have become upright in stance and come to rely more and more on our senses of sight and hearing, a 'trained' nose is capable of identifying hundreds of different odours – a skill much valued in the perfume industry.

Sense of Smell

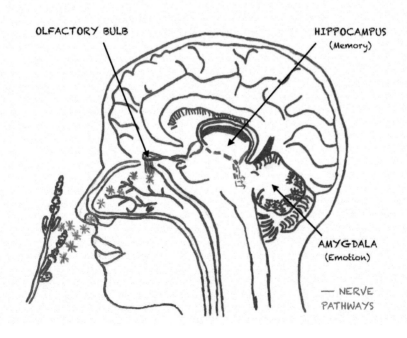

Diagram of the Olfactory pathway[10]. Our sense of smell – the pathway from flower to brain

The essential oil molecules are absorbed by the hair-like cilia of the olfactory bulb – an extension of the forebrain, and are then in direct contact with nerves and are converted to a nervous impulse that is transmitted to the part of the hind brain known as the hypothalamus. This is part of the limbic system, also known as the 'old brain' because of its primitive function and earlier evolutionary development. The limbic system is the home of our emotions, sexual feelings, memory and learning – all of which can be evoked by the sense of smell. Molecules that have entered the body via the skin and blood system can also reach the brain as they are small enough to pass through the protective blood/brain barrier. Thus these oils have the capacity to act on both the physical body and on the brain – the most ancient parts of the brain especially, with their deep connections to our memories, our emotions and our psyches.

A detour back into history

Besides the use of plant essences in the forms of essential oils and floral waters, another very different path can be traced in the use of plants in the perfumed gardens of ancient Persia. A perfumed garden was designed to be an 'Earthly paradise' – as the Garden of Eden was. As its name suggests, plant scents played a central role, and symmetry in architecture and design, elements of sunlight and shade and the movement of water all contributed to the aesthetics. Love in its highest and deepest sense was evoked and this led to eroticism – in its philosophical meaning of fusion with 'Other'. Plants grown in these gardens were sensuous, highly perfumed – especially at night – and, of course, beautiful (e.g. roses, jasmine, orange blossom – and in China, where this custom was adopted, also tree peonies). The custom also spread to India and a famous example of an Indian perfumed garden was at the Taj Mahal monument in Agra, created by the Mughal emperor Shah Jahan to show his eternal love for his dead wife Mumtaz Mahal. The Mahtab Garden (the Moonlight Garden) across the river contained white luminescent flowers of scented jasmine, stocks and champa (*Magnolia* family). Interestingly, so many of the plants grown in these gardens feature in the sensual perfumes created in the French perfumery companies in Grasse in Provence.

And from eroticism to recreational drugs: although the following examples are not essences, the significant effect on the psyche after imbibing, 'snorting' or inhaling extracts of the plants make them worthy of inclusion here. Aldous

Huxley – intellectual, philosopher and English writer of over fifty books – grew increasingly interested in both Eastern and Western mysticism, as described in 'The Perennial Philosophy', published in 1945. Later, in 1954, he wrote 'Doors of Perception', which described his experiments on himself under the influence of mescalin from the peyote cactus. These cacti affect the mind, producing striking psychedelic experiences. His first experience was with less than half a gramme of mescalin, which he took under medical supervision. He then waited patiently to see what would happen. He did not have to wait long and on opening his eyes found that everything had been transformed. He recalls the insights as ranging from 'purely aesthetic' to 'sacramental vision'. In 1956 he published 'Heaven and Hell', which continued on the theme of both the philosophical and the psychological significance of these findings. Huxley was deeply influenced by the spirituality of William Blake, who had written 'The Marriage of Heaven and Hell' so long ago in 1793, and like Blake, had made the connection between these alterations in perception with spiritual development. Peyote/mescalin was later described as an 'entheogen', which is a substance that alters perception and Consciousness and engenders spiritual development in a sacred context. There was another connection, as mentioned by Huxley:

'The mystical experience is doubly valuable; it is valuable because it gives the experiencer a better understanding of himself and the world and because it may help him to lead a less self-centered and more creative life.'

This link with creativity led to the creation of a huge movement in the decade 1960 to 1970, which included 'spiritual adventuring' (e.g. of Timothy Leary, connected with Indian mysticism) and the teachings of spiritual gurus (e.g. the Maharishi Mahesh Yogi, who later devised the Transcendental Meditation technique and attracted followers like the Beatles, the Beach Boys and countless others).

All these examples of the interactions at the deepest psychic and spiritual levels between plants and humans, spanning the whole of history and so many cultures, give us an insight, not so much into Nature's 'intention' – which is unknowable – but into the closeness of our relationship with the plant kingdom.

Chapter notes

1.   Lawless, Julia. Aromatherapy and the Mind: the psychological and emotional effects of Essential Oils. 1998. Thorsons. An Imprint of HarperCollins. ISBN 0 7225 2927 9. Her beautiful chapter on Scent, Soul and Psyche speaks of the Garden of the Soul and the role that scent plays in inspiring the imagination.

2.   Damian, Peter and Kate. Scent & Psyche Healing Arts Press.Vermont. 1995. ISBN 0-89281-530-2. An in-depth treatment on the subject.

3.   Gattefossé, Réne-Maurice. Gattefossé's Aromatherapy. 1993. (First published in French 1937 as 'Aromathérapie: Les Huiles essentielles, hormones végétales'.) C.W. Daniel Co Ltd. ISBN 0 85207 236 8

4.   Valnet, Jean. The Practice of Aromatherapy. 1982. C.W. Daniel Co Ltd. ISBN 085207 143

5.   Maury, Marguerite. Guide to Aromatherapy. The Secret of Life & Youth. 1989. C.W. Daniel Company Ltd. ISBN 0 85207 163 9

6.   The following practising aromatherapists supported the holistic and vital properties of essential oils, capable of influencing the bodies, Emotions and Spirits of their clients:

     Price, Shirley. Aromatherapy and your emotions. How to use essential oils to balance body & Mind. 2000. Thorsons. An Imprint of HarperCollins. ISBN 0 7225 3862 6

     Tisserand, Robert. The Art of Aromatherapy. 1997. C.W. Daniel Co Ltd. ISBN 0 85207 140 X

     Mailhebiau, Philippe. Portrait in Oils. 1995. C.W. Daniel Co Ltd. ISBN 0 85207 237 6

     Davis, Patricia. Subtle Aromatherapy. 1991. C.W. Daniel Co Ltd. ISBN 0 85207 227 9 7-9. Davis suggests that the best way to understand plant energies is to spend time with the plants – as Edward Bach did.

7–9.   Valerie Ann Worwood trilogy:

     The Fragrant Pharmacy. a complete guide to Aromatherapy and Essential Oils. 1991. Bantam Books. ISBN 0 553 40397 4

     The Fragrant Mind. Aromatherapy for Personality, Mind, Mood and Emotion. 1995. Bantam Books. ISBN 0 553 40799 6

     The Fragrant Heavens, The Spiritual dimension of Fragrance and Aromatherapy. 1999. Bantam Books. ISBN 0-553-50579-3

And how those plants grew… Soledad and the sunflowers

XI

Evolving life in the garden...
and in the meadows beyond

'I know a bank where the wild thyme blows,
Where oxlips and the nodding violet grows,
Quite over-canopied with luscious woodbine,
With sweet musk-roses and with eglantine:
There sleeps Titania sometime of the night,
Lull'd in these flowers with dances and delight'
SPOKEN BY OBERON. WILLIAM SHAKESPEARE,
'A MIDSUMMER NIGHT'S DREAM', ACT 2, SCENE 1

Setting up the garden and developing the ground rules was the first step, but as any gardener knows, a garden is a living and dynamic process, constantly evolving with and without one's care and attention. Since my endeavours spanned many years, my original ideas evolved too – but I held true to the basic premise that I wanted to create a garden with as many connections as possible to the cosmos, the Elements and the local environment with its customs, flora and fauna. My reason for doing this has been because I believe that these connections are the basis of good health in plants and therefore in us.

To give some examples of how I did this, I've selected excerpts from my entries in *L'Almanach Savoyard 2005* (since this was a year when I made copious notes on my activities). It was during the early years especially that this little book advised and encouraged me. Month by month, it gave details of work to be done and timings of important events. The following account/descriptions/ mind ramblings came from my diaries of that year with additions and prompts from the *Almanach*.

The gardening year

After the winter mantle of snow had melted and the deep frost and frozen earth began to thaw, life stirred, gradually to start with, sometimes in fits and starts. Since Chevenoz is an Alpine *commune*, the stirring came later than at lower altitudes. But when it did, the intense sun's rays on the south-facing slope penetrated the earth quickly, warming and coaxing it from its winter slumbers back into life. The ice crystals in the soil melted – the melt getting deeper each day; the earth steamed in the sunlight; insects started to emerge. The nights were cold, the light was bright.

My gardening year 2005 started in:

March/April

The preparatory months. There is always a huge range of conditions in these two months, from icy winter to warm spring weather. So work was intermittent and chosen to suit the conditions. On March 20 the sun rose exactly in the east and set exactly in the west (the equinox). Jupiter, Saturn and Mars were visible at times in the night. Venus was the evening star. The *Almanach* gave dates for the return of the swallows and cuckoos somewhere between April 7 and 18. During these months less precisely, bats and hedgehogs were predicted to wake from their winter slumbers and the first songs of blackbirds and the skylarks could be heard.

During this time, my tasks were to:

- Rake over the weed seedlings. The Chelsea Physic Garden definition of a weed: a plant growing where you don't want it to be! So I left some of the red dead nettles and ground ivy flowers for the bees and to attract the first insects
- Tidy up the perennials, do some transplanting
- Spread the compost and hoe in the leaf mould.

Then the rain came – in stair rods then in sheets, then thunderstorms, then hailstones – golf ball sized. The earth got a thorough drenching.

- Then further preparatory work to redefine the paths, tidy up the plots.

- Cut out the dead wood of the roses. The Damasks were not pruned in the conventional sense, only reduced in height if they had become unbalanced in the winter winds and rocked at their roots. Many of the larger ones were in rose obelisks that I was lucky enough to buy in bulk at a good price.
- All staking had to wait until the earth had thoroughly thawed.

Bird song filled the air in the mornings. A black squirrel woke up and searched for buried treasures. I witnessed a raging battle between the squirrel and a magpie – the squirrel was hissing and lashing its claws, the magpie screeching, squawking and flapping its wings and tail, beak snapping savagely. After about five minutes of chasing through upper tree branches, or hiding under fallen tree trunks, where the squirrel had a distinct advantage, the squirrel emerged victorious and the magpie flew off. The hunt for buried walnuts continued. High drama in the orchard, then silence.

May

In this glorious month, the great blessing for May 1 was the flowering of *muguets* (lily-of-the-valley). On that morning bunches of them were always for sale in Abondance market and the local supermarket. I had a large clump sheltered under the hazelnut trees behind the shed and Jeanne had planted hers in a sheltered corner of her *potager*. As April progressed, we monitored their progress, excitedly waiting to pick that first bunch to give to each other. This year I was lucky; I rose early and picked two beautiful posies – one for Jeanne and the other for us. What bounty, what a gift.

This was a month of joyful activity everywhere. Life was burgeoning, you could feel it in your bones. The days got noticeably longer and warmer and lighter. Everything was jubilantly noisier – the birds, the cows and calves, the dogs, the donkeys, the children. At night the foxes howled, and the cats, and the owls. In the valley the stags were marking their territories and signalling their presence. The cows were set free from their long winter's incarceration in the barn and with bells round their necks returned to the buttercup-laden meadows, where they cavorted and tossed their heads. The air resonated with the sound of cowbells, which travelled long distances through the clear air. Then on May 1 (sunny and beautiful), I started to sow the seeds. As soon as the soil had warmed, seeds could germinate in a few days – some even overnight. The beautifully prepared planting beds became green with chickweed, young dandelions and speedwells, which later bore vivid blue flowers. Now was the time to try to bring some order to the order beds. Hoeing, weeding and transplanting the *Calendulas*, the chamomiles and the clary sages eventually established the plots of herbs to be harvested for products later in the year.

The *Almanach* noted that Saturn and Mars were visible at dusk and Jupiter during the night. Venus was still the evening star. This was the time to gather meadow plants for medicinal use: fumitory, mallow, walnut leaves, lime flowers, arnica, meadowsweet, *Hypericum*, meadow sage, chamomile, soapwort roots, wild chicory, borage and burdock.

So much activity was swirling around with the arrival of the summer birds – the swallows, martins and swifts, the thrushes, the finches, and the graceful dancing pied wagtails. They set about prospecting for and deciding on nesting sites; bringing in the nest material, sometimes being very creative using natural and synthetic materials; weaving their nests in so many different shapes and sizes; and then, after so much activity, settling down to lay eggs. The larger birds – the magpies, the green- and pied-woodpeckers, the crows, the jays – competed loudly for territory, resulting in a cacophony in the clear air. Suddenly all was quiet, life was expectant. We all waited. Then came two other harbingers of spring: the first crickets arrived in the meadows and the first cuckoo signalled its presence from the wooded valley of the Dranse (late this year, or had I not heard it earlier?).

June

A glorious time in the mountains. Long days, clear star-filled nights, bright moons. Everything growing so fast and so strongly – 'the grand period of growth', as it is described. But everything changes around the solstice. The four days between the official first day of summer (around June 21) and Midsummer's Day (June 24) are extraordinary. This is high summer, four long days of equal length when the Earth stays still! After that the days start getting shorter until the winter solstice (when a similar lag phase causes four winter days to be the shortest days of the year). After the longest days, the growth in plants is different. It can be seen clearly that the marked extension of stems and growth of leaves stops, and flowers start to form fruits and seeds. After maturity, a gradual senescence begins.

Harvesting the plots

During this time:

+ *Calendula* flowers were harvested daily, dried on the racks, then packed in bottles of oil and left for three weeks on the balcony to infuse
+ *Hypericum* (flower of St John, whose Feast Day is June 24) flowering tops were chopped and steeped in oil in jars and put on the balcony for three weeks
+ Each day the contents of the jars were stirred and the bottles turned
+ Weeds were hoed and seeds sown for next year's perennials
+ Rose petals were dried in the shade of the rafters in the barn.

July

Heat wave time (*La Canicule*), when temperatures reached above 30°C and the air was very still and dry. It was too hot to work in these conditions. Jeanne taught me to shut the shutters in early morning (she closed hers the previous night) to conserve the cooler conditions in the house. This was a good policy. In the Alps, after a few scorching days the cumulus clouds bank up along the mountain ranges and then break out in huge thunderstorms. Sheet and forked lightning streak both along the length of the valley and down to Earth – sometimes hissing and so bright that you see colour in the night. Following very close on the lightning's tail, booming and crackling thunder claps shake the house, and on occasions strike. All appliances need to be unplugged – especially the television. A huge pear tree was struck in half in one storm, and another time the house was struck, leaving a black carbon 'butterfly' half a metre across on the wall by the television aerial plug. Driving hailstones could follow the thunder, crashing against the windows. If the shutters weren't shut by this stage, especially on the west side of the house where the bad weather traditionally comes from, then it was too late. To open a window to close the external shutters would be disastrous. Also, there were daily power cuts in these times and they could last for hours. This showed us how powerful mountain conditions could be with the four Elements coming together in these spectacular displays.

During this time:

+ *Calendula* oil was pressed and filtered
+ *Hypericum* oil was pressed and the oil phase was left to clear
+ Lavender was harvested for distillations
+ Carrot seed heads were gathered and prepared for distillation
+ Other distillations included *Melissa*, hyssop, rosemary, rose geranium
+ More *Calendula* flowers were dried for oil preparation
+ Dried other herbs, *Tilleul* flowers and more rose petals
+ The meadow was scythed for hay.

Another venture in the garden was to conserve an Alpine meadow. As the years passed, agricultural practices in the valley evolved. One of special significance was the frequency of mowing and haymaking. Over time, the surrounding meadows contained more coarse grasses and *Compositae* plants (thistles, dandelions, hawkweeds) and sorrel. The beautiful geraniums, harebells, yellow rattle, dog daisies and fine grasses were fast disappearing. We decided to leave an area as a meadow and cut it in late June/early July as hay for the cows. After a period of two to three years this project succeeded. This year, by late June the grasses were varied and exquisite. Some of them were almost one metre high, with inflorescences glistening in the sunshine and wafting in the summer breezes, releasing clouds of golden pollen into the air. The most prized were: sweet vernal grass, which had been so abundant in the meadows below the house and gave off a wondrous smell as you trod on it – the roots/stolons are perfumed, hence its name; the beautiful yellow oat grass, which shone in the afternoon light; the pink/silver inflorescences of Yorkshire fog; the delicate deep maroon of velvet bent; and the most valued of all – the graceful quaking grass. I read once in a botany book that grass flowers were 'insignificant' – but these were not! They were art forms – varied, colourful and incredibly beautiful. That summer, I noted the following fine grasses in our meadow:

The graceful bents:

+ *Agrostis capillaris* (common bent)
+ *Agrostis canina* (velvet bent)
+ *Agrostis stolonifera* (creeping bent)

The meadow grasses:

+ *Poa annua* (annual meadow grass)
+ *Poa angustifolia* (narrow-leaved meadow grass)

The handsome fine grasses:

+ *Briza media* (the ever-dancing quaking grass)
+ *Cynosurus cristata* (crested dogtail)
+ *Holcus lanatus* (Yorkshire fog, with its inflorescences forming patches of silvery purple haze)
+ *Phleum pratense* (timothy grass)
+ *Anthoxanthum odoratum* (sweet vernal grass with perfumed roots)

And the coarser grasses (but beautiful nevertheless):

+ *Arrhenatherum elatius* (false oat grass)
+ *Bromus sterilis* (barren brome)
+ *Dactylis glomerata* (cocksfoot)
+ *Elymus repens* (couch grass)
+ *Helictotrichon pubescens* (hairy oat grass)
+ *Lolium perenne* (perennial rye grass)
+ *Trisetum flavescens* (the shimmering golden yellow oat grass)

The meadow in June

Scattered among them were luminescent white dog daisies, sun-yellow heartsease and bird's-foot trefoil, brilliant blue speedwells, delicate blue harebells, purple bugles, meadow sage and geraniums, blood-red salad burnet and pink sainfoin. This was my hay!

In the heat of July noons we went down to the cool and refreshing Lac Léman for a swim and picnic under the lakeside trees. It was also time to enjoy the balmy summer evenings. One night, sitting on the balcony on my pouffe, looking up at the crescent moon and her accompanying planet Venus, I noticed a spider's web attached to the balcony rails. Looking closely, I saw that the spider had incorporated one of my finest silver-grey hairs into the web.

August

The days were drawing in and the evenings were considerably cooler. Jeanne used to say that August 15 (a public holiday in France, and a much-celebrated day in Chevenoz, to honour the Virgin's assumption into Heaven) was the last day of Summer. The weather in August in the mountains can be good, but it can also be cold and very wet. Jeanne was correct. By August, I usually tried to have done most of my distillations and pressed most of the infused oils.

During this time:

+ Essential oils were pipetted into small bottles
+ Floral waters were decanted into polypropylene bottles for transport
+ Infused oils were filtered and bottled
+ Washing up – *ad infinitum*. All the glassware was washed until it sparkled, and was thoroughly dried then stored away for next year
+ The still and condensers were thoroughly cleaned
+ The herbs were clipped and pruned after harvesting
+ The rest of the garden was tidied up.

As if to celebrate the end of glorious summer, around August 10 to 13, the heavens gave us a wondrous spectacle – the Perseid shower. As the Earth passed through the meteor belt, the night sky was filled with shooting stars. Those on the night of August 10 are known as the Tears of St Laurent (whose Feast Day it is). On these nights we sat on the balcony and watch the display – best after midnight, hundreds of shooting stars – some even glowing red as they approach Earth, and we wished.

This was also the time when the birds no longer sang in the morning and the migrating birds – the nightingales, the house martins and the swallows – started to line up on the telegraph wires in preparation for their long journeys southwards.

September

The month of the autumn equinox, when day and night are the same length. Here in Chevenoz, a glorious month with beautiful balmy sunshine and clear skies with especially beautiful light. Autumn crocuses appeared in the meadows with their long pale pinky/purple flowers, cars were seen parked in fields near woods where local people all have their secret caches of delicious *chanterelles* and *bolets*, which spring out of the earth in profusion overnight after rain. The wild boars and their piglets came up to the orchard nightly to enjoy the bounty and feed on the fallen plums, pears and apples and later to search for roots and grubs and generally do what pigs are thought to do.

One beautiful September afternoon, I was sitting on the balcony and noticed that the air was glistening. On closer examination, I saw that it was full of gossamer threads reaching from the apple tree leaf canopy down to the ground, all aligned in the direction of the wind, like golden tresses. This was the flight of the codling moth larvae. Each thread was attached to the leaf where the moth had left its cocoon and each larva was letting itself down to the earth gradually – a place where it would spend the winter months in the leaf litter. This spectacle lasted for a few hours and the next day was no more – the migration was complete.

L'Almanach quote: 'in this month the stars are more brilliant due to the low moisture content of the atmosphere'. This is true. The Milky Way was clearly visible as a wide band across the sky from south (SSSW) to north (NNNE). We watched more shooting stars as we passed through the Leonides, and Saturn and Venus graced the morning sky.

October

There is always an excitement and urgency about this month, when mushrooms are abundant in the markets, the hunters distribute venison and *sanglier* (wild boar) from their local hunting sessions, and dusks are enlivened by the sounds of the rutting stags in the meadows near the woods.

Here in my Chevenoz garden, decay set in. Armies of mildew spores attacked the roses, the *Calendula* and *Melissa*, turning the leaves silver white; the rose leaves developed black spot; apple leaves got leaf curl. It was almost as if the plants had done their job and lost the will to live. They submitted to forces greater than themselves. As in spring, a marked change occurred. After a couple of days of rain in the middle of the month, autumn orchestrated a finale of balmy and misty days, with the spectacular colours of the bronzed beech trees among the dark green conifers, the ferns; the reds of the dogwoods, viburnums, pear trees and the wild and cultivated cherries; the orange rowans; the yellows of the willows down by the Dranse, sycamores, silver birches and poplars, all against the backcloth of a mid-blue sky. Then swiftly the winds, rain and falling temperatures that followed caused the leaves to fall, swirling noisily in the wind to the ground. It was all over in a week and the clearing-up process began so that I could put the garden to bed for the winter sleep.

This was the time for my annual bonfire. I found a good spot on the plots for the fire and then selected all the woody stems – of *Melissa*, clary sage, lavender trimmings, hyssop, *Artemisia*, *Calendula*, *Hypericum* – creating a huge mound of aromatic plants resembling a funeral pyre. I waited until dusk, which came early in these ever-shortening days, and as the church bells chimed five, I lit the plywood fruit trays that I used as tinder. The fire lit quickly as the leaves were so dry and with flames to start with, a column of incense rose up in the still air, intensely aromatic and tinged silver/purple in the fading light; red sparks followed and crackles, and then later flames again, brilliant red and gold tongues of fire rising into the mists. I stood with this fire and inhaled its aroma, watching the smoke rise, leaning on my pitchfork, mug of tea in hand, tending the fire, keeping the hot centre fed with leaves and stems. As ever, there was so much to do practically, ritualistically and meditatively – until eventually it was spent. It needed a couple of visits during the night to fork over the embers and keep feeding the fire. The next morning all that remained was fine, grey ash – nothing compared to the mountain there the night before. Later I spread this precious remnant of the year's abundant growth over the plots. That was the end of the gardening year – a time to give thanks.

Work done this month:

+ Walnuts were harvested and dried in the midday sun
+ Quince were harvested and left to 'sweat'
+ Apples and plums were picked
+ Compotes were prepared and bottled
+ Grapes were harvested daily
+ Pruning and tidying up – so much to do…
+ The ceremonial bonfire at Hallowe'en.

The rhythms that I followed over the course of a year in my Chevenoz garden were essentially shamanic. They connected with the seasons, the sun, the moon and the planets, with their effects on the growth of plants. At a basic level they were about expansion and contraction, birth, growth and death. This was the garden year. The eight shamanic/pagan festivals celebrated by people living close to the Earth in the northern hemisphere marked these rhythms with the 'Quarter Days': the Winter Solstice, the Spring Equinox, the Summer Solstice and the Autumn Equinox. Between these festivals were the 'Eighth Days' dividing the year into eight equal parts: Imbolc in February, Beltane in May, Lughnasadh in August and Samhain in October.

In Chevenoz these festivals were still 'Earthy'. Just as May 1 was a garden celebration with its *mugeuts*, so was June 21, August 15 and October 31. But here there was a fusion of the important growing and harvest times in Nature with Catholicism. The ancient pagan celebration of May Day with its fertility rites became a celebration of Mary the Virgin; the summer solstice was the feast of the blessed apostle St John; Mary's assumption to heaven marked the end of the harvest; and the beginning of winter starts with a holy evening (Hallowe'en) followed by the feast of All Saints (*Tous Saints*) on November 1 and the feast of All Souls on November 2, when everyone puts chrysanthemums (a symbol of death) on the family graves. So the concept of the death of Nature and the end of the year when, by pagan belief, the veil between the material world and the world of Spirit is thinnest, became a Christian celebration of the saints and all humans who had died.

This was the end of my gardening year – seven months of deep involvement with Nature and my plants and intense physical work. Besides the preparations of tinctures, essential oils and dried herbs, which I was committed to send to my clients, I also prepared extracts and tisanes for myself from the herbs that had drifted into my garden from the surrounding meadows. In this area I was advised by the *Almanach* and local custom, and also by Jeanne, who remembered from her childhood what her mother had done.

Local home pharmacies – Jeanne's mother's medicine cabinet...

In the lifetime of Jeanne's mother, one of the most important tasks of the mother of a Savoyard household was to gather, prepare and store a range of herbs to be used throughout the year to cure the family's wounds, illnesses and discomforts. Visits to doctors were rare events in these rural communities. But within a couple of generations this tradition has virtually disappeared with the expansion of universal health care in France and the ease of mobility of the population. To counteract this, a movement called *Le Patrimoine* has been established to record many rural and oral traditions and preserve them as history or for later use.

In summer 2005, we took Jeanne to a *Le Patrimoine* exhibition in a nearby town curated by the parish priest, who had been researching Savoyard culture. He was particularly interested in herbal medicine and had found and exhibited many of the plants that until recently had been in common use. We looked around and Jeanne became very animated as she remembered so many of them from her mother's medicine store in their cellar. A few remnants still exist in Chevenoz today, like the old men who arrive in the meadows in April with their Opinel penknives and buckets to dig out the emerging dandelion shoots and the young nettles – both to make soups to benefit kidneys and livers suffering from a winter steeped in *eau de vie*. I was interested to see so many plants also recommended by *L'Almanach*. Looking through the '*travaux du mois*' notes in *L'Almanach Savoyard 2005*, I compiled the following list of plants to be gathered, month by month. I have selected medicinal properties for all these plants[1]. Jeanne remembered that her mother used them in similar ways.

Note:

- Category * plants in the list below were those that were already growing in my garden.
- Category ** plants were all growing in surrounding meadows, *alpages*, woods or hedgerows – all easily found and collected for a medicine chest.
- It is only the category *** plants – marsh mallow, soapwort and hops – that were absent from our local flora. Marsh mallow and soapwort would surely grow on the banks of the Dranse, and since beer has been drunk here for centuries, hops would have been available in local gardens.

January

** Pine buds – anti-inflammatory and expectorant. Remedy for coughs/catarrh
** Bramble leaves – astringent and tonic. Remedy for dysentery and diarrhoea
* Rosemary – used throughout history as a mind stimulant, mood lifter, and for curing headaches
* Birch bark – skin diseases, eczema
** Willow bark – treatment of worms, acid stomach

March

** Coltsfoot flowers – cough remedy
* Primrose flowers – antispasmodic, emetic, vermifuge

April

* Nettle leaves – relief of bronchial or asthmatic symptoms

May

* Hawthorn flowers – heart palpitations, sore throats
* Borage flowers – fevers and lung complaints

**   Pellitory by the wall – relieving toothache

*   Cornflowers – eyewash ('*Casse lunettes*')

*   Wild pansy – treatment of epilepsy, asthma, heart tonic (also called heartsease)

*   Elderflowers – sore throats, haemorrhoids

*   Sage flowers and leaves – there is an old French saying translated as: 'Sage helps the nerves and by its powerful might palsy is cured and fever put to flight'

June

*   Fumitory – a purifier of the blood – so for skin disorders, a purge

*   Mallow – inflammation/irritation of alimentary canal and urinary tract, coughs and colds

*** Marsh mallow – as mallow, but more effective

*   Walnut leaves – skin disease, eczema

*   Linden flowers – tisane used for nervous vomiting, indigestion or hysteria

**   Arnica – for bruising and burns

*   Meadowsweet – children's diarrhoea, diuretic

*   *Hypericum* – for bruising, burns, depression

*   Meadow sage – mouth ulcers, indigestion, tonic

*   German chamomile – calming, antispasmodic, sedative

*** Soapwort roots – jaundice, itching, rheumatism

**   Wild chicory – tonic, laxative, diuretic

*   Couch grass roots – treatment of worms

*   Burdock – blood purifier, diuretic, causes sweating

July

*   *Melissa* (lemon balm) – calming, for fevers, causes sweating

*   Mint – diarrhoea, flatulence

*   Wormwood – aids digestion, stomach pain

**   Yellow gentian roots – digestive problems, liver problems

*   Agrimony – liver complaints, jaundice

*   Peach leaves – sedative, diuretic, expectorant

August

*   *Artemisia* – bitters (as in Absinthe)
** Melilot – to put in a herb cheese, for abdominal and rheumatic pains

September

*** Hop flowers – sedative, stomach and liver tonic
*   Valerian – nervous tension and anxiety, antispasmodic, sedative

These plants could be found in the local environment and could either be picked from where they grew at the appropriate time or else seeds blew or were carried into gardens – as so many useful plants have arrived in my garden. And this raises the important topic of foraging. In bygone days, people in this region spent most of their time – at least in the summer months – in Nature. They knew their native surrounds intimately, noticed what grew around them and, by handed down tradition, knew how they could be used. Plants were available and they were free.

And further afield

Realising that this kind of knowledge was fast disappearing, an interesting study was done in the Vercor region of the Southern Alps and its results were published in 1993[2]. It was an ethno-botanical study to record traditional knowledge for future generations. In this region traditionally there were many shepherds who roamed the mountains with their sheep, and often their grandchildren accompanied them. They would recognise and collect plants as food and medicines for themselves and their families, and an oral tradition was passed down through the generations. Besides the shepherds, there were woodcutters, herdsmen and those working in the fields who all came to recognise and benefit from their local flora. Year by year they collected the same plants from the same locations and took care to make sure they would leave enough plants or seeds for future seasons. Often collecting was seen as a pleasant pastime rather than a chore and sufficient of a particular plant was gathered to last the family for the entire year.

Identification of the plants was never by botanical name and usually in *patois* (the dialect of the region). A plant could have a very local name, being called something very different in a neighbouring *commune*. The use of the plant was always the same though. These people knew in what circumstances and how to use them. Interestingly, if two plants had very similar modes of action, they were called the same name even if they looked rather different (they were often of the same genus botanically). There was also a very narrow divide between plants used as food and plants used as medicine. In early spring, when people were suffering from a long hard winter and there was little variety of stored food left in cellars, young leaves of plants like plantains, primroses, sorrel and cress were foraged to put in potato soups, which were eaten daily. These soups were seen as cleansing for the blood, the intestine and the liver, and very beneficial.

From this sort of existence, a calendar for collecting plants emerged (as the one above from *L'Almanach Savoyard*). Sometimes the harvest of a particular plant became associated with a special feast day – perhaps because this was a day of rest and celebration and families had time to enjoy picnicking and dancing and being in the mountains. An example of this is the feast of St John on June 24, which by tradition was the day to gather mountain violets (*Viola odorata L.*) to be used in the winter months to cure bronchitis and winter chills.

The study showed that the inhabitants of the Vercors region used over one hundred plants for medicinal use alone (other uses were as food, as materials for building, as materials to make household implements like brooms and baskets, and as veterinary products). Their medicinal uses were to treat injuries, wounds, infections – especially childhood ones, fevers, coughs and colds. In particular, there was a range of herbs to treat menstruation or the lack of it, pregnancy, lactation and other problems associated with childbirth and rearing. In discussion with these people, it became clear that the way in which these plants were used was closer to mediaeval herbalism than modern herbal use. Their actual modes of action were seldom known or even questioned, and the language used to express what they did was archaic. This was the nature of traditional knowledge. Their main thesis was that the 'illness' circulated in the body and could be 'drawn out' as blood or pus by poultices (e.g. by a fresh vervain and egg white preparation wrapped in cotton cloth and put on a deep bruise or haematoma); could be flushed out in urine (using diuretics like dandelion leaves tisane) or sweating (using elderflower tisane); or could be somehow improved by heat – either in food taken into the stomach (e.g. cooked maize flour) to warm the body, or by external hot compresses (e.g. pine oil) for alleviating muscle aches and sprains. Liqueurs and wines were very popular too. Each family prepared their own, which were brought proudly to the table as *apéritifs* and liqueurs/*digestifs*, and very often special curative powers were attributed to these concoctions. These were made by steeping aromatic plants in wine or *eau de vie*. Gentian wine was used as a strengthening tonic; walnut liqueur was effective in treatment of chest pain; angelica and juniper liqueurs were used to warm the body in treatment of influenza. With the additional effect of the alcohol in them, these liqueurs were sometimes elevated to sacred status and made using well-guarded secret recipes in monasteries and abbeys throughout the land. For children and those who couldn't take an alcoholic extraction, a syrup was prepared.

This study describes the deep connection and affection between these mountain people and their rich Alpine flora. Many of those interviewed had lived through the Second World War when food was in desperate short supply and there was a revival of traditional ways of existence. But many of these traditions were kept on by choice and appreciation of their benefits. It is only now, with mechanised agricultural methods and such an exodus of young people from the *communes* to the towns, that this way of life is fast disappearing. The flora still exists thanks to the creation of a vast protected national park and this study has aimed to preserve the knowledge for use by everyone who can access these wonderful plants.

These modes of peasant life – in my own garden, in Jeanne's mother's garden and within a whole community – all had a precious quality. And this stems from the close connection we have all had to Nature, living as one with its rhythms of the sun and the seasons, the moon and its phases, the planets and their influences. This is the meaning of the word 'peasant' – one living close to the land. Foraging and harvesting these plants for healing medicines and for food gave us all access to the underlying Power of the universe. As the arch-forager Patience Gray says in her book 'Honey from a Weed'[3]: 'weeds have energy'. We received it. What a gift.

Chapter notes

1.   Grieve, Mrs M. FRHS. A Modern Herbal. Edited by Mrs C.F. Leyel. First published in 1931 by Jonathan Cape. Current edition published in 1994 by Cresset Books. ISBN 1-85501-249-9

2.   Bonnelle, Claire. *Des hommes et des plantes*. 1993. CPIE Vercors, F-38250

3.   Gray, Patience. Honey from a Weed. 2009. Paperback edition. Prospect Books. ISBN 978-1-903018-20-0

Frontispiece from La Pharmacopée Française 1937

XII

Creativity, Spirit and Subtle Energy

'By psychology's 'mortal' sin
I mean the sin of deadening…'
JAMES HILLMAN[1]

Dream on waking (this morning)

I was in a strange farmyard/ranch-type place. Ben and a rancher (?) were with me. We were walking down an empty street with ancient wooden buildings on either side. Suddenly the rancher looked up behind him and saw a huge snake on the roof of one of the buildings. It raised its head and hissed at him. He waved it away with both arms, seemingly unperturbed, and kept walking. The snake was aroused and purposefully slid down off the roof and started to follow us. Ben and the man were walking on, talking, and I had turned round to look at it. It was staring straight at me, intently, and quickened its pace, slithering like a river of quicksilver. It was enormous! I knew I couldn't turn around, nor walk backwards quickly enough. It was coming closer and mesmerising me, its long tongue flickering and reaching towards me. Panicking, I looked for an escape route and realised that in a few paces I could side-step and rush down a little alleyway, but I saw it was a dead-end. Then the snake was upon me — so I just grabbed it. With all my strength, I grasped its 'neck' — just behind its head — with my two hands and held it tight, in front of my face — looking straight into its eyes. Its power was astounding and somehow I wasn't afraid. Ben and the man were watching me with interest… I woke up.

> *Personal symbolism: Yesterday I had been thinking about the Rod of Asclepius – the staff with the snake entwined, the staff of healing (from the gods) and decided to put the frontispiece from La Pharmacopée Française with the palm tree and snake at the beginning of this chapter.*
>
> *Symbolism: Snake represents spirituality/deep powerful life force.*

Creativity and Spirit

All these activities in herbal medicine and working with Nicholas and Jonathan opened up new channels of creativity within me. I started to sing again – firstly with Jill Purce on a Mongolian Overtone Chanting course[2]. Voice is a way for us to participate in the vibratory universe and has been used since ancient times in ritual and spiritual practice. On this workshop, we endeavoured to learn the technique of using voice to produce a harmonic spectrum of 'unearthly' sounds, floating above the deeper voices of the chanters. This 'open throat' singing is practised widely in Central Asia, Tibet and Mongolia in religious ceremonies. The aim is to develop the spiritual potential of the voice as a magical instrument for healing and meditation. An advocate of mind-body medicine, Dr Deepak Chopra described Jill's techniques as 'learning to peel the layers of your soul and discover the grandeur of your being'.

This was enough to rekindle my love of singing. Later I joined a choir in Islington where we sang mostly world folk songs in parts, without musical scores, but with a very talented young teacher who had a beautiful voice. This was new territory for me and involved a lot of listening and engaging. We learned or improvised harmonies and had to develop trust in both ourselves and our companions. The choir was young and modern and after our first year singing together, on May 1 we performed a 'Beltane Concert' in the lovely Union Chapel in Upper Street, Islington. Appreciating the meaning of Beltane and remembering my Catholic rituals of May altars, I volunteered to provide 'greenery' with which to decorate the enormous Union Chapel with the help of other choir members. A friend was head gardener on a large Hertfordshire estate and agreed to gather suitable foliage for me. So on the morning of the concert I went there and packed the car full to the roof with the beautiful foliage and blossoms he had gathered – scented May blossom, service tree blossom, wild cherry, the newly opened lime green leafy beech and delicate birch branchlets, evergreen yew, ivy and pine. The car smelled so deliciously intoxicating that I had to drive back to London with the windows wide open for fear of reaching a trance state. After many hours' work, the chapel looked radiantly alive and the concert was a wonderful experience, bringing our spirituality close to the Earth.

A couple of nights later I had the following dream:

I am in a strange house. It seems very empty and in a state of renovation and redecoration. The ceilings are all very high and some walls have actually been knocked down. I wander around, wondering what to do. Eventually I arrive in a large sort of canteen/dining hall. There are lots of young women present. They are having a banquet and enjoying each other's company. Suddenly, amid cheering, someone brings in a huge plate of candied fruits and passes them round, offering them to everyone. I wasn't part of the group and didn't think they were for me. Then a young woman offers me some and offers to show me around. We go out into a courtyard of a sort of university campus. The buildings are all made of golden sandstone and there are caskets of brilliant precious stones lying around the place. It is really beautiful. She tells me I have a lot of learning to do at this place…

…I go into another room that has a very different atmosphere. Dee (my mother) was there and my eldest sister, Val. They seem very anxious, talking in whispers to each other. Suddenly my dead sister Jan arrives. She is strange and pale but happy, and has a beautiful girl child in her arms. The child has lustrous long black/green hair and a clear and beautifully luminescent pale skin. We haven't seen Jan for a very long time and welcome her. Dee and Val speak to Jan and are very concerned about something. After a while I go up to Jan and greet her and the child. I then say that I am very surprised that she has a child with such lovely dark hair. I look at it closely and stroke it. I notice that along the hairline it is dark green. The rest is black, lustrous and wavy. It is quite spectacular. I say, 'That's funny that you have a child like that, I was always the dark one!' She is silent for a moment and then says, 'The child is yours! I took her from you a long time ago. I don't need her anymore. Here, take her.' And she flings the child into my arms and leaves the room. I clutch the child to my heart. I wake up.

Symbolism: The child was Clara in Isabel Allende's 'House of the Spirits'. Clara was renowned for her beautiful wavy black/green hair (in the book it was her elder sister Rosa who had the black/green hair. In my mind it was Clara). Green hair: the hair of the Earth Maiden sculpture in the Lost Gardens of Heligan.

Later that night I dreamed again:

I was back in my childhood home 'Lindens'. I was a young girl and was standing around in the hall by the front door, leaning against the banisters. I think I was listless and waiting for something to happen. Suddenly the front door burst open and a huge red and white bird strutted in. It had a wonderful long tail made of red and white feathers, spread behind it like a peacock's tail (when not in a fan). Beside the bird was her chick – smaller and less spectacular. As they came in together, I rushed at them, trying to get them out again and to slam the door shut. I ran forward with my arms outstretched and the mother bird immediately charged at me, taking off into flight down the hall – straight into my face. WOW. I woke up.

Symbolism: This was a 'Big Dream' since it was taking place in my beloved childhood home. The bird was a phoenix. The striking in the face was a definite 'wake-up call'. The impact was spectacular – and another of those 'in my face' endings in my dreams.

I regard both these dreams in shamanic terminology as spontaneous Soul Retrievals – and as in all Soul Retrievals for me, I resist them very strongly. The first was a Soul part returned by my sister Jan, who had regarded me as 'The Lucky One', and the second was a return of 'something' transformed from my past (from the ashes) – brought about by a phoenix 'fusing' with me. As with all these 'Big Dreams', from this time on, I was changed.

Another creative venture was to take up wood carving at the City Lit in the heart of London. Again, this broke new ground – and in a very challenging way. In the first lesson, our tutor came in and briefly showed us the rudiments of wood carving. She then gave us the concept of a circle to design our carving and make a maquette/model of it in plasticine. The next lesson, she taught us how to use chisels and mallet and how to saw off a piece of the required size from a large block of linden wood, and then told us to get started. I found this approach to teaching bewildering, having been well schooled and directed during my formal education as well as in my language courses in French and German in Basel. However, I was ready to fight my demons while the creative process was coming into being, and my first carving was based on the infinity form and produced a goddess – part human and part plant. It's now, in later years, that I realise her deep shamanic significance. This was the beginning of my human/plant creations. My next carving was inspired by a beautiful sculpture I had found on a building on the corner of Albemarle Street in London. High up above the street, on a turn-of-the-century building with a red brick and white Portland stone facade, was a young man, rising out of a Greek-style urn/gynaecium (seed pod), with the helmet of a warrior/hero and outstretched arms turning into weaving plant tendrils. To my mind he was exquisite. I started by photographing him, then drawing him – delicately, with charcoals, upside-down – and then the hardest part of all, which was to turn a shallow relief-work sculpture into a three-dimensional maquette. I then carved him from a piece of linden wood. It was later that I found a photo of the same sculpture in a book entitled 'Green Man – the Archetype of our Oneness with the Earth' by William Anderson[3]. So the theme repeated itself.

My third serious carving was another Green Man – this time from a carving made in 1415 by John Watlington with Brice the Dutchman on oak wood, from Norwich Cathedral[3]. Here was a face almost hidden behind oak leaves. It was immensely difficult to get the proportions right and I thought I was carving an older man, even an ancient man, as so many Green Men are. However, as images evolve unexpectedly – especially in carving – my Green Man was still young and beautiful, with hooded eyes, as my first one had been. Perhaps he was not yet mature?

All three of these carvings were of the same theme – an unconscious choice on my part – of the human/plant connection.

Understanding how to carve in three dimensions encouraged me to start drawing again. During my botanical studies I had had ample drawing practice. Although I always tried to make my drawings and compositions attractive, art was not considered part of this exercise. In fact, objectivity was the aim – to draw accurately those parts of the plant that were botanically significant and justified the plant's classification. I now started drawing plants again, putting my own expression and interpretation into my creations. But however beautiful the plants were, my drawings lacked something that I really wanted to be there. Then I found a lovely little book of paintings by Charles Rennie Mackintosh[4] and decided to copy them instead of living plants. Doing this revealed a very interesting fact: in copying what I saw, my curves were never extreme enough! To get the right effect, when copying, I needed to emphasise a line more than my eye told me to. Since this was so difficult to do, I started to draw objects upside down and eventually with my left hand (I was born a 'lefty'). These methods yielded the desired effects. I realised that I needed to use other parts of my brain than the ones I had been trained to use. Once I

The Goddess

A Carving of the Green Man of Albemarle Street

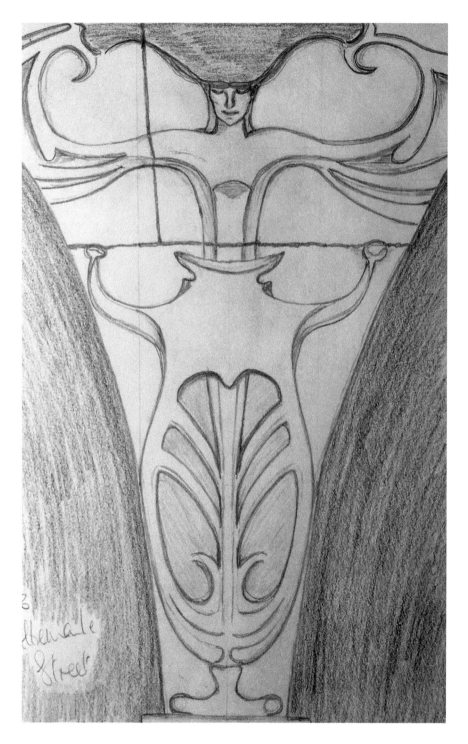

Drawing of the Green Man of Albemarle Street.

Drawing of the Green Man – close-up of his face

An angel from 'Angeli Ministrantes' by Edward
Burne-Jones, drawn with my left hand

understood this, I experimented in all sorts of ways: with charcoals on rough paper, in semi-darkness, with my eyes half closed. My best results were faces drawn upside down. This eliminated those perceptions and anxieties of what a nose should look like, how to create expressions in eyes, details in hair – and the capturing of body language and emotions. These methods are well understood by art teachers, but for me this was experimenting and being creative in a way that I hadn't been since childhood. I also learned to approach a creative project and go through the stages of enthusiasm and blocks and even despair. I came to understand this process and could mostly work through it. Usually the worst part was just before the creative energies came streaming through.

I used this approach in quilt making too. My first attempt was the very regular, huge and orthodox American quilt. It was technically well designed and executed – its appearance being greatly enhanced by the beautiful Liberty fabrics they gave us. I was well pleased with it. The second quilt was made of attractive Nigerian batik design cotton and after quilting it, I used more freestyle silk overstitching. Later quilts for Soledad's crib were a mixture of collage and quilting, full of symbolism and freestyle. Later I decided to transform my mother's mink coat into my shamanic mat. In an act of feared huge destruction, I dismantled my mother's beloved fur coat that had been given to me by my sisters after her death (but not worn for almost fifteen years). I re-modelled the fur into a mat and then, to do the act justice, made a collage to line the reverse side. This was stitched onto a beautiful piece of dark green Indian wild silk given to me by Gail. The collage was an adaptation of an iris flower that I had found in a mosaic in Knossos in Crete, with its bulb and roots in the deep earth and its flower connecting to the moon above the mountains surrounding our house in Chevenoz. Everything in the design was deeply symbolic for me and represented the three shamanic Worlds of Lower World, Middle World and Upper World, and the connections between them and all living things. I made this in semi-trance state over a period of around three days. During this time I hardly stopped – sewing day and night. My desire to create something beautiful from such an important object in my life was intense.

I now regard all these endeavours as spiritual practices. Somehow, while doing them I needed to use parts of myself in ways I hadn't done for a long time. The results were significantly greater because of this. I was beginning to understand creativity.

Soledad's quilt – the Sun

Soledad's quilt – the Moon

A modern idea of creativity

Recently I came across a YouTube video of Patti Smith receiving the Nobel Prize for Literature in the name of her poet and songwriter friend Bob Dylan. The choice of Dylan for the Literature prize in 2016 was considered to be an unusual choice and it was awarded for 'having created new poetic expressions within the great American songwriting tradition'. As an American songwriter, punk singer, poet and author, Patti was a suitable substitute to speak on the topic of creativity. A short time previously she had given an inspiring lecture at Yale University on 'The Compulsion to Write' (September 2016), at which my beloved granddaughter Soledad sat, transfixed. After the Nobel ceremony, Patti gave an interview on Swedish television with a theologian on the subject of spirituality. Using a description of God shared by many other philosophers and theologians as 'a beautiful open concept not contained by limiting ideas', she proclaimed that 'all art belongs to God' and the role of the artist is to 'dive into their innermost, highest or deepest Being, which reflects God, and then return to the world to reflect this and share it with others'. The product could be lofty or lowly – both equally being a work of art, whether a Rembrandt or a loaf of bread, if made with intention and love. They went on to discuss the meaning of the word 'icon': an icon reflects something 'Other', a sort of window. So in creating an icon, an artist reflects that deeper dimension.

This discussion was very meaningful to me and put my prior work in a context. My herbal products were 'works of art' – and I say this humbly. They were produced from beautiful plants in a wonderful healing garden in a superb location. My intention was to make each stage of the process as perfect and as sacred (the connection with the Divine) as possible. And in my work with plants, it was also the Power of the plants themselves (another connection with the Divine) that needed to come into play. I knew that a plant growing in a suitable environment in full health was the essence of vitality and there was nothing that I needed to, or could, do to improve on that. But in my dealings with the plants – by cultivation, by harvesting and by the various processes I used to prepare the plant products, I needed to connect with other forces in Nature or with the plant's Consciousness or Spirit so that I could conserve that natural energy. My belief is that this energy plays an essential part in the healing process. This is not a new idea. Others have certainly done it before. But it was the 'doing' it that was the breakthrough for me.

In all my years of searching and researching, with ideas leading on one to another, I seem to have drifted further and further away from my scientific training. I don't say 'roots' here, as my roots have always been deeply embedded in Nature and my imagination. In these searching years, in particular I have been impressed by the concepts of Energy – the force that empowers and leads to growth – and Spirit – that which enlivens and uplifts. Of course, these terms are defined and described in many philosophical and religious contexts, but I have been in the business of developing my own understanding and spirituality. I had rejected the rigid and immature Catholicism of my youth and didn't want to adhere to any other formalised religion. In hindsight, I realise that I had rejected too much – I had thrown the baby out with the bathwater.

But I have not been idle during the intervening years. Over a period of more than twenty years, I have continued to work with Jonathan Horwitz[5]. It has been a very long journey – in both senses of the word – and one on which I have been a sometime willing and sometime very reluctant pilgrim. Alongside this work and the Jungian analysis working on dreams and symbolism, I realise that some very profound changes have occurred in my psyche and in my ways of 'knowing'. But it is only in latter years that I have had the openness, courage and privilege to meet and work with plant spirits, even though this is what traditional shamans have done the world over. My spirit guides have come from the mythological, human cultural and animal worlds. I had no plant spirits to support me. And I wondered about this on many occasions. Why should it be that someone who has had an affinity with plants all her life, whose childhood garden was her mother, who had magical experiences with flowers, ferns and pollen grains as a child, did not connect with plant spirits? I had done 'medicine walks' on courses, meditated on plants and connected with them and saw them as healers, but the deep and crucial connection had not been made. And this was where I came to realise that in my culture and education, plants have not been considered to be as 'alive' as animals are. My experience as a teacher had shown me the antipathy of students, both boys and girls, to plants. When introducing a new topic in biology lessons, I got used to the groans emitted when I told them it was about plants and not animals. I had to draw them into the world of plant appreciation. It was not a given. Plants were seen as inherently inanimate and therefore, by comparison, less interesting. A scientific view of plants and all the terminology used in botany makes plants inferior to animals. Biology as science is anthropocentric – with man in the centre – and after that it is zoocentric – animals next. The laws of the physical sciences have been adapted to try to make sense of biology and then animals especially, in ways that they are similar to man. But to make concessions for plants and the ways that they differ from animals is not so commonplace. We understand the language of biology used to describe animal characteristics: 'instincts', 'movement', 'senses'. We share them. In botany, the terms 'tropisms', 'sessile' and 'receptors' are not emotive. And science progresses by extending areas of current research (the 'known' paradigm) that are judged by peers studying in that area. This makes it difficult to branch into new fields of research.

Thus for years my view of plants had been clouded by this scientific viewpoint. I had known very early on that to study botany at university took the love out of it. It also took away other connections – for all academic botanists. Those 'net absorbers of the sun's energy, source of all food for all non-green living creatures on this planet, and providers of oxygen that sustains life' became inanimate fodder disconnected from their true essence and their spirits.

As that wonderful professor emeritus of Botany from the University of Montpelier, Francis Hallé, who spent forty years in tropical rainforests studying tree canopies, explains in his book 'Éloge de la Plante' (translated as 'In Praise of Plants'[6]):

> 'With such a dearth of botanical research in areas where plants differ from animals, who has the greater experience, knowledge and authority, the scientist or the shaman who has lived in close proximity with the rainforests all his life and knows the plants like family?'

An example on this theme is the effect of the moon on plants. Traditional knowledge gathered over centuries takes this as a basic truth: the pine wood for Stradivarius violins, by tradition, was cut at certain prescribed times according to moon cycles; many Austrian timber yards supplying wood carvers and house builders dated their timbers accordingly. Our local carpenter Roger knew 'in his bones' when to cut wood for fire-lighting (dry), rafters (flexible), houses (fire-resistant), but science without thorough investigation dismisses these ideas – mostly. The breeding cycles of certain animals are known to be influenced by the moon, like the spectacular migration of the Christmas Island red crabs to the sea for spawning, but only recently has a leading scientific journal published research findings that tree trunk circumferences fluctuate with the tides[7].

Shamanic practices III

In early 2016 I had got to a time in my life when I felt energetically blocked again. My sleep patterns became disrupted, so there were lots of cups of tisanes in the night, and I felt that I had started to contract. I decided it was time to look for another shamanic course with Jonathan Horwitz. I came across a course in Schumacher College, Dartington, in Devon, and immediately had a compelling need to go on it. The closing date was nigh, so I immediately applied online and then had a problem paying the deposit – it wouldn't take my money! I phoned the secretary at Schumacher College and she wasn't available, so I left a message. A couple of hours later she rang me to explain that the website couldn't take my money as the course had been full. But, by chance, someone had cancelled in the last hour, so would I like his place?

The course was a three-week elective course for sixteen young students from around the world, all studying master's degree courses in Holistic Science, Environment and Sustainability, and Design. Alongside them were six of us 'outsiders', mature students, all with a broad range of relevant experiences to bring to the course.

We had three weeks in early spring time in glorious Devonian countryside with no commitments other than attention, in the company of intelligent, caring, questing and like-minded people. We followed a broad-themed and in-depth programme looking at aspects of 'Mind in Nature'. Tutors Rupert Sheldrake and Stephan Harding set the scene with a week of lectures studying the History of Ideas. They took us on a journey from the shamans and hunter-gatherers, through the mediaeval *anima mundi* and the Protestant Reformation in England to the 17th-century origins of modern science with Cartesian dualism that resulted in the Mind-Body split into a distant heavenly spiritual 'God' and a mechanical World.

Rupert's lectures on the History of Ideas described how we had arrived at our mechanistic worldview. He outlined the ten dogmas from his book 'The Science Delusion'[8] and then systematically debunked them. The last of his dogmas to refute, that mechanical medicine is the only one that works, resonated strongly with me. Rupert's sessions were interspersed with Stephan's examples of types of intelligence or Consciousness found in living systems. In fact, Stephan went further – describing an 'Animate Earth'[9] where all life is conscious and connected with rocks, air, water and earth. He described an experience he had while studying the muntjac deer, where after making eye contact with the animal he had been anticipating for over an hour, he became 'at one' with it, and then suddenly understood its relationship with its environment, and outwards with the whole Earth. This 'knowing' is reminiscent of Evelyn Roe's experience with her water lily, and perhaps of Edward Bach's experience with the plants that he used for his Remedies.

The second week of the course was a complete contrast to this intellectual approach – with Jonathan Horwitz and Zara Waldebäck. We were plunged back into an animate world: a world of panentheism where the divine pervades every part of the universe and beyond it. Shamanic work in Nature was what had attracted me to the course, and it was during this time that I really made contact with plant spirits. I felt supported enough to go deeper. And so I did in this vacuum. Or was it a cocoon?

During the course I had the following dream:

I was being driven along a strange street (was it Downtown New York?) in an old black car with *****. We were in a run-down area with closed shops and no life. The car drew up onto the sidewalk and someone from the outside opened the car door (like chauffeurs do for dignitaries); he reached into the car and pulled me out. Immediately I dropped from the car, dead... I actually watched myself falling onto the pavement, wearing the green cardigan I had been wearing that day. Wake up time...

On Jonathan's advice, the next day I Journeyed to my Spirits to ask for meaning and the way forward:

Journey: I was led to the depths of the Earth/Hell?? via the Grand Canyon – doing a 'Thelma and Louise' exit in the company of my spirit guide *****. He was in black leathers on a motorbike... We set off at great speed and over the rim. We then fell a very long way down and eventually arrived in a sort of atrium. It was very calm and dark. I was prepared and ceremonially laid on a bier by my Spirits and a golden-haired boy. In procession they pushed me into the fiery interior of a huge caldron/incinerator and the enormous doors slammed shut. Inside, the flames glowed yellow then red and finally a brilliant white. The heat was unbearable and I was consumed by the flames for what seemed like a very long time. Suddenly I was pushed to one side of the chamber and unceremoniously doused in a cold water sprinkler system as the returning drums sounded. A voice said, 'this will anneal all pain'.

Note I write 'anneal' because that is how I thought I heard it. The scientific term means 'to allow a metal to cool slowly, in order to remove internal stresses and toughen it'. The original sense was 'set on fire', hence (in late Middle English) 'subject to fire, alter by heating'. There is another word 'anele' that sounds the same and means 'the sacrament of anointing at time of death'. All three meanings are suitable!

For years I have been very impressed by how my dreams are able to take my Journeys to another level of understanding (and vice versa). My Jungian work tells me this was an alchemical transformation. I came out distinctly changed. In shamanic terms, I understood what sacred meant.

I had my first real experiences of plant spirits during this course, where I met the Spirit of Yew. In answer to my question, 'who are you?', I was told 'I am YOU'! And I felt the connection. Later, in a dancing ritual, I experienced being 'embodied' by the Spirit of a linden tree. These intensely moving experiences I can only describe in Jungian terms as 'numinous', and in Jonathan's term as 'a deep and felt understanding'. After these experiences, I became open enough to work with plant spirits – a central shamanic practice in healing rites – and to regard the work as central in my description of plant healing[10].

It was now that I began to see the commonality between so many ideas. Shamanic Journeying is an archaic method of reaching a state of Consciousness beyond the Will and the Ego – described as experiencing a 'Non-Ordinary Reality' of the spirit world. Unlike meditation, where the mind is emptied of thoughts and images, shamanic Journeying uses imagination – i.e. uses images to describe sensations and ideas – as dreams do. And it is here that there are similarities between shamanism and Goethe's technique of internalising images and Bach's technique of listening to plants 'talking to him'. Of course, language to describe these other-worldly events is inadequate. When we say 'plants talking', it is our minds trying to make sense of what we are beholding using archetypal images and words – our very effective communication tools! In all these cases, barriers are broken down and deep connection and understanding is made with the essence of the 'Other' within the spirit world. I came away from the course enriched by the experience and my understanding of the healing nature of plants now had another dimension – a *felt* understanding of their spirits. This was a huge step forward.

And interestingly, neither Rupert's nor Stephan's descriptions emphasised the categories of sentient and non-sentient beings (they both described a world where everything is animate). But this idea of sentience is certainly accepted in mainstream science. The idea originated from Aristotle when he made the distinction, and animals were seen to be sentient – they could learn and had a memory – whereas plants were classed as insensitive – they could not. This of course had profound implications for our attitudes to plants and the role of 'economic botany' in our culture, where plants have been seen as commodities.

Recent research by an Australian ecologist and academic Monica Gagliano[11] has shown that plants are sentient beings and have the capacity to learn from experience. This fact has been difficult to incorporate into the current scientific paradigm, where plants are considered to be non-sentient, not least because the researcher has successfully bridged two worlds and has been guided in her scientific research by wisdom from shamanic Journeys, where she has conversed with powerful plant spirits. But perhaps with research like this and attitudes to Consciousness changing, a paradigm shift is underway?

Vitalism

This idea has its roots in ancient Egypt and has been a subject for discussion by philosophers and scientists throughout history. It is the belief that living organisms are fundamentally different from non-living entities because they contain some non-physical element or are governed by different principles than are inanimate objects. Its vital principle has been referred to as the 'vital spark', 'energy', '*élan vital*', 'Soul', and a term relating especially to plants: *Viriditas*. This last term is especially interesting as it has been used by theologians to relate both to nature and to the spiritual health of an individual. Pope Gregory the Great (540 – 604) used *Viriditas* as a metaphor for greenness, lushness and good health and described it as the intrinsic power to heal. He likened this to the spiritual condition of man. This theme was also used much later by Hildegard of Bingen (1098 – 1179), a Benedictine abbess, theologian, visionary mystic, poet – another polymath in fact. She wrote many texts on botany, herbs and medicine. An enduring theme of hers was *Viriditas*: the greening power, vitality and growth of plants. Like Gregory, she also used it to symbolize human health and spirituality, thus connecting the 'green' health of the natural world and the holistic and spiritual health of the human person.

As the Western worldview became more and more mechanistic and biology was described according to physico-chemical laws, this theory lost its adherents. One of the last scientists to support it was Louis Pasteur, who described the fermentation process as 'special reactions that only occur in living organisms. These are irreducibly vital phenomena'.

From then on, science concentrated on matter and energy, and to speak of any property related solely to living organisms was no longer part of the current paradigm. The nearest concept to *Viriditas* here was 'homeostasis' – a state of balance and 'staying the same', but this has no spiritual connection. But that was only in Western scientific culture. The Eastern worldview is still based on Qi or *Prana* – a 'vital' force, central to their concept of life and health.

But there are instances in the West where this vital force has been defined. It is thought to be equivalent to Qi and to *Prana*. In some contexts it has been called 'Orgone' and Subtle Energy. Dowsers adept at sensing it (or at least an unexplained force) call it Earth Magnetism. Following from Steiner's work on Subtle Energy, it is also considered to be the energy that emanates not only from the auras of living beings but also from inanimate objects (hence calling it Subtle Energy rather than Vital Energy). This makes more sense when considered alongside the more recent work of James Lovelock – a scientist, medical doctor and innovator. In the 1960s, when working with NASA on a programme trying to detect life on Mars, Lovelock put forward his 'Gaia hypothesis', which suggests that living and non-living parts of the Earth form a complex interacting system that can be thought of as a single self-regulating organism[12]. This would show the connection between living and non-living entities.

In his book 'Return to Subjectivity'[13], J.F. Caddy, a marine biologist who has also done a lot of personal work using himself as the 'sensor', defines Qi as particles of life energy having some sort of intrinsic intelligence or Consciousness. It is the force that permeates the universe and can adopt various forms. As such, it can be picked up by living entities and, it seems, not by machines. But to do so requires the sensing individual to be in a state of 'non-judgmental openness' that includes having an uncritical acceptance of what happens while in this state. The technique requires participation with it (as in the Goethean method of participation described by Evelyn Roe) and the intentional use of imagination (as in shamanic Journeying). Caddy states that subtle energy can be perceived by almost anyone willing to trust their subjective sensations, either through the tactile or visual senses. It is certainly something I learned to do the first time John showed me, and something my grandchildren especially can do with ease.

Also in his book, he quotes a recent article in a Mexican daily newspaper that describes the work of a *Curandero* (healer) called Jacinto Madrigal. This man cultivates herbs and sells them in the local flea market. In particular, he uses rue (*Ruta graveolens*), rosemary and basil. His thesis is that each person has an aura surrounding the body that can be damaged by bad energy (perhaps psychic attack or disease?). This makes sense both in shamanic terms and in Chinese medicine – both systems regard disease as caused by the invasion of a pernicious influence or Spirit. In his view, aromatic plants can help restore the aura: 'the scent is important because the scent is the spirit that comes out of the plant; the energy.'

The outcome of these lines of enquiry leads to a belief in an overall spiritual essence that James Lovelock describes as 'making our planet a living entity', that Stephan Harding describes as the connecting force of an 'Animate Earth', and one to which I adhere – where I see my plants and essences as containers or bearers of rich spiritual essence to exist in their own right and also to be used for healing our bodies, emotions and spirits.

Creativity in science

To suggest that creativity belongs to the Arts would be ignorant. Of course, scientists can be creative and many of them truly are so. Unfortunately a lot of science is repetitive and re-affirming or refuting others' results, which is how paradigms are adhered to. But new ideas are emerging from the scientific community, albeit slowly. A young biophysicist, Alexis Pietak, has recently suggested that there are now enough connecting threads of research to postulate the existence of a 'Life Energy' that makes all living organisms different from mechanical tools. These threads come from areas of research as varied as Chaos Theory, quantum mechanics and Entropy and Order – and from these areas of research especially, as they are areas in which the divide between objectivity and subjectivity has become blurred.

As she describes in her brilliantly constructed book 'Life as Energy'[14], the 'livingness' of a life form with its patterns of development and growth is a very real kind of energy (akin to heat and to light), which needs to be and can be recognised by modern science. She argues that by reducing living systems to their smallest material parts (e.g. cells, genes, molecules), something intrinsic to life is lost – a living system becomes the same as a non-living one. And this, we all know intuitively, is not so. The three '-isms' of reductionism, mechanism and materialism have brought this about and have defined the imagery and mindset of scientists. She calls for a different thinking style in the biological sciences (akin to that used in modern physics) of blending rationality with imagination – which she calls Imaginative Rationality. This would bring about a different conceptual metaphor to work with very different possibilities of understanding unfamiliar phenomena. So perhaps slowly those perennially unsolved biological questions concerning embryology, cellular differentiation, and morphology of, for instance, leaf shapes (so interesting to Goethe) could be explained.

Another example that has stayed with me for a long time is the story of Barbara McClintock and her 'jumping genes'. I described her work during one of the very few school assembly presentations that I ever gave (a supposedly 'religious' occasion). Here was a scientist in the late 1940s who discovered something that challenged existing models of genetics. Working on the maize plant, she found that their genes (elements that governed all aspects of how the plant was and behaved) were not fixed along the chromosomes like beads on a string (as was previously thought) but could *move*. The wonderful quote in a book on McClintock's work by Evelyn Fox Keller[15] describes the mental state Barbara was in when she made this breakthough:

> 'When you suddenly see the problem, something happens that you have the answer – before you are able to put it into words. It is all done subconsciously. This has happened many times to me, and I know when to take it seriously. I'm so absolutely sure. I don't talk about it. I don't have to tell anyone about it. I'm just SURE this is it.'

Keller describes McClintock: 'her virtuosity resided in her capacity to observe, to process and interpret what she had observed… She was developing skills which she could hardly identify herself, much less impart to others.' A colleague once remarked that McClintock could write the 'autobiography' of each plant she worked with. 'Her respect for the unfathomable workings of the mind was matched by her regard for the complex workings of the plant, but she was confident that, with due attentiveness, she could trust the intuitions the one produced of the other.'

As ever, to challenge existing models was fraught with difficulties and McClintock was only formally recognised for her exceptional work with the Nobel Prize in Physiology and Medicine in 1983. In her press statement about the Nobel Prize, McClintock noted: 'It might seem unfair to reward a person for having so much pleasure, over the years, asking the maize plant to solve specific problems and then watching its responses.'

But this sort of thinking has already been mentioned from time to time in scientific discourse. Evelyn Fox Keller describes McClintock talking about the deepest and most personal dimension of her life as a scientist, and looking down her microscope at the maize cells: 'I was part of the system. I was right down there with them, and everything got big... It surprised me because I actually felt as if I was right down there and these were my friends'. Keller then adds: 'Throughout history, artists, poets, lovers and mystics have known and written about the 'knowing' that comes from loss of self – from the state of subjective fusion with the objective knowledge. Scientists have known this too'.

Another scientist who researched in what seemed to be very creative yet unconnected ways was the Hungarian biochemist Albert Szent-Györgyi. I remember so long ago looking in wonder at an enormous wall chart produced by the German pharmaceutical company Boehringer Ingelheim. It was called 'Biochemical Pathways'[16]. Here were all the known biochemical pathways intricately and artistically woven together with all their connections and feedback loops. It was truly a wonder of dedication and research to understand all these processes taking place within a living cell. I was nearing completion of my Botany degree and was at a stage when a lot of the pathways should have been very meaningful to me. And they were. But something was missing. I remember wondering where in that complexity was the essence of life that held it all together, that made it different from test tube reactions and made it work? After all, we had been studying BIOchemistry – the chemistry of life. Was it a co-enzyme? an oxygen carrier pigment like haemoglobin or chlorophyll? something small, universal and seemingly insignificant? I had been excited reading the research of Albert Szent-Györgyi. He was born in Budapest in 1893 and throughout his long and active research life, it seems as if he was searching for a life force. His first famous research was the discovery of a molecule that he called hexuranic acid (later to be known as vitamin C). Further research in cellular respiration discovered a small molecule called adenosine triphosphate (ATP). This molecule is now known to be the primary energy source in animal cells – a sort of energy currency.

In 1937, Szent-Györgyi received the Nobel Prize for Physiology and Medicine for his work on vitamin C and cellular respiration. Later still, he worked on muscle contraction and the effect of ATP on the two muscle components myosin and actin, which cause contraction. This demonstrated the basic process at the molecular level of muscular movement. Finally (in this story at least) he applied his knowledge of the functioning of ATP to a system of luminescence. Fireflies, or lightning bugs, make light in their bodies. It's a way for them to attract and find mates. On summer evenings after dusk, fireflies can be seen like hovering and darting sparks of pale yellow or reddish-green light – a wonderful sight! The light is produced in the tails of the males, which contain a complex molecule called luciferin (note the archetypal reference) and a smaller molecule, an enzyme called luciferase, which helps the reaction occur. The process needs energy and this is supplied by ATP. Luciferin combines with oxygen and in the process, ATP gives up its energy, changes to a smaller molecule and light is emitted. It's one of those beautiful reactions where matter and energy (in this case light) are interchangeable.

My next story to describe creativity in science – trawled from 'meaningful' memories that I have cherished and kept deep in my psyche – is about the research of Candace Pert. In 1997 I read her book entitled 'Molecules of Emotion'[17]. Dr Pert was a neuropharmacologist who originally became famous for speaking up after being excluded from the prestigious Albert Lasker Award in 1975. She had done much of the seminal work on the research on the opioid receptors in the brain that received morphine and other psycho-active drugs and gave rise to the pain-relieving molecules called endorphins. Candace was a pioneer and later became an activist, and certainly produced a paradigm shift in the scientific world by suddenly bringing two disciplines together – immunology and neuropharmacology. So much work had been done on a group of molecules called peptides, often with highly significant actions in the body. These are molecules like insulin (involved in sugar metabolism), prolactin (involved in milk production), oxytocin (in uterine contractions), and all the gut enzymes (involved in digestion). Pert's work showed that these important molecules, which it had been known for some time had receptors in the brain, also had receptors at their points of action. This was her discovery of the amazing connection between the physical body and the mind. Later, she studied how neuropeptides in the brain could pass to the body (not via the blood – which would have been acceptable in the old model – but via the nerves and synapses) and bring about reactions in the relevant organs. She coined the word 'BodyMind' – just one word to emphasise the connection. These molecules became known as 'Molecules of Emotion' and are found in every system of our bodies, creating a BodyMind's intelligence.

> '*I'm a scientist. We don't talk about the Spirit.*
> *Soul is a four-letter word in our tradition.*'
> CANDACE PERT

This impressive scientist and exceptionally spirited woman later talked a lot about psychosomatic illness, emotions, Soul, and also about Spirit and a concept of God. Her work was gladly received by aromatherapists and other holistic complementary therapists who used energy and MindBody connections. Aromatherapists especially no longer needed to separate the effects of essential oils on the body and organs from the effects that they had emotionally and on the Spirit.

And finally, Monica Gagliano's work already mentioned in this chapter needs to be included in my examples of creativity in science. Interestingly, the work of all these scientists looks at connections, communication and the possibility for messages or energy to move in ways not previously understood.

So this brings me back to the theme of this chapter: the links between creativity, spirituality and Subtle Energy, and an understanding of the deeper meaning of connection as the removal of boundaries – here the boundaries that contain the human mind. Connection can be brought about through meditation, for instance, or through shamanic work, so the altered state of Consciousness described by McClintock is akin to shamanic Journeying. The shaman 'meets' and 'converses' with the spirit world and, using human imagination and creativity, gives spirit or energy a recognisable form.

This can be seen in a recent Journey of mine. In February 2020, England was being ravaged by Storm Ciara and on the south coast (where we live in England) the effects were drastic. Our shamanic drumming group was due to meet and our topic for discussion and work was the Spirit of Weather. In preparation I had been reading 'Weather Shamanism' by Nan Moss and David Corbin[18]. I had found the content challenging as it had led me to new territory in shamanic work. Rain dancing and rituals for influencing weather have always been an essential component of shamanic practice, but I had seen it as far beyond my capabilities and experience. In essence, it required me to recognise myself as an essential and vital co-creator of our world. I read the whole book and felt that I had hardly understood a word of it, until suddenly I understood it all. It was shamanism at its deepest level – to be totally connected to Nature.

On the morning of our meeting, the extreme weather conditions – gale force winds uprooting trees and torrential rain and storms – caused our group members to cancel. The meeting wasn't going to happen. The very theme of the meeting was the reason that they couldn't attend! With the storm lashing at my windows, I decided to Journey by myself:

Mission: I'm going on a Journey to meet the Spirit of Storm Ciara.

I call in my Spirits and they arrive. They say it will be a Middle World Journey and we set off in a little sailing boat from the beautiful white chalk cliffs of Seaford. It is calm and sunny, a wonderful day, and we head out to sea. Out in the Channel it becomes night and then day again and we are becalmed – it is grey and misty and still. We are there for a very long time. I say it is like the poem, The Ancient Mariner. I ask again if I can meet the Spirit of Storm Ciara and I suddenly see thunder and lightning in the distant sky. We abandon the boat and fly into the storm clouds – the flashing lightning and clapping thunder. I ask if this is Ciara. They say it is part of her. I ask if she is in pain and they say it is her job to smooth out the anger in the world: from the sun, the Earth and from people. They show me the anger from the Amazon and Australian bush fires, the scorched Earth from global warming, American politics, Brexit, and then more locally, the anger in Seaford concerning an important social and political issue. Anger and distress is everywhere. We get tossed into the storm and atmosphere across the ocean – raging winds, lashing rain, huge waves – to land and then across the land – hot and turbulent, burning and seething. More distress everywhere. Gradually the strength of the storm subsides until everything is calm. There were no words to describe it, no images to inform me, but I distinctly feel it happening – with my shamanic bones and with my physical body – the balancing of the weather. We are weather and weather is us.

They say: 'Ciara deals with this storm, that is her purpose – to restore balance to the Earth. Your job is to accept it and be part of it, to accept the weather Spirits and be open to them – a complete giving and receiving between us. Always welcome the weather, know it and its purpose.'

Drums to return. I give thanks.

Within two weeks of this Journey, the world was gripped by the spread of Coronavirus and its disease Covid-19. A seemingly 'inanimate' entity, a minute and beautiful molecular sphere hitherto unknown to humans was presumed to have left its stable niche in the bat population of eastern China and had infected market traders dealing in the sale of live wild animals. The disease spread like wildfire. It became a pandemic. The frantic world came to a halt. It was time to self-isolate and turn inwards, to contemplate the state of our Earth and our contribution.

'Whole body and Mind seeing is the total merging of subject and object, of seer and seen, of self and other. It is essentially the experience of enlightenment – a profound achievement, but it is not the endpoint. The journey continues straight ahead down the other side back into the world.

It is in the ordinariness of our lives that the intimate experience of the self merging with the absolute can begin to express itself.[19]

There are many ways of reaching this point. Whether singing mindfully, sewing or carving or gardening mindfully, or being totally engrossed in a creative project or scientific research, there is always the possibility of pushing back the boundaries of separation and merging with something greater – an energy or Spirit or vitality that permeates the cosmos. Plants are totally connected and in a state of 'wholeness'. This gives them their 'green fuse'. Francis Hallé (reference cited) describes very vividly how a plant's function is to take in and concentrate energy – from the cosmos as well as from the sun – and thus provide food for all animal life forms. Animals in turn disperse energy back into the atmosphere. In Western science, this energy is perceived to be predominantly the energy forms heat and light. But Eastern philosophy suggests that *Prana* emanates from the sun. Listening to Rupert Sheldrake's lecture at Schumacher College on 'Is the sun conscious?' he suggests that it is, along with all other bodies in the solar system. Could it be that this Consciousness or Qi or Spirit received by plants from the sun and the planets is also involved in the healing of emotions (Soul), Spirit and human disease?

'I'm aware of the mystery around us,
so I write about coincidences, premonitions,
emotions, dreams, the power of nature, magic.'
ISABEL ALLENDE

Chapter notes

1.   Hillman, James. The Soul's Code. 1997. Bantam Books. ISBN 0-553-50634-X

2.   Jill Purce http //www.jillpurce.com/ The Healing Voice https://www.youtube.com/watch?v=yoj6FAarThQ

3.   Anderson, William and, Hicks, Clive. Green Man – the Archetype of our Oneness with the Earth. 1990. Harper Collins. ISBN 0-00-599255

4.   Robertson, Pamela. Charles Rennie Mackintosh – Art is the Flower. 1997. Pavilion Books. ISBN 10 1857939123

5.   See http://www.shamanism.dk/who.htm. Jonathan Horwitz, Annette Høst and Zara Waldebäck.

6.   Hallé, Francis. Eloge de la Plante, pour une nouvelle Biologie. 1999, Edition du Seuil, Paris. Translated by David Lee in 2002: In Praise of Plants. Timber Press, USA. ISBN 0-88192-550-0

7.   Nature Scientific Correspondence: Vol 392/16 April 1998. Tree stem diameters fluctuate with tides. Ernst Zuercher, Swiss Federal Institute of Technology, Zurich & Maria- Giulia Cantiani, University of Trento, Italy.

8.   Sheldrake, Rupert. The Science Delusion. 2012. Coronet. An imprint of Hodder & Stoughton. ISBN 978 1 444 72790 01

9.   Harding, Stephan. Animate Earth: Science, Intuition and Gaia: Second edition. 2009. Green Books Ltd. ISBN 978 1 900322 54 6

10.   See Cowan, Eliot. Plant Spirit Medicine. 1995. Swan Raven & Co, USA. ISBN 0-926524-09-7 for further details of working with plant spirits.

11.   Gagliano, Monica. Thus Spoke the Plant. 2018. North Atlantic Books, CA. ISBN 978 1 623172 43 5

12.   Lovelock, James. Gaia – a New Look at Life on Earth 1982. Oxford University Press. ISBN 0-19-286218-9

13.   Caddy, John. A Return to Subjectivity. 2006. Trafford Publishing. ISBN 1-4120-8366-4

        For an in-depth description of the various components of Qi, see p198 'Defining Vital Energy'. His description of Chinese 'Energy masters', of healers and those adepts who work with auras shows that much is known and practised in these areas. This description also goes some way to explain the difference between the Energy of living and non-living objects.

14.   Pietak, Alexis Mari. Life as Energy – Opening the Mind to a New Science of Life. 2011. Floris Books. ISBN 978

15.   Keller, Evelyn Fox. A Feeling for the Organism. The life and work of Barbara McClintock. 1983. W.H. Freeman & Co, New York. ISBN 0-7167-1504-X (paperback)

16.   Reference to the wall chart: https://www.roche.com/sustainability/philanthropy/science_education/pathways.htm

17.   Pert, Candice. Molecules of Emotion: why you feel the way you feel. 1998. Simon & Schuster UK Ltd. ISBN 0-671-03397-2

18.   Moss, Nan and Corbin, David. Weather Shamanism: Harmonising our connection with the Elements. 2008. Bear & Co publishers. ISBN 978 1591439219

19.   Loori, John Daido. The Zen of Creativity. 2005. Ballantire Books. Trade Paperback Edition. Copyright 2004 Dharma Communication.

XIII

Plant profiles

Returning to the plants in my garden, I am now ready to describe them in more holistic terms. My experiences during the latter years, and in particular my acceptance that plants through their connections share the vitality and energy that pervades all of Nature and the cosmos, required that I explained more of my ideas to make sense of these more complete descriptions. I now profile three plants of special importance in my garden and in my affections and show their capabilities to heal us physically, emotionally and spiritually.

In this section I am including a new venture – making shamanic journeys to the Spirits of plants. Although it is something I now find easy to do, especially when sensually aroused by the plant's perfume, it is also something that is extremely difficult to portray. The dreamlike qualities of these journeys, which take place when I am in 'trance' state, have to be recorded in words that mirror our western world view. Quoting Leroy Little Bear – a First People and North American Elder and Harvard University professor who has a different worldview: ' You cross a boundary and have an experience but when you come back it is very difficult to have the language to explain it. '

And so it is in my journeys. In them I cross into the 'dream world' of dynamic relationship and connection with plants and then return to this reality and try to describe these events with images, symbols, scene shifts, shape shifts, conversations, perhaps even without words, and above all with intense emotions and a felt understanding.

Three such journeys are recorded below.

Lavender and the bumblebee

Lavender *(Lavandula angustifolia/officinalis/vera)*

This grey, narrow-leaved, highly aromatic and small perennial bush with characteristic purple flowers arranged on spikelets has had a very long connection with humanity, known to Egyptian, Roman and Turkish cultures since ancient times. Its name comes from the Latin *'lavare'* meaning 'to wash' as it was used to scent bath water and heal skin disorders. As a herb, it became easily cultivated and is mentioned in the ancient herbal texts of Dioscorides, Galen and Pliny, and much later by the Abbess Hildegard of Bingen (around AD 1098). Its cultivation in monastery and apothecary gardens made it a very important plant in all later European herbals and pharmacopoeias – where it was designated *L. officinalis*.

Plant cultivation

Lavender is native to the Mediterranean region, where three species can be found: *L. angustifolia* (known as true lavender), *L. stoechas* and *L. spica* (known as spike lavender). The lavender plants that I grew in Chevenoz were chosen for their essential oil qualities as well as for their suitability for this climate. There were four types:

- *Lavandula angustifolia* 'No. 9' from Downderry Herbs, UK. This was bred in New Zealand and had an excellent oil profile. It was winter-hardy and had compact bushes with dark and compact flowering spikes.
- *Lavandula angustifolia 'Maillette'* cultivated in Southern France. This was a more straggly bush with an abundance of long flowering spikes and pale flowers.
- *Lavandula vera* from Basel – a good cultivar with compact bushes and dark, highly aromatic flowers.
- *Lavandula angustifolia* from *Les Courmettes* on the hills above Cannes, Provence. I took cuttings from a plant that I found in a meadow, high up and overlooking the Mediterranean Sea, and cultivated them. This was a strong and upright plant with large pale lilac flowers and a sweet honey perfume. I have always propagated it by cuttings.

These four cultivars were all well suited to the growing conditions in Chevenoz and flowered around the same time – which was important for my distillations. And true to their correspondences, they brought a vibrant and wonderful life force to the garden throughout their flowering season. So many different species of wild 'furry' bumblebees and hive-fuls of domestic honeybees came foraging each day, making the air buzz with their activities. With systematic visitations from flower to flower, the bees sucked out the nectar and at the same time got heavier and heavier with legs clothed in golden yellow pollen breeches. I knew this was important for the nature of the garden and thus had a dilemma: I grew these plants especially to make lavender oil – and needed to harvest a lot of flowers for this. My gain was the bees' great loss. So the compromise was to set aside plants solely for the bees and our enjoyment. I made two large borders alongside our stone table so we could sit and watch the activity: at breakfast it was light, gentle and more haphazard, but at noon and lunchtime the dedication and the co-ordination was an entrancing and mesmerising sound and sight, an invitation to another reality. In return, the local bee-keeper Alexandre's honey was as nectar, the food of the gods – golden, lavender-scented, health-giving and brimming with life.

The process of growing sufficient plants for distillation took several years. The planting recommendation from the British Pharmacopoeia was to plant eighteen inches apart. Since all my plants were small when I got them, this left a large amount of bare earth between plants. Bare earth in these growing conditions invited large weeds, so my strategy was to double plant, i.e. nine inches apart, and then after a year transplant every other plant into a new bed. After three years I had three large beds of mature plants.

Harvesting and distillation

Lavender distillations became a highlight of my gardening year. I did this according to the *Calendrier Lunaire* – looking for a time when the bees told me that the flowers were ready to harvest, the moon was in high ascendancy, the constellations favoured harvesting of flowers, the weather was dry, and preferably around the July full moon (how strange that such synchronicity occurred year after year). I cut handfuls of flowering spikes with a traditional sickle to prevent bruising of the flowers and losing oil, which is stored in glands at their bases[1]. Because the bees visited the lavender plots as well as their own 'garden', I had to wear leather gloves to protect my hands. The flowers were gathered up on dark blue calico sheets that I had bought from Thonon market and carried up to the barn. There I left them to wilt for a couple of hours on the *Cave* floor before distillation. The wilted plant material allowed me to pack the still more tightly but also resulted in some loss of oil due to evaporation.

Over the years, I have done more than sixty beautiful lavender distillations. Each one lasted around forty-five minutes and during this time the barn became infused with the balmy scent of lavender, which calmed our bodies and enlivened our senses. After the work of collecting the distillate, changing the collecting bottles and decanting the oil, I would turn off the still and, in a state of altered Consciousness, rest until the following day. It was at this next stage that I could assess the quality and quantity of the oil and the hydrolat. Chevenoz lavender oil was pale yellow in colour and had an intense and sweetish honey smell – not as peppery as Provence lavender oil. The hydrolat smelled even more honey-like. For each distillation I usually obtained around 70ml of oil, which needed to be left to 'air' for around forty-eight hours before decanting into 10ml purple oil bottles. This was an average yield of around 0.6% (volume of essential oil to plant mass in grammes). As Tim Denny suggested (in personal communication), when I used the still extension and increased the height of plant material to beyond 70cm, the oil yield increased by approximately 20% (i.e. to between 0.7% and 0.9%), as stated in the British Pharmacopoeia.

Charles Wells of Essentially Oils commissioned analyses of both my lavender oil and hydrolats, which were performed by Dr Bill Morden at the Laboratory of the Government Chemist and published in Len Price's book on Hydrolats[2]. The active principles as given in essential oil composition tables are: **esters,** including linalyl acetate (37–54 %) and lavandulyl acetate (0.3–6%); **monoterpenic alcohols,** including linalool (27–50%) and terpinen-4-ol (0.03–6%); **monoterpenes,** including cis- and trans-ocimenes (3.9%); and **oxides,** including 1,8-cineole (0.7–2.3%).

The analysis of *Herbes de Chevenoz* lavender essential oil had peaks from the gas chromatograph traces corresponding to linalyl acetate (% peak area 40.24), lavandulyl acetate (% peak area 6.29) and linalool (% peak area 20.65). Terpinenol and ocimenes were also present in smaller quantities. For results of the gas chromatography analysis, see Appendix IV.

Uses

In mediaeval times

It was seen as a very powerful herb and described as 'Masculine with ruling planet Mercury and under the influence of the Element Fire'[3]. It has been an ingredient of mediaeval strewing herbs, and later of *Eau de Cologne* and as an important constituent of *Herbes de Provence*.

Culpeper[4] lists its virtues as:

'for griefs and pains of the head and brain that proceed from a cold cause, as apoplexy, falling sickness, the dropsy, cramps, convulsions, palsy and often faintings. It strengthens the stomach and freeth the liver and spleen from obstruction, provoking women's courses. The flowers steeped in wine promotes urine and cures flatulency and colic.'

In modern herbal medicine

The tincture or tisane is used to alleviate depressive headaches; the essential oil is used to alleviate rheumatic pain.

In Western medicine

Lavender oil remained in the British Pharmacopoeia until 1988 (it is still present in *La Pharmacopée Française*). It was used as a carminative, tonic and antidepressant. Other formulations, *Spiritus Lavandulae* and *Tinctura Lavandulae Composita*, were removed from BP in 1932. *Spiritus Lavandulae* was used as an antiseptic and a revulsive agent, and the composite tincture was a mixture with spirit of rosemary and nutmeg, cloves and cinnamon, and used as a stimulant and stomachic in cases of languor and flatulence.

Medicinal properties

The oil has a very broad spectrum of actions and is especially used to treat burns and to calm skin rashes and sunburn. It also has many other uses as analgesic, antibacterial, anti-fungal, anti-infectious, anti-inflammatory, antirheumatic, antispasmodic, calmative, mild cardiotonic, cholagogic, cicatrisant, hypotensive and vermifuge. Every household definitely needs a bottle of lavender oil in the medicine cabinet!

In aromatherapy

Used in soaps and perfumes from the Provence lavender fields, and also those around Hitchin in Hertfordshire and Mitcham in Surrey. Lavender oil calms tension, stress and trauma, and relieves insomnia, depression and mental exhaustion. It is a balancer – being calmative at low concentrations and a stimulant at higher concentrations.

In Chinese medicine

Lavender's Energy is Cool and Dry and its associated Elements are Fire and Wood. Its primary actions and uses are cooling, dispersing and relaxing, and it does this by:

+ regulating the Qi of the Liver and the Heart, pacifying Liver-Yang, clearing Heart-Fire, calming the Shen, uplifting the Spirit
+ clearing Damp-Heat from the Lower Burner, restraining infection, killing parasites

+ cooling the Blood, and clearing Heat – benefitting the skin and promoting tissue repair.

Its psychological and spiritual uses stem from its ability to calm and stabilise the Qi of the Heart, the home of the Shen (Mind). It works to calm any strong emotions that threaten to overwhelm the Mind. It also releases pent-up energy in the Wood Element, smoothing the flow of Qi energy and easing frustration, irritability and a feeling of being 'blocked' creatively[5].

Plant spirit medicine

In these following three plant profiles, with permission from my Spirits, I record my shamanic Journeys to the Spirits of the plants. These are intensely intimate accounts – which, after much reflection, I have decided to share here. The details are absolutely personal to me – a framework of symbolism that I have built up over the years using my imagination and creativity. It has given me an interim understanding of the energy that I believe pervades everything. I have recounted them here to describe this powerful additional connection that we as humans can have with plants, and a way in which they can be part of a holistic healing system. Something of huge interest to me is that in each account of my meetings with plants, I have felt their presence in my chakras and in my aura – something I had never done in my meetings with other Spirits on the countless Journeys I have done in the last twenty years. I wonder if taking in the plant essence via my nose and its effect on my primitive hind brain has contributed to this.

By 2017, I had enough experience of shamanic Journeying, and had also decided to go deeper in my work with using oils for healing work. With all parameters right for harvesting and distilling according to the *Calendrier Lunaire*, I decided to Journey while doing the distillation. It entailed 'keeping a foot in both worlds', i.e. altering my state of Consciousness sufficiently to Journey and at the same time be aware of the workings of the still. In many respects, this is similar to the sort of altered state of mind recommended by Goethe in his scientific method and that used by Bach in 'letting the plants speak to him'. Since the Journey tape I was using on that occasion lasted twenty minutes, I knew I didn't need to worry about time parameters (e.g. overflowing distillate flasks, the boilers running dry, etc). The date was July 11, 2017. In my Journey book, I had entitled this *'Le Grand Oeuvre'*. It was the first time I had done a Journey during a distillation. I set the still going and once it had settled down, sitting on my cushion on the *Cave* floor and being aware of the distillation and also using Jonathan's drumming tape, I Journeyed to the Spirit of Lavender. I asked, 'How best can we work together to produce the most therapeutic healing oils?'

> *The drums start and IMMEDIATELY I am in the presence of the Spirit of Lavender – a HUGE woman in purple robes and with flowing hair. She is very near me, almost engulfing me. She holds out her arms to me in embrace. I feel very small next to her. I thank her for my harvest and ask her my question: how best can we work together to produce the most therapeutic healing oils? She says we must be 'as one' and I realise we almost are, we are so close together! She holds my hand and leads me towards the still – which is roaring and pumping like an alchemical vessel. She says we must enter it – like the cauldron of my dream… We go in and the noise and power is intense. We get buffeted about, rising and falling – steadily going higher and higher. I realise what an extraordinarily powerful process distillation is. We eventually get to the top and are suddenly released – expanding as vapour, as spirit. We then go up and up – higher and higher in the dark void. My heart is racing and I seem to be in my sixth chakra (between my eyes); everything is deep purple. The perfume and intensity is almost too much to bear – but it is completely supportive, enveloping; it is at the same time calming and stimulating. I grasp her and she says, 'Now you know my Power.' This is her Essence – concentrated Spirit. Then it became too much for me to bear. I had experienced her deep purple 'mothering' love and I felt I was going to burst/pass out/on? I pleaded with her to stop and release me.*
>
> *She leads me to the cooling condenser and we sink down through the copper spiral into the pool. When I am more composed (but still hugely elated), I ask her if there is anything I must do. She says that when the oils are in the purple bottles, I must put them all together and we will do a ritual by holding our hands over them to bless them and contain this power within them. This will make them the most therapeutic healing oils. She says always to do this after completing a distillation. A power ritual for all oils. I agree to do so…*
>
> *Drums to return. I give thanks.*

This is now my practice after a distillation – to perform a 'containment' blessing with the Spirit of the plant.

Back in this reality, I checked the course of the distillation and then sat quietly and reflected. The sound of the pump had returned to its Ordinary Reality 'gurgling'. The air was rich with the scent of lavender. I felt extraordinarily 'whole' with both a calmness and elation/joy, which is a very unusual mix. I knew that I had indeed connected to the Spirit of Lavender; we had become 'as one'. And in that time, as Steiner, Goethe and Evelyn Roe have all said, I came to know Lavender in a way that no measurement could ever attain.

Examining this account, I realise that lavender is one of the most energetically powerful of oils. The progression from the calm and loving protection at the beginning to the intensity of later stages gave me an understanding at the psychic level of the physiological description of lavender oil as an adaptogen (calming at low concentrations and stimulant at high concentrations). It was both the intense purple colour involved and the feeling that I was existing in the region of my 'Third Eye' that made me realise that this oil was resonating with me at a very high energetic/spiritual level.

Section notes

1. Günther, Ernest. The Essential Oils. 1948. NY Volumes I to VI Van Nostrand Co: Vol III p440 Lavandula officinalis. Cut with a sickle. French lavender has a characteristic sweetness due to a high ester content. (50–55% ester). Yield 0.8%.

2. Price, Len and Shirley. Understanding Hydrolats: the specific Hydrosols for Aromatherapy. 2004. Churchill Livingstone, an imprint of Elsevier Ltd. ISBN 0443 07316 3

3. Cunningham, Scott. Encyclopedia of Magical Herbs. 1997. Llewellyn Publications, Minnesota, USA. ISBN 0-87542-122-9. p25. Gender is a way of categorising by their basic type of vibration. Masculine denotes strong fiery vibrations and Feminine denotes a more subtle, softer vibration (early herbals used the terms Hot and Cold).

4. Culpeper, Nicholas. Culpeper's Complete Herbal. 1992. Bloomsbury Books under licence from Omega Books. ISBN 1 85471 140 7

5. Mojay, Gabriel. Course notes (as before).

The Swedish Juniper grove

Common juniper (*Juniperus communis*)

Common juniper is found growing on chalk and limestone in forests and mountainous regions in Northern Europe and beyond. Many other species of juniper are also found worldwide. *Juniperus communis* grows as a tree/shrub up to six metres tall or in its prostrate form lying close to the ground. As a conifer, it bears cones and has needle-like evergreen leaves. There are usually two forms of the plant – the female berry-producing form and the male catkin/pollen-bearing form. The berries take up to three years to ripen from green to dark bluish black and all stages can be seen on the same bush.

Since pre-historic times and in many cultures, juniper has been regarded as a sacred tree and used in ritual, as incense, for healing and in food. Traces of juniper berries have been found in pre-historic archaeological remains from lakeside dwelling communities around Geneva (named after the juniper bush – *Genévrier* in French). In European cultures, juniper berries have been considered more magical than medicinal: sprays of berries hung on doors were thought to keep witches at bay on May Eve; smoke from a juniper wood fire kept demons away.

In other cultures, juniper is associated with symbolism of overcoming death at the beginning of eternal life. There is a Celtic custom, originating back to ancient times, of burning juniper branches at a funeral and paving the path of the final journey of the deceased to the grave with them. In Greco-Roman mythology, juniper symbolised protection, confidence and initiative; it was dedicated to Hermes (Mercury). In North Russia, juniper was considered a symbol of longevity and an infusion of the berries was thought to restore lost youth. According to the Bashkir legends from the Ural Mountains, juniper drives away evil spirits from the house and guards from evil incantations.

The overwhelming presence of juniper bushes in the wide open spaces of New Mexico is a wonder to behold. It is one of the few plants that can survive the arid and mountainous desert of the northern territory and the clear air there has a purity and spirituality like no other.

Rituals using juniper can be found worldwide. In Tibet, juniper branches are burned on rooftops in early morning to aid prayer, to purify and to connect, and Tibetan incense is 80% juniper; Native American cultures burn trees and branches in welcoming ceremonies; many cultures use juniper in burial and embalming rites; and up until the 19th century, juniper sprigs were burned in French hospitals to purify the air and prevent the spread of infectious diseases.

Juniper berries in the snow

Ground-up berries and dry juniper bark mixed to a paste with melted beeswax and then moulded into a small pyramid ignites well and the smoke can be used as an incense and purifier/protector.

Perhaps it's the universality of juniper with its large number of species, its evergreen and robust appearance and piquant smell that has attracted humans to it, but in all these traditional uses, the underlying theme is one of sacredness, of purification and renewal, and of protection from all evils (spirits and infections). As modern medicine has become concerned with the physical body, chemical analysis of juniper and studies of modes of action of these components still uphold the characteristics of juniper as purifier, cleanser and protector.

Plant cultivation

My attempts to cultivate juniper came to nothing. I sourced *Juniperus communis* in both England and France and made a small plantation of the plants I managed to purchase. Juniper is slow-growing and the root systems take a considerable time to establish. After the first winter, my losses were considerable. Talking to neighbours – many of whom had juniper bushes in their '*potagers*' – I was told it would be best to go and dig up bushes from the mountains. I preferred to take cuttings from both male and female plants and wait patiently. Each year I had losses and after four years, I had three bushes remaining – one female and two males. If these reached maturity, they would certainly provide enough plant material for distillations. I remember one late spring morning seeing the finest golden pollen grains wafting in the wind from the male catkins and feeling hopeful. Later that year, I noticed the formation of very small green berries on the female bush and thought I was in business. Alas, that winter the deer came up into the orchard, as was their custom, and jumped over the fence into my plots (which was not), trampled the remaining juniper plants and ripped off the succulent and tasty bark. From then on, I resorted to wild crafting. Our years of walking in the mountains and talking to locals gave me a good idea of where to search. Literature cites that good quality juniper essential oil should be made from juniper berries, but I thought this was not environmentally tenable – so decided to make mine from the berries and the aromatic spines/leaves.

One late spring morning, we set off on our search with rucksacks, secateurs and very thick gardening gloves. The location was along a steepish mountain track leading up to a forest. As we went up, we noticed that a woodman was cleaning the encroaching scrubland and pruning wild roses, thistles and dogwoods before the cattle were let out to graze for the summer. And suddenly, there on our path, was a large female juniper bush! It was tree-like in form, about 1.5m tall, recently felled and in beautiful condition. I imagined the woodman was saving it to take it home to smoke his *saucissons*. After a rocky descent to find him, I enquired and he said no, he was going to burn it along with everything else he had cut down. I could have it gladly as it would save him the trouble. We ceremonially bore it down the track and into the back of the Land Rover, and took it home. This was to be my first juniper distillation.

Distillation of juniper berries and needles

Branchlets need to be cut into very short pieces in order to pack the still effectively. I beat them and their attached berries with a meat tenderiser to break down the tough cuticle of the spines and open the hard berries. Even with this treatment, the oil is released very slowly and usually the first three litres of distillate is collected without any oil.

My most successful distillation of juniper oil has been of approximately 10kg of juniper, which I distilled twice. In this way I collected nine litres of hydrolat and obtained 17ml of oil. The first distillation yielded very little oil but a highly aromatic hydrolat. I then left the still overnight and repeated the distillation the next morning. From this second distillation, both oil and hydrolat were excellent. The need to warm up the damp plant mass for the second distillation yielded 800ml of light brown reflux from the base of the still. The yield was 1.7% oil. Other distillations have yielded excellent hydrolat but in the region of 1.2% oil.

The active principles as given in essential oil composition tables are: **terpenes**, including a- and b-pinenes (40–90%); sabinene (10–40%); limonene; b-caryophyllene; and germcrene-B **alcohols**, including terpineol-4.

Uses

In mediaeval herbalism

The mediaeval correspondences assigned to juniper and cited by Scott Cunningham[1] are: gender: Masculine; ruling planet: Sun; Element: Water (and Metal). As with lavender, these correspondences make juniper a powerful and protective herb.

Culpeper[2] starts his long list of uses by saying: 'This admirable solar shrub is scarce to be paralleled for its virtues'. Among so many other virtues, he describes it as an admirable counter-poison and a resister of pestilence, and notes that it provokes urine copiously, cures the dropsy, provokes the terms, strengthens the stomach, helps the memory, and fortifies the sight. In his entire herbal, this list must be one of the most comprehensive.

In modern herbal medicine

Mrs Grieve[3] cites many uses including 'many traditional uses in UK and in Europe of its diuretic and antibacterial properties as well as a carminative in indigestion and as a poultice for arthritic joints and pain'.

In Western medicine

Oleum Juniperi and *Spiritus Juniperi* (oil dissolved in alcohol) were in the British Pharmacopoeia until 1932. Preparations of Juniper Oil and Juniper Spirit were both included in the British Pharmaceutical Codex 1949 and used as diuretic, antiseptic, carminative and anti-inflammatory agents[4]. Cade oil made from another species – *Juniperus oxycedrus* – was removed from the BP in 1963. It had been used for rheumatic pain, as a diuretic, as a carminative and antiseptic. It is still included in other European pharmacopoeias.

The medicinal properties cited here are antibacterial, antirheumatic, diuretic, depurative, neurotonic and general tonic. It is also regarded as anti-catarrhal, anti-infectious, decongestant, expectorant, lymphatic decongestant and rubefacient.

A publication commissioned by the Royal Pharmaceutical Society of Great Britain and completed in 1995, entitled 'Herbal Medicines – a Guide for Health-Care Professionals'[5] has a long entry for juniper, with historical uses for humans and animals. (Sadly there is no entry for lavender, despite its inclusion in the British Pharmacopoeia for so long.) The 'Pharmaceutical Comment' at the end of the juniper text states: 'Many of the traditional uses documented for juniper can be supported by documented pharmacological actions or known constituents…' So here two worlds come together!

In aromatherapy

Juniper essential oil can be inhaled as a vapour for respiratory infections and absorbed through the skin in therapeutic massage.

In Chinese medicine

Juniper's Energy is described as Hot and Dry and its associated Elements are Water and Metal. Its primary actions and uses are as:

+ a powerful tonic for Kidney-Yang and Spleen-Yang;
+ diuretic and decongestant – it clears Damp-Cold from the urino-genital, gastro-intestinal and respiratory systems; and
+ an alleviator of joint pain and neuralgia.

Its psychological uses are to drive out negative influences and fears; to consolidate willpower; to replace stasis with movement and openness. Spiritually, it has always been associated with purification[6].

In plant spirit medicine

To connect with the Spirit of Juniper, I made an incense out of berries, leaves and beeswax and using this in ritual, ignited it and inhaled the smoke until I reached an altered state of Consciousness and was ready to Journey. I then recorded the conversations of the Journey. This is a partial transcript:

'I'm going on a Journey to meet the Spirit of Juniper – to ask him to show me his healing power.'

I'm walking along the path from *******, up through the woods among huge mossy stones and tall dark conifer trees. The slanting sun is shining between the upright trunks and sunbeams flitter in the air. I go through the gate and over the mud and across the wide track. Then I start my ascent towards the juniper grove. I walk up and then along a ridge and finally up the steep path. Eventually I reach the two huge juniper trees at the summit. One of them is tall, tall, up to the sky, and the other one has branches spread wide and generous. I kneel before them and tell them how happy I am to have returned here to this sacred spot in the Swedish forest.

I look up and see the tall tree has suddenly changed to his Spirit form. He says to me: 'Come, stand in front of me. We've known each other for a long time. Your Juniper distillations have always been so important to you. How sacred you see the oil. How you have always known to use it for protection – on handkerchiefs in turbulent aeroplanes across the oceans!'

And suddenly we take off! We're sitting in a very small plane high up over the forests. He is the pilot and I am sitting behind. Then we go up over the high mountains and through a snowstorm. We fly our little plane through the driving snow, on and on towards a yellow glow in the distance. As we approach, we land. I ask him: 'May I get to know you better? Can we work together to protect and heal?'

He replied: 'Look, I can protect you!' And he cast this gossamer web over me. It was sort of continuous with him and it covered every pore of me and was absorbed – in through my skin.

He continued: 'Now you're protected. Now you are me! I am you! We are one. I can give you that skill, that Power when I'm with you. It can come out through your hands. You can cast it around people. You could do it to '**' if he would let you. You could burn juniper oil, cast your hands over it and then you could surround his head with it. This oil has powers extreme and deep.' Then he showed me a sort of auric picture of a man with glowing chakras and auras.

He continued: 'Put your hands round this man's head.' And he stood behind me, his body close up against my spine. He repeated: 'Hold your hands around his head.'

And I did. And I watched as his whole aura turned into blue smoke and floated up, high, high. I went with it.

I asked: 'Is this the Power?'

He replied: 'Yes.'

… And we went so high up, up, up through the void, through the darkness, always following this green light which I knew was the 'aura of the chakras'. And we continued to go up and up.

The Spirit of Juniper: 'Now put that green light on your Wisdom. On your *******.'

And I put it on. I waited, I waited and then the whole of my body shimmered, shimmered with a brilliant light. It wasn't green but it was like a very tall triangle – like the Shard. And I stood in this high up place and let myself feel this Juniper Power down to my core and along my edges. I knew I had no fear. I knew I was totally protected – so high up.

The Spirit of Juniper then commanded me: 'Now fly!'

And I just dived off the highest precipice! Head first. I could see the World was so far below. I put my arms out and I glided down, down, down. With no fear! Down, down. I was totally alone in this huge void and I flew like a bird, then I soared, I spiralled up and fearlessly swooped down. I could fly!

Then I understood the protective power of Juniper.

And I floated back, down, down to the juniper hill, to the juniper grove and sat beneath him (the tree). I then asked him: 'Can I use this Journey in my book?'

He replied: 'Yes, but you must protect yourself as well. You can adapt it. [Hence the asterisks.] But yes, use it. So people can see the Power of plant spirits – all true to our essences, all true to our qualities in their virtual

247

dimension. My power above all is to protect; to keep FEAR at bay – the fear that contracts the kidneys, that freezes water, and most importantly, that is the opposite of love. We know you use your imagination in these Journeys – to give yourself 'hooks' to describe the indescribable and what is going on energetically. This is your 'insight'. But given to you by us.'
Drums to go back. I give thanks to the Spirit of Juniper. I'm back.

Section notes

1. Cunningham, Scott. Encyclopedia of Magical Herbs. 1997. Llewellyn Publications, Minnesota, USA. ISBN 0-87542-122-9.

2. Culpeper, Nicholas. Culpeper's Complete Herbal. 1992. Bloomsbury Books under licence from Omega Books. ISBN 1 85471 140 7

3. Grieve, Mrs M. FRHS. A Modern Herbal. Edited by Mrs C.F. Leyel. First published in 1931 by Jonathan Cape. Current edition published in 1994 by Cresset Books. ISBN 1-85501-249-9

4. Newall, I. and Wren, R.W. Potter's New Cyclopaedia of Botanical Drugs and Preparations. First published in 1907. Completely revised edition by Williamson and Evans. 1988. C.W. Daniel Company Ltd. ISBN 0 85207 197 3

5. Carol A., Anderson, Linda. A., Phillipson, J. David. Herbal Medicines: A Guide for Health-care professionals. 1996. London Pharmaceutical Press. ISBN 0 85369 289 0

6. Mojay, Gabriel. Course notes (as before).

Rose petals (Rosa gallica)

Rose *(Rosa damascena, Rosa gallica)*

Rose is associated with beauty, with love and with passion. It has held a special place in the medicine and perfumery of ancient Persian, Egyptian, Indian, Greek, Roman and Chinese civilisations, as well as in Western herbalism (e.g. *Rosa gallica*, the Apothecary's Rose – used as petals, tinctures, tisanes and sugared buds).

Of around 300 species of rose in the world, thirty are scented enough to be described as *'odorata'*. The three roses used to produce 'Otto' or in distillation for essential oil are *Rosa gallica, R. damascena* (originating from Damascus), and *R. centifolia* (from Provence, also known as the cabbage rose). The chief rose growing areas now are in Bulgaria where *R. damascena* is predominantly grown.

I've used rose purposely, as we all recognise the place that it holds in the realms of ritual and symbolism (the 'Herb of Love' sacred to Aphrodite; the Damask rose is the 'Holy Rose' – a symbol of God's love for the World and often portrayed around statues of the Blessed Virgin – as when she appeared to Saint Bernadette at Lourdes; the Greek poetess Sappho called rose the 'Queen of Flowers').

The following is an attempt to suggest how a rose preparation acts on the body, Soul and Spirit. It is necessarily incomplete and the information presented comes from a wide variety of sources – with different authenticities.

Uses

In mediaeval herbalism

The mediaeval correspondences assigned to rose and cited by Scott Cunningham[1] are: gender: Feminine; ruling planet: Venus; Element: Fire. So rose is a powerful archetypal feminine, loving and passionate force.

The entry for rose in Culpeper's Herbal is one of the longest in the book. He cites the government and virtues of rose at length, separating the virtues of different coloured roses and explaining each individually. He also separates the virtues of different parts of the plant – the petals, the roots, the leaves and even the stamens of the flowers – and different preparations. Such was the importance of rose in mediaeval herbalism. In essence, the quality of rose is Cool and Dry.

In modern herbal medicine

Grieve's entry for rose covers eight pages – perhaps the longest entry in the book. It covers the history of its use, its constituents and the uses of Otto of rose, rose water and rose hips. She quotes Culpeper – 'it strengtheneth the heart, the stomach, the liver and the retentive faculty' – and the uses from the British Pharmacopoeia of that time (1931), but suggests that their current use is mostly as flavour and perfume (see notes below). In this unlikely entry, she finishes with recipes for crystallised roses and rose petal sandwiches.

In Western medicine

Rose has a very broad spectrum of action. It acts as anti-inflammatory, astringent, digestive stimulant, expectorant, neurotonic, blood tonic, uterine tonic, aphrodisiac, anti-depressive, calmative, sedative, and has many other properties. It is also used to treat dry and inflamed skin, as astringent for diarrhoea, to relieve colic, in cough syrups, and as a tonic.

Seven rose formulations were removed from the British Pharmacopoeia in 1932: *Aqua Rosae*, *Oleum Rosae*, *Unguentum Aquae Rosae*, *Confectio Rosae Gallicae*, *Infusum Rosae Acidum*, *Rosa Gallica Petala*, and *Syrupus Rosae*. These were used for a variety of conditions: to reduce nausea; to normalise blood pressure and stimulate circulation of blood; to tone the spleen, liver and gall bladder and to normalise digestion. Rose preparations were also often used as flavouring agents.

In aromatherapy

Rosa damascena essential oil/floral water

These powerful scents have a remarkable influence on a human being. As described earlier, once registered, scent stimuli travel rapidly to the limbic system of the brain. This primitive part of the brain is made up of the hippocampus (involved with memory) and the even more primitive amagdala (involved with emotions). The brain then stimulates the release of hormones and neurochemicals that alter body physiology and human behaviour. Because of their high concentration, in this way, plant oils especially have an intrinsic energy that can have profound effects on emotions.

But other formulations of plant extracts are also effective. This has been demonstrated by the work of Edward Bach – a pioneer in this field – and his Flower Remedies, and also Rudolf Steiner with tinctures. More modern research has been done by Charlie Zhang (Universities of Zhejiang, China, and Siegen, Germany) on the relationship between the Electromagnetic Body versus the Chemical Body[2]. The Electromagnetic Body consists of the seven chakras with connecting meridians, forming a network continuous with the aura surrounding the body. It is this Electromagnetic Body that is the common base for many complementary therapies.

The active principles are: **alcohols,** including citronellol (34–55%), geraniol (30–40%) nerol (8.5%) and phenyl ethanol (1.5–3%), **terpenes** – stearoptene (16–22%), nonadecane/nonadecene (2–15%); and **numerous trace compounds** – perhaps up to 300 constituents, only 100 of which have been identified so far.

Effects on the nervous system and emotions: rose calms the parasympathetic nervous system. As a nerve tonic it can be used in treatment of depression, anxiety and grief.

Spiritual aspects: The use of plant essences in ritual, in magic, as incenses and in ecstatic practice is universal. Rose extracts have more use in these practices than most other plants. They have the ability to transport the user to another 'plane' of Consciousness or reality in meditation, relaxation and ecstasy – the third essential part of Wholeness.

In Chinese medicine:
Energy: Cool and Moist; Associated Element: Fire.

Primary actions and uses:

+ Rose petals or rosehips in preparations are used as Qi stimulants
+ Blood tonics to stimulate stagnant Liver energies
+ Kidney tonics.

These treatments act on both the Organs and the corresponding Emotions – so Heart/Love, Liver/Anger and Kidney/Fear. Using these connections, the effects of rose can be clearly seen (e.g. in the treatment of depression due to repressed anger; anxiety due to fear; and grief due to loss of love).

Spiritually, it regulates the Qi, calms the Shen and uplifts the Spirit. Rose is a gentle Heart tonic. It thus supports and calms the Heart, nourishing the Heart-Yin and restoring a sense of security and wellbeing[3].

Plant spirit medicine

My personal addition to this profile comes (as in the previous two plant profiles) from a shamanic Journey. My belief is that there are many ways to 'meet' plant spirits. With lavender, I inhaled its essential oil; with juniper I burned an incense. For this Journey, I gathered a huge bouquet of exquisite *Rosa gallica* flowers from my garden. I spent some time with them, as suggested by Evelyn Roe (reference cited). I observed their form and colour, breathed in their perfume and eventually changed my perception, bringing them within myself (the Goethean method). I then sat with them in my head and my head in the bouquet, and with headphones on, listening to my drumming tape, I Journeyed to the Spirit of Rose. My intention was: 'I am going on a Journey to meet the Spirit of *Rosa gallica* – the Apothecary's Rose – to ask her if she will be an important part of my book.'

> *I am standing on the ********** and call in my Spirits. Immediately many of them arrive at the same time. I ask them to take me to meet the Spirit of Rosa gallica. They say, 'This is a Journey about wisdom, you must learn – it is an Upper World Journey.'*
>
> *We set off and when we get to **** the bonfire is bigger than usual. I know this is an important Journey. We reach the Upper World and they say they must prepare me. They dress me in the finest clothes – actually, I look like a man, a sort of Prince Charming! We set off, my Spirits and me, in a procession towards and then through a rose plantation – hectares of Rosa gallica bushes in full flower. On and on we go and then we enter a sort of distillery with rose petals everywhere and the scent is quite astounding.*
>
> *Suddenly I am in the still with petals surrounding me. The lid shuts and the distillation begins. I waft up and into a grey tunnel, on and on, up and up, and then I enter a rose red sort of never-ending rose flower. On and on I go through the petals, searching for the Spirit of Rose. I get closer and closer in and don't find anyone – but I can sense a distinct presence and get closer and closer to it. The scent is intense and I am totally in love*

with this presence. She tells me to love with each chakra. I love with the base chakra and feel an intense desire, then the second chakra and my pelvis glows red, and then the third chakra and my lower trunk swells and is totally alive. then my Heart Chakra and I feel pure LOVE – intense and complete… and it is totally reciprocated. We stay like that for what seems a long time.

Later, the light changes from pink/red to bright white/yellow and a young girl appears. She is just a head – she has no body. I ask her if she is the Spirit of Rose and she says, 'No, and of course you realise that we Spirits don't actually have bodies! You also need to know the wisdom of Love. Receive it with your Throat Chakra.' And I did so, and then with my third Eye Chakra and lastly with my seventh Chakra. By this time the light was brilliant white and I met the wisdom of Pure Love. I had reached a state of BLISS.

After a while she tells me, 'This is what plant Spirits are – of course not 'Humans', but sometimes humans need to give us human form in order to perceive us. But this is how we really are – intense feeling/sense/energy for you to connect with…'

I then ask, 'Now I have met you, will you play an important part in my book?'

She replied: 'Yes. Infuse the whole of the book with this love and this wisdom. That will be my contribution, my part in your book.'

Drums to return. I give thanks.

I had never before experienced such consuming and generous love. I have never loved *so* deeply…

When I had come out of the Journey and returned to this reality, I held my hands over the *Rosa gallica* bouquet to feel the Qi. My hands were over one metre apart.

Section notes

1. Cunningham, Scott. Magical Aromatherapy. 1996. Llewellyn Publications, Minnesota, USA (as before)

2. Zhang, Charlie. 1997. Article Electromagnetic Body versus Chemical Body. www.datadiwan.de/SciMedNet/library/articlesN81+/N81Zhang_electrochem.htm

3. Mojay, Gabriel. Course notes (as before).

Lady's mantle (Alchemilla vulgaris) – an important ingredient
of the Breuss Diet and an ancient healing herb

XIV

The Breuss Diet revisited

*'He looked into his own soul with a telescope. What
seemed all irregular, he saw and shewed to be beautiful
constellations, and he added to the consciousness hidden
worlds within worlds.'*

<small>COLERIDGE NOTEBOOKS INTRODUCTION TO C.G. JUNG,
'MEMORIES, DREAMS, REFLECTIONS'</small>

It was a considerable number of years later than my first attempt that I thought
it necessary to revisit the Breuss Diet. I decided to follow it for ten days and to
record, and later research, my reactions. I tried to understand it as a herbalist
and especially from the point of view of energetics and the sense of wellbeing
that I had so definitely experienced the first time. Of course, the second diet did
not have the 'unknown' quality, the intensity or the same purpose as the first one.
But nevertheless, after a few days of adaptation and hunger pangs, I again felt
energised and contented, even light-hearted.

A thread of this research was to consider the various factors that could
have contributed to that sense of wellbeing – be they physical, psychological,
spiritual or energetic. Whether a case of body 'detoxification', an opportunity for
relaxation, good sleep patterns or any other factor, I considered that during the
Diet I reached a state of balance between body and psyche. And this, of course, is
what good health and wellbeing is. The well-known phrase *'Mens sana in corpore
sano'* can be traced back to ancient Greek philosophy, where in around 585 BCE
the philosopher Thales answers the question 'What man is happy?' with 'He
who has a healthy body, a resourceful mind and a docile nature.'

Another consideration was that Herr Breuss knew precisely what he was
doing. Although not a medical doctor, he was a renowned naturopath and healer

with a considerable following. He understood the body's physiological needs, e.g. for elimination of toxins, for water balance, for smooth functioning of the gut, for balancing constituents of the blood, and getting sufficient nutrients to cells for maintenance and energy. The Breuss Diet was designed as a cure for his own duodenal cancer where a diet with almost no roughage but relatively high plant fibre/protein from the beetroot juice, and using herbs that are wound healers and blood staunchers, would surely be highly beneficial. Breuss made various modifications for diets to treat other types of cancer and in the case of breast cancer, he included Tisane III of lady's mantle and white dead nettle.

Plants contain a vast number of chemical constituents – far more different molecules than human cells and so many that have not been identified and, of those that have, so many that are very difficult or even impossible to synthesise. From this bountiful 'pharmacy' of active ingredients present in the eleven herbs and three juices and soups of the diet, there are countless opportunities for healing.

From my subjective experience of the diet, I felt that besides promoting the healthy functioning of my physical body, which allowed me to feel comfortable, rested, satisfied and relaxed, there was another dimension that affected my mood, my energy and my high spirits. I thus turned to the models where I felt I would be most likely to find an answer. I decided to research all the plants in the tisanes and juices.

The first place for me to look seemed obvious – Chinese medicine. Here is a system that treats the physical body, the Emotions and the Spirit – taken here to be the total of all aspects of the psyche. The system of correspondences between the Elements, the Seasons, the Organs and their root Emotions, the Spirit and the effects of imbalance of Qi on mood could give a suitable model for explanation. For the plants I had studied in this system, my source was Gabriel Mojay[1] and his work on essential oils.

But since these are all Western herbs and many are not used in Chinese medicine systems, I also needed to go back to the ancient herbals. I looked for correspondences of these herbs to the planets, the Elements, for balance of the Humours and Temperaments. My sources were John Gerard,[2] Nicholas Culpeper,[3] and also Scott Cunningham[4] from a magical herbalism perspective and because he cited correspondences with the planets. Further research brought me to Graeme Tobyn,[5] who had worked on Culpeper's descriptions and emphasised the concept of *pneuma*, which gave Western herbalism a holistic and energetic basis akin to Qi in Chinese medicine. This fitted in with theories of modern Western herbal energetics as proposed by some enlightened medical herbalists[6] and naturopaths. I added findings from Mrs M. Grieve[7] for good bodily measure!

Finally, I made shamanic Journeys to the Spirits of some of the herbs. I chose those aromatic herbs that I could contact by inhaling their essences as this is a very effective way of reaching a trance state. In my experience, Journeys to plant spirits are Middle World Journeys that often involve a very rapid connection with the plant Spirit. They are sometimes less distinct as a Journey and more a 'felt understanding' of the healing capability of the plant – call it an 'intuition' if you will, or a 'vignette' that portrays the character of the plant spirit. And so it was when I Journeyed to the Spirit of Sage (see below).

The Herbs in Tisane I

Breuss calls this a 'Nieren Tee', which translates as a tea to treat the kidneys. It is made of very ancient herbs, each one of which is beneficial to the kidneys and acts on regulating the consistency and purity of the blood. It also has tonic and stimulating qualities, allaying fears, lethargy and depression. The herbs have correspondences with the Sun, Mars and Saturn, and with the Elements Fire and Earth.

Equisetum arvense (horsetail)

Source: Culpeper
Gender: Feminine; planetary ruler: Saturn.

Uses: To staunch bleeding, heal inward ulcers, provoke urine, ease the bowels, cure inflammations.

Grieve
A very primitive plant related to fossils of the Carboniferous Era. Found in watery habitats.
It acts on kidneys as diuretic and astringent. A blood stauncher.

Scott Cunningham
Gender: Feminine; planetary ruler: Saturn.
Used to charm snakes. For fertility.

Urtica dioica (stinging nettle)

Gerard
Temperament: Dry and a little Hot.
Used to remedy against the venomous qualities of hemlock and quicksilver.

Culpeper
Gender: Masculine; planetary ruler: Mars; deity: Thor.
Uses: For protection, exorcism and healing. Good for lethargy– to rub on the forehead on the temples mixed with salt. Warm, tonic and astringent.

Grieve
Acts on kidneys as astringent and a stimulating tonic.

Scott Cunningham
Gender: Masculine; planetary ruler: Mars; Element: Fire.
Uses: Protection, healing and exorcism. To allay fear and to avert danger.

Polygonum aviculare (knot grass)

Gerard
To feed sick swine; it is mentioned in Shakespeare's 'Midsummer's Night Dream': 'the hindering knotgrass'; efficacious in retarding the growth of children and young domestic animals.

Culpeper
Herb of Saturn and an important wound herb.

Grieve
Acts on kidneys, astringent, diuretic, styptic and vulnerary (blood staunching).

Scott Cunningham
Gender: Feminine; planetary ruler: Saturn; Element: Earth.
Uses: To 'bind' woes and miseries.

Hypericum perforatum (St John's wort)

Gerard
The infused oil is a deep wound curer – 'I know that in all the world there is not a better one'.

Culpeper
Many ancient lores related to this plant, e.g. protection from evil spirits; used in Midsummer's Day celebrations (the Feast Day of Saint John is June 24).
Herb of the Sun under the sign of Leo (so a very powerful herb). A wound herb. Properties of protection, strength and happiness.

Grieve
Acts on kidney-related ailments, astringent, expectorant and powerful nervine.

Scott Cunningham
Gender: Masculine; planetary ruler: sun; Element: Fire.
Uses: To keep mental illness at bay and to cure melancholy. To protect from evil 'influences'.

Hypericum perforatum

The Herbs in Tisane II

These herbs are extremely powerful. They have correspondences with the Sun, Jupiter and Mercury and with the Elements Air and Fire. Physiologically they act on the gut and its smooth function in these new dietary conditions. So this tisane is a regulator and balancer of the alimentary canal, of saliva flow, digestion and the effects of so little bulk passing through the gut. Three of the plants (sage, peppermint and *Melissa*) also have powerful effects on the nervous system and specifically mood. They act as tonic and stimulant and a calmer of the heart and Mind.

Salvia officinalis (sage)

Culpeper

Gender: Masculine; planetary ruler: Jupiter; Element: Air.
A very powerful herb. Uses include: 'it provokes urine, stayeth the bleeding of wounds, and cleaneth ulcers and sores'. Excellent aid to help memory.

Grieve

There have been so many references to this herb throughout history. It was mentioned by Dioscorides, Agrippa, Matthiolus and Pliny.

> '*Cur moriatur homo cui salvia cresit in horto?*' ('Why should a man die if he grows Salvia in his garden?')
>
> PLINY

Also known as *Salvia salvatrix* (Sage the Saviour). Gerard grew it in Holborn in 1597. A culinary and medicinal herb used for many centuries in Europe. It was grown in French graveyards to recognise grief. Used for its volatile oil.

Action: Astringent, stimulant, tonic and carminative. Regulator of saliva flow and action and taken to reduce dyspepsia. Also affecting mood. (Note: it was the sage oil that I craved during preparation of this tisane.)

Scott Cunningham
Gender: Masculine; planetary ruler: Jupiter; Element: Air.
Uses: To ensure long life. For protection, wisdom and longevity. Excellent to help the memory, warming and quickening the senses.

In Chinese medicine
Neutral to slightly Warm, tonifies both Yin and Yang – a balancer.

Shamanic Journey to the Spirit of Sage

Before the Journey I had been inhaling the vapours of sage tea and drinking it for a short while. When I was ready to start the Journey, I prepared myself.

> *Immediately 'I' rose from my supine position, leapt out of the window and confidently strode to the place where I usually start my Journeys. To this day I can feel that youthful leap from our balcony and reassured stride across the terrace with my head held high. It was like this that I meet the Spirit of Sage – a huge, kindly man in a sort of armour with a purple helmet. Returning to my body, I realise that my third chakra is throbbing. He says, 'Put your hands there' – and I feel the Qi/power. As I pull my hands away, I realise it has moved to my second chakra. Again I feel it. He says: 'My power is to know where to balance you.' I then realise that my Third Eye region is intense and throbbing. I ask if this is how he heals and he says: 'My wisdom is to know what you need.'*
>
> *Suddenly he changes to a huge Sage bush and I kneel before him and immerse my head in the bush. He tells me to meditate on his power. I realise my body has blown into a huge golden sphere – that's what I am. He says: 'Feel your body. This is you. How could you die in this perfection?'*
>
> *Drums to return. I give thanks.*

Hypericum perforatum

(as before)

Mentha piperata (peppermint)

Gerard
Sage 'rejoiceth the heart of man'

Culpeper
Gender: Masculine; planetary ruler: Mercury; Element: Air.
Uses: To gain money, healing and protection from evil.

Grieve
Peppermint has ancient connections. It was used by the Romans, Egyptians and Greeks and found in Icelandic and Japanese Pharmacopoeias of the 13th century and the London Pharmacopoeia 1721. Contains menthol, the most extensively used of all essential oils.
Action: Antispasmodic, relieving pain in the alimentary canal; relief of dyspepsia, flatulence, colic and cramps. A stomachic. Also relieves heart palpitations.

Scott Cunningham
Gender: Masculine; planetary ruler: Mercury; Element: Fire; deity: Pluto.
Powers: Purification; healing and psychic powers. Used for divination dreams of the future.

In Chinese medicine
It is Cooling, stimulant, antispasmodic, Dry. It raises Qi to the head, restores the nerves, supports the Shen and uplifts the Spirit.

Melissa officinalis (lemon balm)

Gerard
Called it 'Bawme' that 'comforteth the heart, driveth away melancholy and sadness'. A singular good for the heart. It strengthens the vital spirits (after Avicenna).

Culpeper
Gender: Masculine; planetary ruler: Jupiter; Element: Air; Hot and Dry.
Uses: A wound herb that cures old sores and strengthens Nature much. It cheers the heart and mind by purging melancholy.

Grieve

So many references. Mentioned by Paracelsus in the 13th century – 'to revivify a man'; and by John Evelyn (around 1650) – 'Balm is sovereign for the brain, chasing melancholy'.
Action: Disorders of the nervous system, wound stauncher.

Scott Cunningham

Gender: Masculine; planetary ruler: Jupiter; Element: Air.
Uses: To influence love; a wound stauncher; to quieten the mind and uplift the spirits.

In Chinese medicine

Cool and Dry, to treat stagnation of Qi, for Heat in the Liver and Heart and to calm disturbance of the Mind (Shen).

The Herbs in Tisane III

Tisane III is specific to breast cancer in the Breuss Diet. It is a 'woman's' tisane to regulate hormones and promote a smooth menstrual flow. It is also involved in temperature regulation, which is an important factor in this regime that generates so little energy. It also affects mood and vitality. The herbs have correspondences with the planet Venus and the Element Water.

Alchemilla alpina (Alpine lady's mantle) and *Alchemilla vulgaris* (lady's mantle)

Culpeper
Gender: Feminine; planetary ruler: Venus; Element: Water.
Uses: For love spells and in love potions.

Grieve
Species name from the Arabic '*Alkemelych*', meaning 'alchemy', because of its wonder-working powers, including the magical powers of the dew drops that form at dawn in the base of the furrowed leaves. Its English name is lady's mantle (in German, *Frauenmantele*), used by herbalist Jerome Bock in 1532 in his 'History of Plants'. Culpeper calls it a Herb of Venus.
Actions: High in tannins so is an astringent and styptic; antispasmodic. An important wound herb and useful to regulate menstrual blood flow.

Scott Cunningham
Gender: Feminine; planetary ruler: Venus; Element: Water.
Powers: to evoke Love.

Lamium album (white dead nettle)

Gerard

'Maketh the heart merry and refresheth the vital spirits.'

Grieve

Actions: Promotes perspiration; acts on kidneys; staunches wounds and haemorrhages.

The Herb in Tisane IV

Tisane IV of *Geranium robertianum* is a crucial part of this diet. Its actions to counteract the growth of cancer cells and the effects of radiation are not understood. But my experience was that during the first Diet regime, I needed/appreciated this tea more than any of the others. In fact, I craved it. This herb has correspondences with the planet Venus and the Element Water.

Geranium robertianum (herb robert)

Culpeper
Gender: Feminine; planetary ruler: Venus; Element: Water.
Uses: Cure for the stone (in kidneys?) and effectual in all old ulcers in any part of the body.

Grieve
An important ancient herb.
Actions: Very high in tannins and useful as an astringent, tonic and mouth gargle. Modern texts cite its use to alleviate the effects of radiation.

The juices and soups

Beetroot

Culpeper
Gender: Feminine; planetary ruler: Saturn; Element: Earth.
Use: 'To stay the blood flux, women's courses, and to help the yellow jaundice';
'to purify the head and helpeth the noise in the ears'.

Grieve
First cultivated by the Romans, beetroot is highly nutritious, containing the red pigment betacyanin, and is high in antioxidants. It is claimed to reduce cholesterol levels, in some cases suppress cancer growth, and regulate bowel function.

Beetroot contains 10% glucose sugar that is very easily assimilated.

'Its sugar is a force-giver and an energy creator, a source of vitality to the human body.' It contains 33% starch and gum so releases sugars slowly into the blood stream.

'Modern medicine disregards the beet but of old it was considered to have distinct remedial actions.' It is thus a crucial part of this diet and has correspondences with the planet Saturn and the Element Earth.

In Chinese medicine
It is Cooling and a blood tonic.

Onions

Culpeper

Planetary ruler: Mars; They have warming, expectorant, tonic and diuretic properties. Effective in easing the bowels and drawing putrefaction.

Scott Cunningham

Gender: Masculine; planetary ruler: Mars; Element: Fire; deity: Isis.
Powers: Protection, exorcism, healing, prophetic dreams.

Grapefruit

Fresh fruit rich in vitamin C and vitality. As with all the citrus fruits, grapefruit invigorates and enlivens.

In Chinese medicine

It is Hot, expectorant, tonic and diuretic.

****

These descriptions of the herbs and their properties come from very different sources that use different models of health. However, there are some overriding similarities in the descriptions of their properties: of cleansing and as purifiers; of protecting (from blood loss, from evil, from venom, from infection). On many occasions they are mind-altering in their effects as well.

So by returning to the old herbals and considering the shamanic Journeys as well, besides the physiological effects, I began to understand the nature of that powerful life force/energy and sense of wellbeing that I had experienced during the Diet. These herbs had so many qualities, so much potential for balancing and healing body, Soul and Spirit. So many of the herbs affected my mood and spirit in ways that modern medicine does not take into account.

Going back to my description of mediaeval herbalism, I was able to fit the herbs from the diet into the scheme and could see how the root emotions of worry and fear, of anger, of indifference and of joy could all be balanced by the herbs. And it was this balance that contributed hugely to my feeling of vitality, wellbeing and happiness. Above all, I became aware of the holistic nature of this cure.

The Correspondences of Herbs in the Breuss Diet

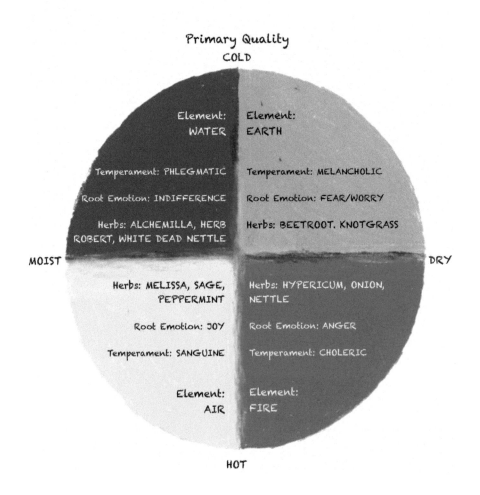

Primary Quality
COLD

Element: WATER

Element: EARTH

Temperament: PHLEGMATIC

Temperament: MELANCHOLIC

Root Emotion: INDIFFERENCE

Root Emotion: FEAR/WORRY

Herbs: ALCHEMILLA, HERB ROBERT, WHITE DEAD NETTLE

Herbs: BEETROOT. KNOTGRASS

MOIST

DRY

Herbs: MELISSA, SAGE, PEPPERMINT

Herbs: HYPERICUM, ONION, NETTLE

Root Emotion: JOY

Root Emotion: ANGER

Temperament: SANGUINE

Temperament: CHOLERIC

Element: AIR

Element: FIRE

HOT

Diagram of Correspondences of the herbs in the Breuss Diet

But this account also raises another dilemma. How can we benefit from this ancient knowledge and practice, and also from Western medicine and surgical techniques? Perhaps I was fortunate; I benefitted from first-rate diagnosis, surgery and radiation – all according to the current Western model of cancer and its treatment. The treatment was over once the radiation finished. Check-ups lasted for years, of course. It was not until after the treatment, because of 'soul searching' and 'unhappiness', that I looked elsewhere for the healing I hadn't received. With no conflict, I could embrace the second approach with openness and optimism.

So often a patient suffering from a chronic disease now has to juggle with treatments. Can you be taking prescribed drugs – perhaps for the rest of your life – and at the same time take significant amounts of herbal treatments? Can you take statins and grapefruit juice? Pharmaceutical research is scanty in matters like this and where there is inconclusive evidence, patients are advised not to take herbs alongside pharmaceutical prescription drugs. Thankfully, medical herbalists are trained in advising in such cases and thus open the doors to diets like the Breuss Diet. Of course, there are sufferers of various diseases who, through their affiliations and belief systems, make a choice to follow an alternative medicine treatment. It could be for a chronic disease for which there appears to be little success of cure using pharmaceutical drugs, or even for a serious medical complaint where the treatment, although it has a high probability of success, is aggressive with unacceptable side effects.

However, there is a movement towards a confluence of ancient healing rites and the best of medical science. This was encouraged by the far-from-proven distinction between complementary and alternative therapies. One could be used alongside Western medicine and the other could not. This type of Third Era Medicine (of which there are many) is an art that considers all possibilities for healing the human body and psyche in a holistic approach – whether by using allopathic medications, herbs, loving touch, scalpel strikes, prayer or meditation – appropriate to the needs of the individual[7].

Chapter notes

1. Mojay, Gabriel. Aromatherapy for Healing the Spirit. 1997. Gaia Books Ltd. London. ISBN 978 0 89281 887 8. Other than the reference to Chinese medicine for *Salvia officinalis*, all Chinese medicine properties come from this source book and course lecture notes.

2.   Culpeper, Nicholas. Culpeper's Complete Herbal. 1992. Bloomsbury Books under licence from Omega Books. ISBN 1 85471 140 7

3.   Gerard's Herbal: The History of Plants. Edited by Marcus Woodward. 1994. Published by Senate, an imprint of Studio Editions Ltd. London. ISBN 1 85958 051 3

4.   Cunningham, Scott. Encyclopedia of Magical Herbs. 1997. Llewellyn Publications, Minnesota, USA. ISBN 0-87542-122-9 and Cunningham, Scott: Magical Aromatherapy. 1996. Llewellyn Publications, Minnesota, USA

5.   Tobyn, Graeme. Culpeper's Medicine. A practice of Western Holistic Medicine. 1997. Element Books Ltd. ISBN 1-85230-943-1

6.   Colorado School of Clinical Herbalism. www.clinicalherbalism.com

7.   Grieve, Mrs M. FRHS. A Modern Herbal. Edited by Mrs C.F. Leyel. First published in 1931 by Jonathan Cape. Current edition published in 1994 by Cresset Books. ISBN 1-85501-249-9

A swallowtail butterfly, a symbol of the Soul and its connection – in this case with the flowers of Buddleja davidii (the butterfly bush)

Epilogue

In the midst of the Covid-19 pandemic, Spring 2020

'The force that through the green fuse drives the flower
Drives my green age; that blasts the roots of trees
Is my destroyer...'

DYLAN THOMAS

These opening lines of the poem by Dylan Thomas, inspired by William Blake's *'O rose, thou art sick',* describe the connection between plants and humanity. That same powerful energy in a flower is also present in us. We share it in Nature and we share the same fate.

Could there ever be an end to this humble attempt to unravel the mystery of this force and of the healing nature of plants? I doubt it, as it has to be a pulling together of personal experience and objective knowledge to create a 'felt understanding' where heart and head are as one. Neither the one nor the other can tell the whole story. We continue to experience and to learn to the end of our days. To be satisfied is to be dead.

I am aware that in all my meanderings, I have scarcely mentioned our complete physical dependence on plants: to provide us with vital oxygen and to relieve us of too much carbon dioxide in the atmosphere; as our primary food source and materials source for building and textiles; as the basis of all our fossil fuels. These are all taught in minute detail in school and university biology courses throughout the Western world. They are essential aspects of our very existence.

Instead, I've spoken about the age-old and universal connections we used to have with plants. My emphasis has been on what we have forgotten, to our great loss: our sacred and energetic connections with plants that bring comfort and heal 'dis-ease' at every level of human distress. With this 'forgetting', we also seem to have lost the gratitude and respect that we once had for plants and their relationship with the Earth. This has deeply affected our attitudes towards the environment.

And for me, this description really brings my experience of the last thirty years into a coherence. I have tried to weave together the creation of my beautiful and highly productive herb garden; my reading and studying of philosophy, herbal medicine, psychology, aromatherapy and holistic science; my practical and spiritual activities with my herbs; and my shamanic existence. My creative pursuits of singing, art, wood-carving and quilt-making all strengthened my relationship with plants until, in many ways, we became 'as one'. Although I have always loved them, I now also have the deepest heartfelt respect for them – with their connections to the luminaries, the Elements, the seasons and the Earth; and with their connections communicating with each other and with all other organisms – us included. Plants are truly connected with all of Nature and as such share its omnipresent and vital energy.

But there is still much to understand about the magic of their healing properties and why it should be so that we have such a relationship with plants that they have this capacity to heal us. I have no grand 'Theory of Everything' that could give me the model on which to test my theories. My understanding is interim and evolving. But my strong belief and felt understanding is that everything on this Earth *is* connected; we have all evolved from that first stirring of life on this planet, we are all part of the worldwide web of Nature. And we are only a part of it and, although blessed with a powerful Consciousness, do not own it. The shamanic practice of 'giving and receiving' holds true. *All* our activities have profound effects on the delicate balance of the Qi or 'Subtle energy' or 'Grace' or 'Spirit' that permeates the Earth and the cosmos. My garden and my interactions with it are a contribution to maintaining this balance and to pay homage and give thanks to this beautiful planet Earth and her vital and healing green mantle.

I wanted to call my book 'In Praise of Plants' but Francis Hallé coined the phrase, in the English translation at least. His French title is 'Éloge de la Plante. Pour une nouvelle Biologie'. So, as we share this sentiment with such enthusiasm, I wholeheartedly endorse his ideas:

'We need to perceive {the plant} with all our senses, not in an intellectual, devitalised way... More interesting is the truth that attracts the gardener *and his or her accomplices, including the horticulturalist and the herbalist, the grape grower and the healer, the landscape painter and the poet. They do not doubt their responsibility for maintaining a very ancient knowledge of life, full of the future and indissolubly linked to the human species.'*

In the intervening years, my garden has returned to meadow as it was so long ago. The trees we planted have now grown in stature and in grace. Yesterday the meadow was cloaked in pale yellow primroses and deep purple, scented violets on the sunny slope. Today they all lie beneath this morning's deep snowy blanket. As I write, the crows have been a constant presence in the orchard, sitting for hours in a howling snow blizzard, still as frozen black statues on the icy branches of the pear tree. Their presence has been a huge comfort and encouragement to me to try to 'suffuse my writing with spiritual brilliance and far-reaching preciousness for humanity', as I was told to do by Spirits in a recent Journey.

The world has suddenly been gripped in fear of a virus for which, as yet, there is no synthetic 'cure'. Governments the world over are relying on 'the science' to understand Coronavirus and the disease it causes, Covid-19. All hope is being placed on a vaccine. Now is the time, more than any other, for us to turn to a Third Era Medicine and the plant kingdom with its bountiful medicine chest to look for holistic remedies to keep us strong and heal us body, Soul and Spirit – and at the same time, to heal our relationship with our beautiful planet Earth.

'So I threw the dice and wrote a book for my contemporaries or for posterity. I don't care. It may take 100 years for my book to find readers.'

Kepler, 'Harmonia mundi – Kepler's Planetary Music'[1]

Hilary Miflin
Chevenoz
March 5th, 2020

Notes

1. https://explore/scimednet.org by Paul Keiniewicz SMN

Vervain (Verbena officinalis)
Herb of Grace

Appendix I

Research background: the following information has been compiled from British Pharmacopoeias in the Wellcome Library (personal research).

The Medical Act of 1858 gave rise to the formation of the General Medical Council in Great Britain and to the production of the first British Pharmacopoeia. This single pharmacopoeia replaced those of London, Dublin and Edinburgh.

The British Pharmacopoeia 1864 1st Edition had many imperfections and half of the 28,000 copies were destroyed. However, this was the starting point and the General Medical Council published an edition at intervals until 1993. They were decreed to 'cause to be published under their direction a book containing a list of medicines and compounds and the manner of preparing them... To be called 'The British Pharmacopoeia'... and to alter and amend as the Council deems necessary'.

By investigating this first BP 1864, I have compiled a list of all plant species used as herbs or formulations of herbs, as shown in **Table I**. This is made up of around 138 plant species from around the world – very few of which are still included in the British Pharmacopoeia 1993. There is also a list of those plants that are native British (i.e. have been used traditionally by herbalists and healers since ancient times), shown in **Table II**. In the intervening years since 1864, some plant species have been added to the original list, but overall there has been a systematic deletion of herbs and formulations, and replacement by synthetic molecules.

In the index of BP 1864, the number of entries of plants and their formulations is around 450. This represents 60% of all entries and includes 138 plant species and 310 formulations of them. The most common plant formulations are shown in **Table II** below (241 formulations). The most common non-plant entries include inorganic salts, acid and ammonium preparations, solutions, mineral preparations, liquors and unguents.

It is this species list (**Table I**) that I use as the starting point to research the deletion of plant species and formulations from the British Pharmacopoeia, as shown in **Table IV** (species names alphabetically ordered) and **Table V** (chronologically ordered – which shows when the most deletions occurred, in 1932). **Table VI** shows the remaining plant formulations in BP 1993 – just nineteen entries.

Table I: (compiled from) British Pharmacopoeia 1864 plant species list

Index Name	Species Name	Common Name	Origin
Acacia	*Acacia Linn.*	Gum Arabic	E. Africa
Aconitum	*Aconitum napellus Linn.*	Monkshood	cultivated in Britain
Aloe barbadensis	*Aloe vulgaris Lam Encycl. plate 109, Steph. and Church. Med. Bot.*	Barbadoes Aloes	Barbadoes
Aloe socotrina	*One or more species of Aloe Linn.*	Socotrina Aloes	Socotra
Amygdala	*Amygdalus communis var dulcis DC.*	Sweet Almond*	cultivated Malaga
Anethum	*Anethum graveolens Linn.*	Dill*	cultivated in England
Anisi Oleum	*Pimpinella Anisum Linn.*	Oil of Anise	distilled in Europe
Anthemis	*Anthemis nobilis Linn.*	Chamomile flowers*	wild and cultivated in England
Armoracia	*Cochlearia Armoracia Linn.*	Horseradish root	cultivated in Britain
Arnica	*Arnica montana Linn.*	Arnica root	collected Middle/S Europe
Assafoetida	*Narthex Assafoetida Falconer*	Assafoetida	Affghanistan & Punjaub
Aurantii Aqua & Cortex	*Citrus Bigaradia Risso*	Orange flower water / Bitter Orange peel	France
Balsumum Peruvianum	*Myrospermum Pereirae Royle, Mat. Med.*	Balsum of Peru	Salvador in Guatemala
Balsumum Tolutanum	*Myrospermum toluiferum DC.*	Balsum of Tolu	New Granada
Belladonna	*Atropa Belladonna Linn.*	Deadly Nightshade	cultivated in Britain

Bucco	*Barosma spp betulina, crenulata, serrtifolia*	Bucho	Cape of Good Hope
Burgundy Pitch Spruce Fir	*Abies excelsa Lamarck*	Pix Burgundica	Switzerland
Cajuput oil	*Melaleuca minor DC.*	Oil of Cajeput	Molucca Islands
Calumba	*Cocculus palmatus DC.*	Calumbo	Mozambique
Cambogia	*Garcinia Linn.*	Gamboge	China
Camphora	*Camphora officinarum Nees, Laurineae*	Camphor	China
Cannabis indica	*Cannabis sativa Linn.*	Indian Hemp	India
Capsicum	*Capsicum fastigiatum Blume, Bijdr.*	Capsicum	Guinea, E/W Indies
Cardamomum	*Elettaria Cardamomum Maton*	Cardamoms	Malabar
Carui	*Carum Carui Linn.*	Caraway*	Cultivated in England & Germany
Caryophyllum	*Caryophyllus aromaticus Linn.*	Cloves*	Penang, Bencoolen & Amboyna
Cascarilla	*Croton Eluteria Bennett*	Cascarilla	Bahamas Islands
Cassia	*Cassia Fistula Linn.*	Cassia Pulp	E/W Indies
Catechu nigrum	*Acacia Catechu Willd. Enum.*	Black Catechu	Peru
Catechu pallidum	*Uncaria Gambir Roxburgh, Flor. Ind.*	Pale Catechu	Singapore
Cetraria	*Cetraria islandica Acharius, Lichenogr.*	Iceland Moss	N. Europe
Chinchona flava	*Cinchona Calisaya Weddell*	Yellow-Cinchona Bark	Bolivia, S. Peru
Chinchona pallida	*Cinchona Comdaminea DC. Vars*	Pale-Cinchona Bark	Equador
Chinchona rubra	*Cinchona succirubra Pavon*	Red-Cinchona Bark	Chimborazo
Chirata	*Ophelia Chirata DC.*	Chiretta	N.India
Cinnamon	*Cinnamomum cassia*	Oleum Cinnamomi	Ceylon
Cocculus	*Anamirta Cocculus Wight & Arnott*	Cocculus Indicus	Malabar
Colchici Cormus & Semen	*Colchicum autumnale Linn.*	Colchicum Corm	Indigenous
Colocynthis	*Citrullus Colocynthis Schrad.*	Colocynth	Smyrna, Trieste, France, Spain

Conium	Conium maculatum Linn.	Hemlock	wild British plants
Copaiba	Copaifera multijuga Hayne	Copaiva*	Brazil
Coriandrum	Coriandrum sativum Linn.	Coriander*	cultivated in Britain
Crocus	Crocus sativus Linn.	Saffron	Spain, France, Naples
Cubeba	Cubeba officinalis Miquel	Cubebs*	Java. Oil distilled in England
Cusparia	Galipea Cusparia DC.	Cusparia Bark	tropical S. America
Cusso	Brayera anthelmintica DC	Kousso	Abyssinia
Digitalis	Digitalis purpurea Linn.	Digitalis	wild indigenous plants
Dulcamara	Solanum Dulcamara Linn.	Dulcamara	indigenous plants
Elaterium	Ecbalium officinarum Richard	Elaterium	not stated
Elemi	probably Canarium commune Linn.?	Elemi	Manilla
Ergota	Secale cereale Linn.	Ergot	not stated
Ficus	Ficus Carica Linn.	Fig	Smyrna
Filix	Aspidium Filix mas Swartz	Fern Root	indigenous
Foeniculum	Foeniculum dulce DC.	Sweet Fennel Root	Malta
Galbanum	unascertained Umbelliferous plant	Galbanum	India, The Levant
Galla	from Quercus infectoria Olivier	Galls	not stated
Gentiana	Gentiana lutea Linn.	Gentian	Alps, Apennines
Glycyrrhiza	Glycyrrhiza glabra Linn.	Liquorice Root	cultivated in England
Granati Radix	Punica Granatum Linn.	Pomegranate Root	Germany
Guaiaci Lignum	Guaiacum officinale Linn.	Guaiac Wood	St Domingo & Jamaica
Guaiaci Resina	Guaiacum officinale Linn.	Guaiac Resin	St Domingo & Jamaica
Hemidesmus	Hemidesmus indicus DC.	Hemidesmus	India
Hordeum	Hordeum distichon Linn.	Pearl Barley	cultivated in Britain
Hyoscyamus	Hyoscyamus niger Linn.	Hyoscyamus	Indigenous

Ipecacuanha	*Cephaelis Ipecacuanha DC.*	Ipecacuan	Brazil
Jalapa	*Exogonium Purga Bentham*	Jalap	Mexico
Kamela	*Rottlera tinctoria Roxb. Corom.*	Kamela	India
Kino	*Pterocarpus Marsupium DC.*	Kino	Malabar
Krameria	*Krameria triandra Ruiz & Pavon*	Rhatany	Peru
Laurocerasus	*Prunus Laurocerasus Linn.*	Cherry-Laurel leaves"	cultivated in England
Limonis Cortex	*Citrus Limonum DC.*	Lemon Peel	S. Europe
Limonis Oleum	*as above*	Lemon Oil	as above
Limonis Succus	*as above*	Lemon Juice	as above
Lini Farina	*Linum usitatissumum Linn.*	Linseed Meal	cultivated in Britain
Lini Oleum	*as above*	Linseed Oil	as above
Lini semen	*as above*	Linseed	as above
Lobelia	*Lobelia inflata Linn.*	Lobelia	N. America
Lupulus	*Humulus Lupulus Linn.*	Hop	cultivated in England
Manna	*Fraxinus Ornus Linn.*	Manna	Sicily & S. Europe
Mastiche	*Pistacia Lentiscus Linn.*	Mastich	Turkey & the Levant
Matica	*Artanthe elongata Miquel*	Matico	Peru
Menthae piperitae Oleum	*Mentha piperata Linn.*	English Oil of Peppermint"	Oil distilled in England
Menthae viridis Oleum	*Menthae viridis Linn.*	English Oil of Spearmint	Oil distilled in England
Mezereum	*Daphne Mezereum Linn.*	Mezereon	not stated
Mori Succus	*Morus nigra Linn.*	Mulberry Juice	cultivated in Britain
Myristica	*Myristica officinalis Linn.*	Nutmeg (and concrete oil)*	Sumatra & Molucca Islands
Myrrha	*Balsamodendron Myrrha Ehren.*	Myrrh*	Arabia Felix & Abyssinia
Nectrandra	*Nectrandra Rodiaei Schomburgk.*	Bebeeru Bark	British Guiana
Nux vomica	*Strychnos Nux vomica Linn.*	Nux Vomica	E. Indies

Oleum Crotonis	*Croton tiglium Linn.*	Croton Oil	expressed from seeds in England
Oleum Juniperi	*Juniperus communis Linn.*	English Oil of Juniper	Oil distilled in England
Oleum Lavandulae	*Lavandula vera DC.*	English Lavender Oil	Oil distilled in England
Oleum Olivae	*Olea europaea Linn.*	Olive Oil	S. Europe
Opium	*Papaver somniferum Linn.*	Opium	Asia Minor
Papaver	*Papaver somniferum Linn.*	Poppy Capsules	cultivated in Britain
Pareira	*Cissampelos Pareira Linn.*	Pareira	Brazil
Peppermint	*Mentha piperita*	Oleum Menthae Piperitae	England
Pimenta	*Eugenia Pimenta DC.*	Pimento*	W.Indies
Piper	*Piper nigrum Linn.*	Black Pepper	W. Indies
Podophyllum	*Podophyllum peltatum Linn.*	Podophyllum	N.America
Prunum	*Prunus domestica Linn.*	Prune	S. Europe
Pterocarpus	*Pterocarpus santalinus Linn.*	Red Sandal-Wood	Coromandel & Ceylon
Quassia	*Picraena excelsa Lindl.*	Quassia	Jamaica
Quercus	*Quercus pedunculata Willd.*	Oak bark	plants growing in Britain
Rheum	*Rheum spp. Linn.*	Rhubarb	Chinese Thibet & Tartary
Rhoeas	*Papaver Rhoeas Linn.*	Red-Poppy Petals	indigenous plants
Ricini Oleum	*Ricinus communis Linn.*	Castor Oil	E. Indies & America
Rosa canina	*Rosa canina Linn.*	Hips	indigenous plants
Rosa centifolia	*Rosa centifolia Linn.*	Cabbage-Rose Petals"	plants cultivated in Britain
Rosa gallica	*Rosa gallica Linn.*	Red-Rose Petals	plants cultivated in Britain
Rosmarini Oleum	*Rosmarinus officinalis Linn.*	English Oil of Rosemary	Oil distilled in England
Rutae Oleum	*Ruta graveolens Linn.*	English Oil of Rue	Oil distilled in England
Sabadilla	*Asagraea officinalis Lindl.*	Cevadilla	Vera Cruz & Mexico
Sabina	*Juniperus Sabina Linn.*	Savin*	plants cultivated in Britain

Sambucus	Sambucus nigra Linn.	Elder Flowers	indigenous plants
Santonica	Artemisia spp. Linn.	Santonica	Russia
Sarsa	Smilax officinalis Humb. & Bonpl.	Jamaica Sarsaparilla	Jamaica
Sassafras	Sassafras officinale Nees, Laurineae	Sassafras	N. America
Scammonium	Convolvulus Scammonia Linn.	Scammony	Syria
Scilla	Urginea Scilla Steinheil.	Squill	Mediterrean coasts
Scoparius	Sarothamnus Scoparius Wimmer.	Broom Tops	indigenous plants
Senega	Polygala Senega Linn.	Senega	N.America
Senna alexandrina	Cassia lanceolata Lamarck, Encyc.	Alexandrian Senna	Alexandria
Senna indica	Cassia elongata Lemaire	Tinnevelly Senna	S. India
Serpentaria	Aristolochia Serpentaria Linn.	Serpentary	N.America
Sinapis	Sinapis nigra Linn.& S. alba Linn.	Mustard	cultivated in England
Spearmint	Mentha viridis	Oleum Menthae viridis	England
Stramonii Folia & Semina	Datura Stramonium Linn.	Stramonium Leaves & Seeds	cultivated in Britain
Styrax Praeparatus	Liquidambar orientale Miller's Dict.	Prepared Storax	Asia Minor
Tabacum	Nicotiana Tabacum Linn.	Leaf Tobacco	Cultivated in America
Tamarindus	Tamarindus indica Linn.	Tamarind	W. Indies
Taraxacum	Taraxacum Dens Leonis DC.	Dandelion Root	meadows and pastures in Britain
Terebinthina Canadensis	Abies balsamea Aiton, Hort. Kew	Canada Balsam*	Canada
Thus Americanum	Pinus Taeda Linn.	Common Frankincense	N.America
Tragacantha	Astragalus verus Olivier, Voy., DC	Tragacanth	Asia Minor
Ulmus	Elm Bark Ulmus campestris Linn.	Elm bark	indigenous & cultivated in Britain
Uva Ursi	Arctostaphylos Uva Ursi Spreng. Syst.	Bearberry Leaves	indigenous plants
Uvae	Vitis vinifera Linn.	Raisins	Spain
Valeriana	Valeriana officinalis Linn.	Valerian	indigenous & cultivated in Britain

Zingiber	*Zingiber officinale Roscoe*	Ginger	W. Indies, India
		Cinnamon	Ceylon
		* denotes Oil in addition to herb e.g. Dill and Oil of Dill	

(138 species)

Table II: The plants in Table I were represented in the following most common formulations in the British Pharmacopoeia 1864

Formulation	Number of entries	Including
Tinctures	54	Lavender
Extracts	31	
Unguents	14	
Oils	27	Rosemary, Lavender, Juniper
Infusions	27	Infusum Rosae Acidum
Spirits	8	Juniper, Lavender, Rosemary
Syrups	12	Rosa gallica syrup
Decoctions	13	
Waters	12	Rose
Confections	7	Confectio Rosae caninae, Confectio Rosae gallicae
Pills	13	
Liniments	10	
Enemas	5	
Powders	8	

(241 entries)

Of these 138 plant species, forty-eight were native British plants/cultivated in Britain or in very common use.

Table III: Native British plants from Table I

Common Name	Origin
Monkshood	cultivated in Britain
Dill	cultivated in England
Oil of Anise	distilled in Europe
Chamomile flowers	wild and cultivated in England
Horseradish root	cultivated in Britain
Arnica root	collected Middle/S Europe
Deadly Nightshade	cultivated in Britain
Caraway	cultivated in England & Germany
Iceland Moss	N. Europe
Colchicum Corm	Indigenous
Hemlock	wild British plants
Coriander	cultivated in Britain
Digitalis (Foxglove)	wild indigenous plants
Dulcamara (Bittersweet)	indigenous plants
Ergot	indigenous
Fern Root	indigenous
Galls	indigenous
Gentian	Alps, Apennines
Liquorice Root	cultivated in England
Pearl Barley	cultivated in Britain
Hyoscyamus (Henbane)	indigenous
Cherry-Laurel leaves	cultivated in England
Lemon Peel/oil/juice	S. Europe
Linseed Meal/oil/seed	cultivated in Britain
Hop	cultivated in England
English Oil of Peppermint	oil distilled in England
English Oil of Spearmint	oil distilled in England
Mulberry Juice	cultivated in Britain
Croton Oil (Spurge)	expressed from seeds in England
English Oil of Juniper	oil distilled in England
English Lavender Oil	oil distilled in England
Olive Oil	S. Europe
Poppy Capsules	cultivated in Britain
Oak bark	plants growing in Britain
Red-Poppy Petals	indigenous plants

Hips	indigenous plants
Cabbage-Rose Petals	plants cultivated in Britain
Red-Rose Petals	plants cultivated in Britain
English Oil of Rosemary	oil distilled in England
English Oil of Rue	oil distilled in England
Savin (Juniper)	plants cultivated in Britain
Elder Flowers	indigenous plants
Broom Tops	indigenous plants
Mustard	cultivated in England
Stramonium Leaves & Seeds (Jimsonweed/ Datura)	cultivated in Britain
Dandelion Root	meadows and pastures in Britain
Elm Bark	indigenous & cultivated in Britain
Bearberry Leaves	indigenous plants
Valerian	indigenous & cultivated in Britain

(48 entries)

This list contains:

- native 'poisonous' plants, always noted in botanical floras: monkshood, nightshades, henbane, bittersweet, rue
- culinary herbs: mustard, caraway, coriander, dill, mints
- flowers: rose, elder, poppy, broom
- roots: dandelion, liquorice, fern, arnica, horseradish
- seeds: poppy, linseed

Interesting to note here is the overlap of food and medicine, and in particular the use of culinary herbs in the British Pharmacopoeia.

From this original research, I was in a position to chart the fate of these plants over time. At intervals over a period of 126 years, thirteen new editions of the British Pharmacopoeia were published – each with additions and deletions of formulations. I could thus survey the plant deletions of each subsequent pharmacopoeia. A list of deleted formulations can be seen in **Table IV**.

Table IV: List of British Pharmacopoeia plant deletions (1867 to 1993)
Species name alphabetical (522 entries)

Year of deletion, Vol. & Page no.	Index name	Species name
1932 p.xxxii	Terebinthina Canadensis	*Abies balsamea Aiton, Hort. Kew*
1932 p.xxxii	Decoctum Acaciae Corticis	*Acacia arabica Willd.*
1993 p.xxxiv	Catechu	*Acacia Catechu Willd. Enum.*
1953 p.xx	Catechu	*Acacia Catechu Willd. Enum.*
1932 p.xxxii	Catechu Nigrum	*Acacia Catechu Willd. Enum.*
1867 p. xviii	Catechu Nigrum	*Acacia Catechu Willd. Enum.*
1993 p.xxxiv	Catechu Tincture	*Acacia Catechu Willd. Enum.*
1993 p.xxxiv	Powdered Catechu	*Acacia Catechu Willd. Enum.*
1953 p.xx	Tinctura Catechu	*Acacia Catechu Willd. Enum.*
1932 p.xxxii	Trochiscus Catechu	*Acacia Catechu Willd. Enum.*
1932 p.xxxii	Acaciae Cortex	*Acacia Linn.*
1958 p.xxiii	Mucilage of Acacia	*Acacia Linn.*
1914 p.xxiii	Succus Acalyphae	*Acalypha indica Linn.*
1953 p.xx	Aconitum	*Aconitum napellus Linn.*
1953 p.xx	Linimentum Aconiti	*Aconitum napellus Linn.*
1932 p.xxxii	Tinctura Aconiti	*Aconitum napellus Linn.*
1932 p.xxxii	Unguentum Aconitinae	*Aconitum napellus Linn.*
1932 p.xxxii	Belae Fructus	*Aegle Marmelos Correa*
1932 p.xxxii	Extractum Belae Liquidum	*Aegle Marmelos Correa*
1932 p.xxxii	Agropyrum	*Agropyrum repens Beauvois*
1932 p.xxxii	Decoctum Agropyri	*Agropyrum repens Beauvois*
1932 p.xxxii	Extractum Agropyri Liquidum	*Agropyrum repens Beauvois*
1953 p.xx	Pilula Aloes	*Aloe sp.*
1993 p.xxxiv	Powdered Aloes	*Aloe sp.*
1932 p.xxxii	Pilula Aloes et Myrrhae	*Aloe sp. & Balsamodendron Myrrha Ehren.*
1948 p.xxix	Pilula Aloes et Ferri	*Aloe sp. & Iron*
1948 p.xxix	Pilula Aloes et Asafoetidae	*Aloe sp. & Narthex Assafoetida Falconer*
1932 p.xxxii	Decoctum Aloes Compositum	*Aloe spp.*
1932 p.xxxii	Extractum Aloes	*Aloe spp.*
1914 p.xxiii	Tinctura Aloes	*Aloe spp.*
1932 p.xxxii	Alstonia	*Alstonia scholaris R. Br.*
1932 p.xxxii	Infusum Alstoniae	*Alstonia scholaris R. Br.*

1932 p.xxxii	Tinctura Alstoniae	*Alstonia scholaris R. Br.*
1932 p.xxxii	Amygdala Amara	*Amygdala communis var dulcis DC*
1932 p.xxxii	Amygdala Dulcis	*Amygdala communis var dulcis DC*
1932 p.xxxii	Mistura Amygdalae	*Amygdala communis var dulcis DC*
1932 p.xxxii	Pulvis Amygdalae Compositus	*Amygdala communis var dulcis DC*
1932 p.xxxii	Pyrethri Radix	*Anacyclus Pyrethrum DC.*
1932 p.xxxii	Tinctura Pyrethri	*Anacyclus Pyrethrum DC.*
1867 p. xviii	Cocculus	*Anamirta Cocculus Wight & Arnott*
1867 p. xviii	Unguentum Cocculus	*Anamirta Cocculus Wight & Arnott*
1914 p.xxiii	Tinctura Andrographidis	*Andrographis paniculata Nees.*
1914 p.xxiii	Liquor Andrographidis Concentratus	*Andrographis paniculata Nees*
1914 p.xxiii	Infusum Andrographidis	*Andrographis paniculata Nees.*
1953 p.xx	Anethum	*Anethum graveolens Linn.*
1948 p.xxix	Aqua Anethi Destillata	*Anethum graveolens Linn.*
1963 p.xxvi	Concentrated Dill Water	*Anethum graveolens Linn.*
1963 p.xxvi	Dill Oil	*Anethum graveolens Linn.*
1932 p.xxxii	Mucilago Gummi Indici	*Anogeissus latifolia Wall.*
1932 p.xxxii	Anthemidis Flores	*Anthemis nobilis Linn.*
1914 p.xxiii	Extractum Anthemidis	*Anthemis nobilis Linn.*
1932 p.xxxii	Oleum Anthemidis	*Anthemis nobilis Linn.*
1932 p.xxxii	Infusum Uvae Ursi	*Arctostaphylos Uva Ursi Spreng. Syst.*
1932 p.xxxii	Uvae Ursi Folia	*Arctostaphylos Uva Ursi Spreng. Syst.*
1885 vol. I/p.xxii	Areca	*Areca Catechu Linn.*
1914 p.xxiii	Aristolochia	*Aristolochia indica Linn.*
1914 p.xxiii	Infusum Serpentariae	*Aristolochia Serpentaria Linn.*
1914 p.xxiii	Liquor Aristolochiae Concentratus	*Aristolochia Serpentaria Linn.*
1914 p.xxiii	Liquor Serpentariae Concentratus	*Aristolochia Serpentaria Linn.*
1948 p.xxix	Serpentaria	*Aristolochia Serpentaria Linn.*
1914 p.xxiii	Tinctura Aristolochiae	*Aristolochia Serpentaria Linn.*

1932 p.xxxii	Tinctura Serpentariae	*Aristolochia Serpentaria Linn.*
1932 p.xxxii	Arnicae Flores	*Arnica montana Linn.*
1914 p.xxiii	Arnicae Rhizoma	*Arnica montana Linn.*
1914 p.xxiii	Tinctura Arnicae	*Arnica montana Linn.*
1932 p.xxxii	Tinctura Arnicae Florum	*Arnica montana Linn.*
1932 p.xxxii	Trochiscus Santonini	*Artemisia cina Berg*
1980 p.xxvii	Male Fern	*Aspidium Filix mas Swartz*
1980 p.xxvii	Male Fern Extract	*Aspidium Filix mas Swartz*
1963 p.xxvi	Male Fern Extract Capsules	*Aspidium Filix mas Swartz*
1988 p.xxxi	Compound Tragacanth Powder	*Astragalus verus Olivier, Voy., DC.*
1968 p.xxix	Tragacanth Mucilage	*Astragalus verus Olivier, Voy., DC.*
1988 p.xxxi	Belladonna Adhesive Plaster	*Atropa Belladonna Linn.*
1958 p.xxiii	Belladonna Root	*Atropa Belladonna Linn.*
1948 p.xxix	Emplastrum Belladonnae	*Atropa Belladonna Linn.*
1948 p.xxix	Extractum Belladonnae Herbae	*Atropa Belladonna Linn.*
1914 p.xxiii	Extractum Belladonnae Viride	*Atropa Belladonna Linn.*
1953 p.xx	Linimentum Belladonnae	*Atropa Belladonna Linn.*
1958 p.xxiii	Liquid Extract of Belladonna	*Atropa Belladonna Linn.*
1885 vol. I/p.xxii	Liquor Atropiae	*Atropa Belladonna Linn.*
1914 p.xxiii	Succus Belladonnae	*Atropa Belladonna Linn.*
1932 p.xxxii	Unguentum Belladonnae	*Atropa Belladonna Linn.*
1953 p.xx	Myrrha	*Balsamodendron myrrha Ehren.*
1953 p.xx	Tinctura Myrrhae	*Balsamodendron Myrrha Ehren.*
1948 p.xxix	Buchu	*Barosma betulina (Thunb.) Bartl. & Wendl.*
1948 p.xxix	Infusum Buchu Concentratum	*Barosma betulina (Thunb.) Bartl. & Wendl.*
1948 p.xxix	Infusum Buchu Recens	*Barosma betulina (Thunb.) Bartl. & Wendl.*
1932 p.xxxii	Tinctura Buchu	*Barosma betulina (Thunb.) Bartl. & Wendl.*
1932 p.xxxii	Berberis	*Berberis vulgare Linn.*
1914 p.xxiii	Liquor Berberidis Concentratus	*Berberis vulgare Linn.*
1932 p.xxxii	Tinctura Berberis	*Berberis vulgare Linn.*
1932 p.xxxii	Linimentum Sinapis	*Brassica nigra (Linn.) Koch*
1932 p.xxxii	Oleum Sinapis Volatile	*Brassica nigra (Linn.) Koch*
1932 p.xxxii	Cusso	*Brayera anthelmintica DC.*

1932 p.xxxii	Butae Gummi	*Butea frondosa Roxb.*
1932 p.xxxii	Butae Semina	*Butea frondosa Roxb.*
1932 p.xxxii	Pulvis Butae Seminum	*Butea frondosa Roxb.*
1914 p.xxiii	Calotropis	*Calotropis procera Ait.*
1914 p.xxiii	Tinctura Calotropis	*Calotropis procera Ait.*
1980 p.xxvii	Camphor Liniment	*Camphora officinarum Nees, Laurineae*
1963 p.xxvi	Camphor Water	*Camphora officinarum Nees, Laurineae*
1993 p.xxxiv	Natural Camphor	*Camphora officinarum Nees, Laurineae*
1953 p.xx	Spiritus Camphorae	*Camphora officinarum Nees, Laurineae*
1932 p.xxxii	Cannabis Indica	*Cannabis sativa Linn.*
1932 p.xxxii	Extractum Cannabis Indicae	*Cannabis sativa Linn.*
1932 p.xxxii	Tinctura Cannabis Indicae	*Cannabis sativa Linn.*
1953 p.xx	Capsicum	*Capsicum fastigiatum Blume, Bijdr.*
1953 p.xx	Tinctura Capsici	*Capsicum fastigiatum Blume, Bijdr.*
1948 p.xxix	Tinctura Capsici Concentrata	*Capsicum fastigiatum Blume, Bijdr.*
1953 p.xx	Unguentum Capsici	*Capsicum fastigiatum Blume, Bijdr.*
1932 p.xxxii	Aqua Carui	*Carum Carui Linn.*
1953 p.xx	Oleum Cari	*Carum Carui Linn.*
1953 p.xx	Infusum Caryophylli	*Caryophyllus aromaticus Linn.*
1953 p.xx	Infusum Caryophylli Concentratum	*Caryophyllus aromaticus Linn.*
1948 p.xxix	Infusum Caryophylli Recens	*Caryophyllus aromaticus Linn.*
1948 p.xxix	Confectio Sennae	*Cassia acutifolia Delile*
1948 p.xxix	Infusum Sennae Recens	*Cassia acutifolia Delile*
1958 p.xxiii	Liquid Extract of Senna	*Cassia acutifolia Delile*
1968 p.xxix	Senna Leaf	*Cassia acutifolia Delile*
1958 p.xxiii	Syrup of Senna	*Cassia acutifolia Delile*
1932 p.xxxii	Tinctura Sennae Composita	*Cassia acutifolia Delile*
1914 p.xxiii	Liquor Sennae Concentratus	*Cassia elongata Lemaire*
1948 p.xxix	Cassia	*Cassia Fistula Linn.*
1932 p.xxxii	Cassiae Fructus	*Cassia Fistula Linn.*

1953 p.xx	Mistura Sennae Composita	*Cassia sp?*
1932 p.xxxii	Trochiscus Ipecacuanhae	*Cephaelis Ipecacuanha DC.*
1932 p.xxxii	Vinum Ipecacuanhae	*Cephaelis Ipecacuanha DC.*
1932 p.xxxii	pilula Ipecacuanhae cum Urginea	*Cephaelis Ipecacuanha DC. & Urginea indica Kunth.*
1932 p.xxxii	Pilula Ipecacuanhae cum Scilla	*Cephaelis Ipecacuanha DC. & urginea Scilla Steinh.*
1958 p.xxiii	Chenopodium Oil	*Chenopodium ambrosioides Linn. var. anthelminticum Gray*
1948 p.xxix	Cinchona	*Chinchona sp.*
1948 p.xxix	Extractum Cinchonae	*Chinchona sp.*
1948 p.xxix	Extractum Cinchonae Liquidum	*Chinchona sp.*
1932 p.xxxii	Infusum Cinchonae Acidum	*Chinchona sp.*
1948 p.xxix	Quininae Tannas	*Chinchona sp.*
1948 p.xxix	Tinctura Cinchonae	*Chinchona sp.*
1948 p.xxix	Tinctura Cinchonae Composita	*Chinchona sp.*
1948 p.xxix	Tinctura Cinchonae Composita Concentrata	*Chinchona sp.*
1932 p.xxxii	Tinctura Quininae	*Chinchona sp.*
1914 p.xxiii	Cimicifugae Rhizoma	*Cimicifuga racemosa Nutt.*
1914 p.xxiii	Extractum Cimicifugae Liquidum	*Cimicifuga racemosa Nutt.*
1914 p.xxiii	Tinctora Cimicifugae	*Cimicifuga racemosa Nutt.*
1932 p.xxxii	Oliveri Cortex	*Cinnamomum Oliveri Bailey*
1932 p.xxxii	Tinctura Oliveri Corticis	*Cinnamomum Oliveri Bailey*
1948 p.xxix	Aqua Cinnamomi Destillata	*Cinnamomum zeylandicum Nees, Laurineae*
1963 p.xxvi	Cinnamon Oil	*Cinnamomum zeylandicum Nees, Laurineae*
1963 p.xxvi	Concentrated Cinnamon Water	*Cinnamomum zeylandicum Nees, Laurineae*
1932 p.xxxii	Pulvis Cinnamomi Compositus	*Cinnamomum zeylandicum Nees, Laurineae*
1932 p.xxxii	Spiritus Cinnamomi	*Cinnamomum zeylandicum Nees, Laurineae*
1932 p.xxxii	Tinctura Cinnamomi	*Cinnamomum zeylandicum Nees, Laurineae*
1914 p.xxiii	Extractum Cissampeli Liquidum	*Cissampelos Pareira Linn.*
1914 p.xxiii	Extractum Pareirae Liquidum	*Cissampelos Pareira Linn.*
1914 p.xxiii	Pareirae Radix	*Cissampelos Pareira Linn.*

1968 p.xxix	Fresh Bitter Orange peel	*Citrus Aurantium Linn.*
1968 p.xxix	Orange Syrup	*Citrus Aurantium Linn.*
1968 p.xxix	Orange Tincture	*Citrus Aurantium Linn.*
1932 p.xxxii	Aqua Aurantii Floris	*Citrus Bigaradia Risso*
1932 p.xxxii	Aurantii Cortex Indicus	*Citrus Bigaradia Risso*
1953 p.xx	Infusum Aurantii	*Citrus Bigaradia Risso*
1932 p.xxxii	Infusum Aurantii Compositum	*Citrus Bigaradia Risso*
1953 p.xx	Infusum Aurantii Concentratum	*Citrus Bigaradia Risso*
1948 p.xxix	Infusum Aurantii Recens	*Citrus Bigaradia Risso*
1932 p.xxxii	Syrupus Aurantii Floris	*Citrus Bigaradia Risso*
1948 p.xxix	Tinctura Aurantii Concentrata	*Citrus Bigaradia Risso*
1932 p.xxxii	Vinum Aurantii	*Citrus Bigaradia Risso*
1963 p.xxvi	Fresh Lemon Peel	*Citrus Limonum DC.*
1958 p.xxiii	Lemon Oil	*Citrus Limonum DC.*
1963 p.xxvi	Lemon Syrup	*Citrus Limonum DC.*
1963 p.xxvi	Lemon Tincture	*Citrus Limonum DC.*
1932 p.xxxii	Succus Limonis	*Citrus Limonum DC.*
1948 p.xxix	Tinctura Limonis Concentrata	*Citrus Limonum DC.*
1932 p.xxxii	Infusum Ergotae	*Claviceps purpurea Tulasne*
1932 p.xxxii	Injectio Ergotae Hypodermica	*Claviceps purpurea Tulasne*
1932 p.xxxii	Tinctura Ergotae Ammoniata	*Claviceps purpurea Tulasne*
1953 p.xx	Calumba	*Cocculus palmatus DC.*
1953 p.xx	Infusum Calumbae	*Cocculus palmatus DC.*
1953 p.xx	Infusum Calumbae Concentratum	*Cocculus palmatus DC.*
1953 p.xx	Infusum Calumbae recens	*Cocculus palmatus DC.*
1914 p.xxiii	Liquor Calumbae Concentratus	*Cocculus palmatus DC.*
1953 p.xx	Tinctura Calumbae	*Cocculus palmatus DC.*
1932 p.xxxii	Armoraciae Radix	*Cochlearia Armoracia Linn.*
1932 p.xxxii	Spiritus Armoraciae Compositus	*Cochlearia Armoracia Linn.*
1953 p.xx	Colchici Semen	*Colchicum autumnale Linn.*
1980 p.xxvii	Colchicum Corm	*Colchicum autumnale Linn.*
1980 p.xxvii	Colchicum Liquid extract	*Colchicum autumnale Linn.*
1980 p.xxvii	Colchicum Tincture	*Colchicum autumnale Linn.*
1932 p.xxxii	Extractum Colchici	*Colchicum autumnale Linn.*
1948 p.xxix	Extractum Colchici Cormi Liquidum	*Colchicum autumnale Linn.*
1953 p.xx	Extractum Colchici Siccum	*Colchicum autumnale Linn.*

1932 p.xxxii	Vinum Colchici	*Colchicum autumnale Linn.*
1914 p.xxiii	Conii Folia	*Conium maculata Linn.*
1914 p.xxiii	Conii Fructus	*Conium maculata Linn.*
1914 p.xxiii	Succus Conii	*Conium maculata Linn.*
1914 p.xxiii	Tinctura Conii	*Conium maculata Linn.*
1914 p.xxiii	Unguentum Conii	*Conium maculata Linn.*
1914 p.xxiii	Pilula Scammonii Composita	*Convolvulus Scammonia Linn.*
1932 p.xxxii	Pulvis Scammoniae Compositus	*Convolvulus Scammonia Linn.*
1932 p.xxxii	Scammoniae Radix	*Convolvulus Scammonia Linn.*
1914 p.xxiii	Scammonium	*Convolvulus Scammonia Linn.*
1948 p.xxix	Copaiba	*Copaifera multijuga Hayne*
1932 p.xxxii	Oleum Copaibae	*Copaifera multijuga Hayne*
1914 p.xxiii	Coscinium	*Coscinium fenestratum Colebr.*
1914 p.xxiii	Infusum Coscinii	*Coscinium fenestratum Colebr.*
1914 p.xxiii	Liquor Coscinii Concentratus	*Coscinium fenestratum Colebr.*
1914 p.xxiii	Tinctura Coscinii	*Coscinium fenestratum Colebr.*
1914 p.xxiii	Crocus	*Crocus sativum Linn.*
1914 p.xxiii	Cuspariae Cortex	*Crocus sativum Linn.*
1914 p.xxiii	Tinctura Croci	*Crocus sativum Linn.*
1932 p.xxxii	Infusum Cascarillae	*Croton Eluteria Bennett*
1932 p.xxxii	Tinctura Cascarillae	*Croton Eluteria Bennett*
1932 p.xxxii	Linimentum Crotonis	*Croton Tiglium Linn.*
1932 p.xxxii	Oleum Crotonis	*Croton tiglium Linn.*
1932 p.xxxii	Cubebae Fructus	*Cubeba officinalis Miquel*
1932 p.xxxii	Oleum Cubebae	*Cubeba officinalis Miquel*
1932 p.xxxii	Tinctura Cubebae	*Cubeba officinalis Miquel*
1932 p.xxxii	Cucurbitae Semina Praeparat	*Cucurbita maxima Duchesne*
1932 p.xxxii	Oleum Graminis Citrati	*Cymbopogon citratus Staph.*
1914 p.xxiii	Mezerei Cortex	*Daphne Mezereum Linn.*
1932 p.xxxii	Daturae Folia	*Datura Metel Linn.*
1932 p.xxxii	Daturae Semina	*Datura Metel Linn.*
1932 p.xxxii	Tinctura Daturae Seminum	*Datura Metel Linn.*
1885 vol. I/p.xxii	Stramonii Folia	*Datura Stramonium Linn.*
1914 p.xxiii	Stramonii Semina	*Datura Stramonium Linn.*
1963 p.xxvi	Stramonium Dry Extract	*Datura Stramonium Linn.*
1973 p.xx	Stramonium Liquid Extract	*Datura Stramonium Linn.*
1988 p.xxxi	Stramonium Tincture	*Datura Stramonium Linn.*
1932 p.xxxii	Staphagriae Semina	*Delphinium Staphisagria Linn.*

1885 vol. I/p.xxii	Digitalinum	*Digitalis purpurea Linn.*
1993 p.xxxiv	Digitalis Tablets	*Digitalis purpurea Linn.*
1948 p.xxix	Infusum Digitalis Recens	*Digitalis purpurea Linn.*
1993 p.xxxiv	Prepared Digitalis	*Digitalis purpurea Linn.*
1958 p.xxiii	Tincture of Digitalis	*Digitalis purpurea Linn.*
1914 p.xxiii	Elaterium	*Ecbalium officinarum Richard*
1914 p.xxiii	Pulvis Elaterini Compositus	*Ecbalium officinarum Richard*
1948 p.xxix	Tinctura Cardomomi Composita Concentrata	*Elleteria Cardamomum Maton*
1932 p.xxxii	Embelia	*Embelia Ribes Burm. F.*
1914 p.xxiii	Cocae Folia	*Erythroxylum coca Lam.*
1914 p.xxiii	Extractum Cocae Liquidum	*Erythroxylum coca Lam.*
1932 p.xxxii	Unguentum Eucalypti	*Eucalyptus polybractea R.T. Baker*
1948 p.xxix	Oleum Santali Australiensis	*Eucarya spicata Sprague & Summerhayes*
1958 p.xxiii	Clove	*Eugenia Caryophyllus (Spreng.) Sprague*
1914 p.xxiii	Aqua Pimentae	*Eugenia Pimenta DC.*
1914 p.xxiii	Oleum Pimentae	*Eugenia Pimenta DC.*
1914 p.xxiii	Pimenta	*Eugenia Pimenta DC.*
1932 p.xxxii	Euonymi Cortex	*Euonymus atropurpureus Jacq.*
1932 p.xxxii	Extractum Euonymi	*Euonymus atropurpureus Jacq.*
1914 p.xxiii	Extractum Jalapae	*Exogonium Purga Bentham*
1948 p.xxix	Jalapa	*Exogonium Purga Bentham*
1948 p.xxix	Jalapa Pulverata	*Exogonium Purga Bentham*
1932 p.xxxii	Jalapae resina	*Exogonium Purga Bentham*
1948 p.xxix	Pulvis Jalapae Compositus	*Exogonium Purga Bentham*
1932 p.xxxii	Tinctura Jalapae	*Exogonium Purga Bentham*
1932 p.xxxii	Tinctura Jalapae Composita	*Exogonium Purga Bentham*
1914 p.xxiii	Sumbul Radix	*Ferula Sumbul Hook.*
1914 p.xxiii	Tinctura Sumbul	*Ferula Sumbul Hook.*
1914 p.xxiii	Ficus	*Ficus Carica Linn.*
1932 p.xxxii	Aqua Foeniculi	*Foeniculum dulce DC.*
1958 p.xxiii	Fennel	*Foeniculum dulce DC.*
1932 p.xxxii	Galla	*from Quercus infectoria Olivier*
1932 p.xxxii	Unguentum Gallae	*from Quercus infectoria Olivier*
1932 p.xxxii	Umguentum Gallae cum Opio	*from Quercus infectoria Olivier & Papaver somniferum Linn.*
1914 p.xxiii	Infusum Cuspariae	*Galipea Cusparia DC.*

1914 p.xxiii	Liquor Cuspariae Concentratus	*Galipea Cusparia DC.*
1914 p.xxiii	Cambogia	*Garcinia Linn.*
1914 p.xxiii	Cambogia Indica	*Garcinia Linn.*
1914 p.xxiii	Pilula Cambogiae Composita	*Garcinia Linn.*
1932 p.xxxii	Oleum Gaultheriae	*Gaultheria procumbens Linn.*
1932 p.xxxii	Gelsemii Radix	*Gelsemium sempervirens Ait.*
1932 p.xxxii	Tinctura Gelsemii	*Gelsemium sempervirens Ait.*
1973 p.xx	Compound Gentian Tincture	*Gentiana lutea Linn.*
1948 p.xxix	Extractum Gentianae	*Gentiana lutea Linn.*
1948 p.xxix	Infusum Gentianae Compositum Recens	*Gentiana lutea Linn.*
1885 vol. I/p.xxii	Mistura Gentianae	*Gentiana lutea Linn.*
1948 p.xxix	Tinctura Gentianae Composita Concentrata	*Gentiana lutea Linn.*
1958 p.xxiii	Compound Powder of Liquorice	*Glycyrrhiza glabra Linn.*
1953 p.xx	Extractum Glycyrhizae	*Glycyrrhiza glabra Linn.*
1914 p.xxiii	Extractum Glycyrrhizae Spirituosum	*Glycyrrhiza glabra Linn.*
1932 p.xxxii	Decoctum Gossypii Radicis Corticis	*Gossypium herbaceum Linn.*
1932 p.xxxii	Extractum Gossypii Radicis Corticis Liquidum	*Gossypium herbaceum Linn.*
1932 p.xxxii	Gossypii Radicis Cortex	*Gossypium herbaceum Linn.*
1932 p.xxxii	Gossypium	*Gossypium herbaceum Linn.*
1973 p.xx	Cottonseed Oil	*Gossypium spp.*
1932 p.xxxii	Extractum Grindeliae Liquidum	*Grindelia camporum Greene*
1932 p.xxxii	Grindelia	*Grindelia camporum Greene*
1932 p.xxxii	Guaiaci Lignum	*Guaiacum officinale Linn.*
1932 p.xxxii	Guaiaci Resina	*Guaiacum officinale Linn.*
1932 p.xxxii	Mistura Guaiaci	*Guaiacum officinale Linn.*
1932 p.xxxii	Tinctura Guaiaci Ammoniata	*Guaiacum officinale Linn.*
1932 p.xxxii	Trochiscus Guaiaci Resinae	*Guaiacum officinale Linn.*
1958 p.xxiii	Dry Extract of Hamamelis	*Hamamelis virginiana Linn.*
1932 p.xxxii	Hamamelidis Cortex	*Hamamelis virginiana Linn.*
1963 p.xxvi	Hamamelis	*Hamamelis virginiana Linn.*
1963 p.xxvi	Hamamelis Liquid Extract	*Hamamelis virginiana Linn.*
1963 p.xxvi	Hamamelis Ointment	*Hamamelis virginiana Linn.*
1932 p.xxxii	Liquor Hamamelidis	*Hamamelis virginiana Linn.*
1932 p.xxxii	Tinctura Hamamelidis	*Hamamelis virginiana Linn.*

1914 p.xxiii	Hemidesmi Radix	*Hemidesmus indicus DC.*
1914 p.xxiii	Syrupus Hemidesmi	*Hemidesmus indicus DC.*
1914 p.xxiii	Liquor Caoutchouc	*Hevea brasiliensis Muell.*
1914 p.xxiii	Infusum Lupuli	*Humulus Lupulus Linn.*
1914 p.xxiii	Lupulus	*Humulus Lupulus Linn.*
1914 p.xxiii	Tinctura Lupuli	*Humulus Lupulus Linn.*
1932 p.xxxii	Extractum Hydrastis Liquidum	*Hydrastis canadensis Linn.*
1932 p.xxxii	Hydrastis Rhizoma	*Hydrastis canadensis Linn.*
1932 p.xxxii	Tinctura Hydrastis	*Hydrastis canadensis Linn.*
1988 p.xxxi	Hyoscine Eye Ointment	*Hyoscyamus niger Linn.*
1973 p.xx	Hyoscyamus Dry Extract	*Hyoscyamus niger Linn.*
1973 p.xx	Hyoscyamus Liquid Extract	*Hyoscyamus niger Linn.*
1988 p.xxxi	Hyoscyamus Tincture	*Hyoscyamus niger Linn.*
1914 p.xxiii	Succus Hyoscyami	*Hyoscyamus niger Linn.*
1932 p.xxxii	Kaladana	*Ipomoea hederacea Jacq.*
1932 p.xxxii	Kaladanae Resina	*Ipomoea hederacea Jacq.*
1932 p.xxxii	Tinctura Kaladanae	*Ipomoea hederacea Jacq.*
1953 p.xx	Ipomoea	*Ipomoea orizabensis (Pelletan) Ledanois*
1953 p.xx	Ipomoeae Resina	*Ipomoea orizabensis (Pelletan) Ledanois*
1932 p.xxxii	Oleum Juniperi	*Juniperus communis Linn.*
1932 p.xxxii	Spiritus Juniperi	*Juniperus communis Linn.*
1963 p.xxvi	Cade Oil	*Juniperus Oxycedrus Linn.*
1953 p.xx	Extractum Krameriae Siccum	*Krameria triandra Ruiz & Pavon*
1932 p.xxxii	Infusum Krameriae	*Krameria triandra Ruiz & Pavon*
1953 p.xx	Krameria	*Krameria triandra Ruiz & Pavon*
1914 p.xxiii	Liquor Krameriae Concentratus	*Krameria triandra Ruiz & Pavon*
1948 p.xxix	Tinctura Krameriae	*Krameria triandra Ruiz & Pavon*
1953 p.xx	Trochisci Krameriae	*Krameria triandra Ruiz & Pavon*
1953 p.xx	Trochisci Krameriae et Cocainae	*Krameria triandra Ruiz & Pavon*
1932 p.xxxii	Spiritus Lavandulae	*Lavandula officinalis Chaix*
1932 p.xxxii	Tinctura Lavandulae Composita	*Lavandula officinalis Chaix*
1988 p.xxxi	Lavender Oil	*Lavandula officinalis Chaix.*
1958 p.xxiii	Lavender Oil	*Lavandula officinalis Chaix.*
1968 p.xxix	Linseed Oil	*Linum usitatissumum Linn.*
1948 p.xxix	Linum	*Linum usitatissumum Linn.*
1948 p.xxix	Linum Contusum	*Linum usitatissumum Linn.*

1993 p.xxxiv	Lobelia	*Lobelia inflata Linn.*
1948 p.xxix	Lobelia	*Lobelia inflata Linn.*
1993 p.xxxiv	Powdered Lobelia	*Lobelia inflata Linn.*
1948 p.xxix	Tinctura Lobeliae Aetherea	*Lobelia inflata Linn.*
1948 p.xxix	Tinctura Lobeliae Aetherea Concentrata	*Lobelia inflata Linn.*
1953 p.xx	Spiritus Cajuputi	*Melaleuca minor DC.*
1914 p.xxiii	Azadirachta Indica	*Melia Azadirachta Linn.*
1914 p.xxiii	Infusum Azadirachtae Indicae	*Melia Azadirachta Linn.*
1914 p.xxiii	Tinctura Azadirachtae Indicae	*Melia Azadirachta Linn.*
1948 p.xxix	Aqua Menthae Piperitae Destillata	*Mentha piperata Linn.*
1980 p.xxvii	Concentrated Peppermint Water	*Mentha piperata Linn.*
1958 p.xxiii	Emulsion of Peppermint	*Mentha piperata Linn.*
1963 p.xxvi	Peppermint Spirit	*Mentha piperata Linn.*
1932 p.xxxii	Aqua Menthae Viridis	*Mentha viridis Linn.*
1932 p.xxxii	Oleum Menthae Viridis	*Mentha viridis Linn.*
1958 p.xxiii	Nutmeg	*Myristica fragrans Houtt.*
1958 p.xxiii	Nutmeg Oil	*Myristica fragrans Houtt.*
1932 p.xxxii	Spiritus Myristiciae	*Myristica officinalis Linn.*
1953 p.xx	Balsumum Peruvianum	*Myrospermum Pereirae Royle, Mat. Med.*
1988 p.xxxi	Tolu Balsam	*Myroxylon balsamum (Linn.) Harms*
1973 p.xx	Tolu Balsam	*Myroxylon balsamum (Linn.) Harms*
1973 p.xx	Tolu Syrup	*Myroxylon balsamum (Linn.) Harms*
1948 p.xxix	Assafoetida	*Narthex Assafoetida Falconer*
1948 p.xxix	Tinctura Assafoetidae	*Narthex Assafoetida Falconer*
1885 vol. I/p.xxii	Enema Tabaci	*Nicotiana Tabacum Linn.*
1980 p.xxvii	Olive Oil	*Olea europaea Linn.*
1932 p.xxxii	Infusum Chiratae	*Ophelia Chirata DC.*
1914 p.xxiii	Liquor Chiratae Concentratus	*Ophelia Chirata DC.*
1932 p.xxxii	Tinctura Chiratae	*Ophelia Chirata DC.*
1932 p.xxxii	Rhoeados Petala	*Papaver Rhoeas Linn.*
1932 p.xxxii	Syrupus Rhoeados	*Papaver Rhoeas Linn.*
1914 p.xxiii	Emplastrum Opii	*Papaver somniferum Linn.*
1932 p.xxxii	Extractum Opii Liquidum	*Papaver somniferum Linn.*

1948 p.xxix	Extractum Opii Siccum	*Papaver somniferum Linn.*
1932 p.xxxii	Linimentum Opii	*Papaver somniferum Linn.*
1914 p.xxiii	Papaveris Capsulae	*Papaver somniferum Linn.*
1993 p.xxxiv	Prepared Opium	*Papaver somniferum Linn.*
1932 p.xxxii	Pulvis Opii Compositus	*Papaver somniferum Linn.*
1932 p.xxxii	Tinctura Opii Ammoniata	*Papaver somniferum Linn.*
1948 p.xxix	Tinctura Opii Camphorata Concentrata	*Papaver somniferum Linn.*
1914 p.xxiii	Extractum Physostigmatis	*Physostigma venenosum Balf.*
1914 p.xxiii	Physostigmatis Semina	*Physostigma venenosum Balf.*
1958 p.xxiii	Concentrated Infusion of Quassia	*Picraena excelsa Lindl.*
1958 p.xxiii	Infusion of Quassia	*Picraena excelsa Lindl.*
1958 p.xxiii	Quassia	*Picraena excelsa Lindl.*
1953 p.xx	Tinctura Quassiae	*Picraena excelsa Lindl.*
1948 p.xxix	Tinctura Quassiae Concentrata	*Picraena excelsa Lindl.*
1914 p.xxiii	Liquor Quassiae Concentratus	*Picreana excelsa Lindl.*
1932 p.xxxii	Extractum Picrorhizae Liquidum	*Picrorhiza Kurroa Royle*
1932 p.xxxii	Tinctura Picrorhizae	*Picrorhiza Kurroa Royle*
1914 p.xxiii	Extractum Jaborandi Liquidum	*Pilocarpus microphyllus Stapf.*
1914 p.xxiii	Jaborandi Folia	*Pilocarpus microphyllus Stapf.*
1914 p.xxiii	Tinctura Jaborandi	*Pilocarpus microphyllus Stapf.*
1932 p.xxxii	Anisi Fructus	*Pimpinella Anisum Linn.*
1932 p.xxxii	Aqua Anisi	*Pimpinella Anisum Linn.*
1932 p.xxxii	Spiritus Anisi	*Pimpinella Anisum Linn.*
1988 p.xxxi	Pumilio Pine Oil	*Pinus mugo Turra var. pumilio zenari*
1948 p.xxix	Emplastrum Colophonii	*Pinus palustris Mill.*
1914 p.xxiii	Thus Americanum	*Pinus Taeda Linn.*
1932 p.xxxii	Extractum Kavae Liquidum	*Piper methysticum Forst.*
1932 p.xxxii	Kavae Rhizoma	*Piper methysticum Forst.*
1932 p.xxxii	Confectio Piperis	*Piper Nigrum Linn.*
1914 p.xxiii	Piper Nigrum	*Piper Nigrum Linn.*
1932 p.xxxii	Decoctum Ispaghulae	*Plantago ovata Forsk.*
1932 p.xxxii	Ispaghula	*Plantago ovata Forsk.*
1953 p.xx	Podophyllum	*Podophyllum peltatum Linn.*
1932 p.xxxii	Tinctura Podophylli	*Podophyllum peltatum Linn.*
1988 p.xxxi	Concentrated Senega Infusion	*Polygala Senaga Linn.*
1953 p.xx	Extractum Senegae Liquidum	*Polygala Senaga Linn.*

1953 p.xx	Infusum Senegae	*Polygala Senaga Linn.*
1953 p.xx	Infusum Senegae Concentratum	*Polygala Senaga Linn.*
1948 p.xxix	Infusum Senegae Recens	*Polygala Senaga Linn.*
1953 p.xx	Senega	*Polygala Senaga Linn.*
1988 p.xxxi	Senega Liquid Extract	*Polygala Senaga Linn.*
1953 p.xx	Tinctura Senegae	*Polygala Senaga Linn.*
1914 p.xxiii	Liquor Senegae Concentratus	*Polygala Senega Linn.*
1958 p.xxiii	Volatile Bitter Almond Oil	*Prunus amygdalus Batsch. Var. amara (D.C.) Focke*
1914 p.xxiii	Prunum	*Prunus domestica Linn.*
1932 p.xxxii	Tinctura Pruni Virginianae	*Prunus domestica Linn.*
1932 p.xxxii	Aqua Laurocerasi	*Prunus Laurocerasus Linn.*
1932 p.xxxii	Laurocerasi Folia	*Prunus Laurocerasus Linn.*
1953 p.xx	Prunus Serotina	*Prunus serotina Ehrh.*
1953 p.xx	Syrupus Pruni Serotinae	*Prunus serotina Ehrh.*
1988 p.xxxi	Wild Cherry Bark	*Prunus serotina Ehrh.*
1988 p.xxxi	Wild Cherry Syrup	*Prunus serotina Ehrh.*
1932 p.xxxii	Kino	*Pterocarpus Marsupium DC.*
1932 p.xxxii	Kino Eucalypti	*Pterocarpus Marsupium DC.*
1932 p.xxxii	Pulvis Kino Compositus	*Pterocarpus Marsupium DC.*
1932 p.xxxii	Tinctura Kino	*Pterocarpus Marsupium DC.*
1932 p.xxxii	Trochiscus Kino Eucalypti	*Pterocarpus Marsupium DC.*
1914 p.xxiii	Decoctum Granati Corticis	*Punica Granatum Linn.*
1914 p.xxiii	Granati Cortex	*Punica Granatum Linn.*
1958 p.xxiii	Liquid Extract of Quillaia	*Quillaia Saponaria Molina*
1948 p.xxix	Tinctura Quilliae	*Quillaia Saponaria Molina*
1885 vol. I/p.xxii	Syrupus Rhamni	*Rhamnus catharticus Linn.*
1993 p.xxxiv	Cascara Elixir	*Rhamnus Purshianus DC.*
1973 p.xx	Cascara Elixir	*Rhamnus Purshianus DC.*
1988 p.xxxi	Cascara Liquid Extract	*Rhamnus Purshianus DC.*
1958 p.xxiii	Compound Powder of Rhubarb	*Rheum sp. Linn.*
1993 p.xxxiv	Compound Rhubarb Mixture	*Rheum sp. Linn.*
1988 p.xxxi	Compound Rhubarb Oral Powder	*Rheum sp. Linn.*
1953 p.xx	Pilula Rhei Composita	*Rheum sp. Linn.*
1932 p.xxxii	extractum Rhei	*Rheum spp. Linn.*
1932 p.xxxii	Infusum Rhei	*Rheum spp. Linn.*
1914 p.xxiii	Liquor Rhei Concentratus	*Rheum spp. Linn.*

1932 p.xxxii	Syrupus Rhei	*Rheum spp. Linn.*
1932 p.xxxii	Mistura Olei Ricini	*Ricinus communis Linn.*
1932 p.xxxii	Aqua Rosae	*Rosa damascena Mill.*
1932 p.xxxii	Oleum Rosae	*Rosa damascena Mill.*
1932 p.xxxii	Unguentum Aquae Rosae	*Rosa damascena Mill.*
1932 p.xxxii	Confectio Rosae Gallicae	*Rosa gallica Linn.*
1932 p.xxxii	Infusum Rosae Acidum	*Rosa gallica Linn.*
1932 p.xxxii	Rosa Gallica Petala	*Rosa gallica Linn.*
1932 p.xxxii	Syrupus Rosae	*Rosa gallica Linn.*
1963 p.xxvi	Rosemary Oil	*Rosmarinus officinalis Linn.*
1932 p.xxxii	Spiritus Rosmarini	*Rosmarinus officinalis Linn.*
1993 p.xxxiv	Concentrated Raspberry Jiuce	*Rubus idaeus Linn.*
1993 p.xxxiv	Raspberry Syrup	*Rubus idaeus Linn.*
1948 p.xxix	Salicinum	*Salix spp.*
1914 p.xxiii	Aqua Sambuci	*Sambucus nigra Linn.*
1914 p.xxiii	Sambuci Flores	*Sambucus nigra Linn.*
1948 p.xxix	Oleum Santali	*Santalum album Linn.*
1932 p.xxxii	Infusum Scoparii	*Sarothamnus Scoparius Wimmer.*
1932 p.xxxii	Succus Scoparii	*Sarothamnus Scoparius Wimmer.*
1914 p.xxiii	Sassafras Radix	*Sassafras officinale Nees, Laurineae*
1953 p.xx	Ergota	*Secale cereale Linn.*
1953 p.xx	Ergota Praeparata	*Secale cereale Linn.*
1932 p.xxxii	Extractum Ergotae	*Secale cereale Linn.*
1953 p.xx	Extractum Ergotae liquidum	*Secale cereale Linn.*
1953 p.xx	Tabellae Ergotae Praeparatae	*Secale cereale Linn.*
1973 p.xx	Sesame Oil	*Sesamum indicum Linn.*
1914 p.xxiii	Sinapis Albae Semina	*Sinapis alba Linn.*
1914 p.xxiii	Sinapis Nigrae Semina	*Sinapis nigra Linn.*
1914 p.xxiii	Sinapis	*Sinapis nigra Linn. & S. alba Linn.*
1914 p.xxiii	Extractum Sarsae Liquidum	*Smilax officinalis Humb. & Bonpl.*
1914 p.xxiii	Liquor Sarsae Compositus Concentratus	*Smilax officinalis Humb. & Bonpl.*
1914 p.xxiii	Sarsae Radix	*Smilax officinalis Humb. & Bonpl.*
1885 vol. I/p.xxii	Dulcamara	*Solanum Dulcamara Linn.*
1885 vol. I/p.xxii	Infusum Dulcamara	*Solanum Dulcamara Linn.*
1932 p.xxxii	Unguentum Staphisagriae	*Staphisagria sp*
1932 p.xxxii	Extractum Strophanthi	*Strophanthus kombe Oliver*

1948 p.xxix	Strophanthinum	*Strophanthus kombe Oliver*
1953 p.xx	Strophanthus	*Strophanthus kombe Oliver*
1953 p.xx	Tinctura Strophanthi	*Strophanthus kombe Oliver*
1958 p.xxiii	Dry Extract of Nux Vomica	*Strychnos Nux Vomica Linn.*
1988 p.xxxi	Nux Vomica	*Strychnos Nux Vomica Linn.*
1988 p.xxxi	Nux Vomica Liquid Extract	*Strychnos Nux Vomica Linn.*
1988 p.xxxi	Nux Vomica Tincture	*Strychnos Nux Vomica Linn.*
1958 p.xxiii	Prepared Nux Vomica	*Strychnos Nux Vomica Linn.*
1963 p.xxvi	Benzoin	*Styrax Benzoin Dryand.*
1963 p.xxvi	Compound Benzoin Tincture	*Styrax Benzoin Dryand.*
1988 p.xxxi	Siam Benzoin	*Styrax tonkinensis Craib.*
1948 p.xxix	Tamarindus	*Tamarindus indica Linn.*
1932 p.xxxii	Extractum Taraxaci	*Taraxacum Dens Leonis DC.*
1914 p.xxiii	Extractum Taraxaci Liquidum	*Taraxacum Dens Leonis DC.*
1932 p.xxxii	Succus Taraxaci	*Taraxacum Dens Leonis DC.*
1932 p.xxxii	Taraxaci Radix	*Taraxacum Dens Leonis DC.*
1885 vol. I/p.xxii	Decoctum Ulmi	*Ulmus campestris Linn.*
1885 vol. I/p.xxii	Ulmi Cortex	*Ulmus campestris Linn.*
1914 p.xxiii	Galbanum	*Umbelliferous plant?*
1914 p.xxiii	Pilula Galbani Composita	*Umbelliferous plant?*
1932 p.xxxii	Pulvis Catechu Compositus	*Uncaria Gambier (Hunter) Roxb.*
1932 p.xxxii	Tinctura Urgineae	*Urginea indica Kunth.*
1932 p.xxxii	Syrupus Urgineae	*Urginea indica Kunth.*
1948 p.xxix	Extractum Scillae Liquidum	*Urginea Scilla Steinheil.*
1932 p.xxxii	Pilula Scillae Composita	*Urginea Scilla Steinheil.*
1988 p.xxxi	Squill Elixir	*Urginea Scilla Steinheil.*
1988 p.xxxi	Squill Tincture	*Urginea Scilla Steinheil.*
1988 p.xxxi	Squill Vinegar	*Urginea Scilla Steinheil.*
1953 p.xx	Syrupus Scillae	*Urginea Scilla Steinheil.*
1953 p.xx	Tinctura Scillae	*Urginea Scilla Steinheil.*
1948 p.xxix	Urginea	*Urginea Scilla Steinheil.*
1953 p.xx	Scilla	*Urginea Scilla Steinheil.*
1953 p.xx	Tinctura Valerianae Ammoniata	*Valeriana officinalis Linn.*
1948 p.xxix	Tinctura Valerianae Ammoniata Concentrata	*Valeriana officinalis Linn.*
1932 p.xxxii	Tinctura Valerianae Indicae Ammoniata	*Valeriana officinalis Linn.*
1953 p.xx	Valeriana	*Valeriana officinalis Linn.*

1948 p.xxix	Valeriana Indica	*Valeriana officinalis Linn.*
1932 p.xxxii	Valerianae Indicae Rhizoma	*Valeriana officinalis Linn.*
1932 p.xxxii	Extractum Viburni Liquidum	*Viburnum prunifolium Linn.*
1932 p.xxxii	Viburnum	*Viburnum prunifolium Linn.*
1968 p.xxix	Ginger Syrup	*Zingiber officinale Roscoe*
1914 p.xxiii	Infusum Tinosporae	
1914 p.xxiii	Infusum Toddaliae	
1914 p.xxiii	Tinctura Tinosporae	
1914 p.xxiii	Tinospora	
1914 p.xxiii	Toddalia	
1914 p.xxiii	Tylophorae Folia	
1932 p.xxxii	Unguentum Hamamelidis	

Table V: Deletions of plant entries from the British Pharmacopoeia between 1864 and 1993
Species name chronological (522 entries)

Year of deletion, Vol. & Page no.	Index name	Species name	No. of species deleted this year
1867 p. xviii	Catechu Nigrum	*Acacia Catechu Willd. Enum.*	
1867 p. xviii	Cocculus	*Anamirta Cocculus Wight & Arnott*	
1867 p. xviii	Unguentum Cocculus	*Anamirta Cocculus Wight & Arnott*	2
1885 vol. I/p.xxii	Areca	*Areca Catechu Linn.*	
1885 vol. I/p.xxii	Liquor Atropiae	*Atropa Belladonna Linn.*	
1885 vol. I/p.xxii	Stramonii Folia	*Datura Stramonium Linn.*	
1885 vol. I/p.xxii	Digitalinum	*Digitalis purpurea Linn.*	
1885 vol. I/p.xxii	Mistura Gentianae	*Gentiana lutea Linn.*	
1885 vol. I/p.xxii	Enema Tabaci	*Nicotiana Tabacum Linn.*	
1885 vol. I/p.xxii	Syrupus Rhamni	*Rhamnus catharticus Linn.*	
1885 vol. I/p.xxii	Dulcamara	*Solanum Dulcamara Linn.*	
1885 vol. I/p.xxii	Infusum Dulcamara	*Solanum Dulcamara Linn.*	

1885 vol. I/p.xxii	Decoctum Ulmi	*Ulmus campestris Linn.*	
1885 vol. I/p.xxii	Ulmi Cortex	*Ulmus campestris Linn.*	9
1914 p.xxiii	Succus Acalyphae	*Acalypha indica Linn.*	
1914 p.xxiii	Tinctura Aloes	*Aloe spp.*	
1914 p.xxiii	Tinctura Andrographidis	*Andrographis paniculata Nees.*	
1914 p.xxiii	Liquor Andrographidis Concentratus	*Andrographis paniculata Nees*	
1914 p.xxiii	Infusum Andrographidis	*Andrographis paniculata Nees.*	
1914 p.xxiii	Extractum Anthemidis	*Anthemis nobilis Linn.*	
1914 p.xxiii	Aristolochia	*Aristolochia indica Linn.*	
1914 p.xxiii	Infusum Serpentariae	*Aristolochia Serpentaria Linn.*	
1914 p.xxiii	Liquor Aristolochiae Concentratus	*Aristolochia Serpentaria Linn.*	
1914 p.xxiii	Liquor Serpentariae Concentratus	*Aristolochia Serpentaria Linn.*	
1914 p.xxiii	Tinctura Aristolochiae	*Aristolochia Serpentaria Linn.*	
1914 p.xxiii	Arnicae Rhizoma	*Arnica montana Linn.*	
1914 p.xxiii	Tinctura Arnicae	*Arnica montana Linn.*	
1914 p.xxiii	Extractum Belladonnae Viride	*Atropa Belladonna Linn.*	
1914 p.xxiii	Succus Belladonnae	*Atropa Belladonna Linn.*	
1914 p.xxiii	Liquor Berberidis Concentratus	*Berberis vulgare Linn.*	
1914 p.xxiii	Calotropis	*Calotropis procera Ait.*	
1914 p.xxiii	Tinctura Calotropis	*Calotropis procera Ait.*	
1914 p.xxiii	Liquor Sennae Concentratus	*Cassia elongata Lemaire*	
1914 p.xxiii	Cimicifugae Rhizoma	*Cimicifuga racemosa Nutt.*	
1914 p.xxiii	Extractum Cimicifugae Liquidum	*Cimicifuga racemosa Nutt.*	
1914 p.xxiii	Tinctora Cimicifugae	*Cimicifuga racemosa Nutt.*	
1914 p.xxiii	Extractum Cissampeli Liquidum	*Cissampelos Pareira Linn.*	

1914 p.xxiii	Extractum Pareirae Liquidum	*Cissampelos Pareira Linn.*	
1914 p.xxiii	Pareirae Radix	*Cissampelos Pareira Linn.*	
1914 p.xxiii	Liquor Calumbae Concentratus	*Cocculus palmatus DC.*	
1914 p.xxiii	Conii Folia	*Conium maculata Linn.*	
1914 p.xxiii	Conii Fructus	*Conium maculata Linn.*	
1914 p.xxiii	Succus Conii	*Conium maculata Linn.*	
1914 p.xxiii	Tinctura Conii	*Conium maculata Linn.*	
1914 p.xxiii	Unguentum Conii	*Conium maculata Linn.*	
1914 p.xxiii	Pilula Scammonii Composita	*Convolvulus Scammonia Linn.*	
1914 p.xxiii	Scammonium	*Convolvulus Scammonia Linn.*	
1914 p.xxiii	Coscinium	*Coscinium fenestratum Colebr.*	
1914 p.xxiii	Infusum Coscinii	*Coscinium fenestratum Colebr.*	
1914 p.xxiii	Liquor Coscinii Concentratus	*Coscinium fenestratum Colebr.*	
1914 p.xxiii	Tinctura Coscinii	*Coscinium fenestratum Colebr.*	
1914 p.xxiii	Crocus	*Crocus sativum Linn.*	
1914 p.xxiii	Cuspariae Cortex	*Crocus sativum Linn.*	
1914 p.xxiii	Tinctura Croci	*Crocus sativum Linn.*	
1914 p.xxiii	Mezerei Cortex	*Daphne Mezereum Linn.*	
1914 p.xxiii	Stramonii Semina	*Datura Stramonium Linn.*	
1914 p.xxiii	Elaterium	*Ecbalium officinarum Richard*	
1914 p.xxiii	Pulvis Elaterini Compositus	*Ecbalium officinarum Richard*	
1914 p.xxiii	Cocae Folia	*Erythroxylum coca Lam.*	
1914 p.xxiii	Extractum Cocae Liquidum	*Erythroxylum coca Lam.*	
1914 p.xxiii	Aqua Pimentae	*Eugenia Pimenta DC.*	
1914 p.xxiii	Oleum Pimentae	*Eugenia Pimenta DC.*	
1914 p.xxiii	Pimenta	*Eugenia Pimenta DC.*	

1914 p.xxiii	Extractum Jalapae	*Exogonium Purga Bentham*	
1914 p.xxiii	Sumbul Radix	*Ferula Sumbul Hook.*	
1914 p.xxiii	Tinctura Sumbul	*Ferula Sumbul Hook.*	
1914 p.xxiii	Ficus	*Ficus Carica Linn.*	
1914 p.xxiii	Infusum Cuspariae	*Galipea Cusparia DC.*	
1914 p.xxiii	Liquor Cuspariae Concentratus	*Galipea Cusparia DC.*	
1914 p.xxiii	Cambogia	*Garcinia Linn.*	
1914 p.xxiii	Cambogia Indica	*Garcinia Linn.*	
1914 p.xxiii	Pilula Cambogiae Composita	*Garcinia Linn.*	
1914 p.xxiii	Extractum Glycyrrhizae Spirituosum	*Glycyrrhiza glabra Linn.*	
1914 p.xxiii	Hemidesmi Radix	*Hemidesmus indicus DC.*	
1914 p.xxiii	Syrupus Hemidesmi	*Hemidesmus indicus DC.*	
1914 p.xxiii	Liquor Caoutchouc	*Hevea brasiliensis Muell.*	
1914 p.xxiii	Infusum Lupuli	*Humulus Lupulus Linn.*	
1914 p.xxiii	Lupulus	*Humulus Lupulus Linn.*	
1914 p.xxiii	Tinctura Lupuli	*Humulus Lupulus Linn.*	
1914 p.xxiii	Succus Hyoscyami	*Hyoscyamus niger Linn.*	
1914 p.xxiii	Liquor Krameriae Concentratus	*Krameria triandra Ruiz & Pavon*	
1914 p.xxiii	Azadirachta Indica	*Melia Azadirachta Linn.*	
1914 p.xxiii	Infusum Azadirachtae Indicae	*Melia Azadirachta Linn.*	
1914 p.xxiii	Tinctura Azadirachtae Indicae	*Melia Azadirachta Linn.*	
1914 p.xxiii	Liquor Chiratae Concentratus	*Ophelia Chirata DC.*	
1914 p.xxiii	Emplastrum Opii	*Papaver somniferum Linn.*	
1914 p.xxiii	Papaveris Capsulae	*Papaver somniferum Linn.*	
1914 p.xxiii	Extractum Physostigmatis	*Physostigma venenosum Balf.*	
1914 p.xxiii	Physostigmatis Semina	*Physostigma venenosum Balf.*	

1914 p.xxiii	Liquor Quassiae Concentratus	*Picreana excelsa Lindl.*	
1914 p.xxiii	Extractum Jaborandi Liquidum	*Pilocarpus microphyllus Stapf.*	
1914 p.xxiii	Jaborandi Folia	*Pilocarpus microphyllus Stapf.*	
1914 p.xxiii	Tinctura Jaborandi	*Pilocarpus microphyllus Stapf.*	
1914 p.xxiii	Thus Americanum	*Pinus Taeda Linn.*	
1914 p.xxiii	Piper Nigrum	*Piper Nigrum Linn.*	
1914 p.xxiii	Liquor Senegae Concentratus	*Polygala Senega Linn.*	
1914 p.xxiii	Prunum	*Prunus domestica Linn.*	
1914 p.xxiii	Decoctum Granati Corticis	*Punica Granatum Linn.*	
1914 p.xxiii	Granati Cortex	*Punica Granatum Linn.*	
1914 p.xxiii	Liquor Rhei Concentratus	*Rheum spp. Linn.*	
1914 p.xxiii	Aqua Sambuci	*Sambucus nigra Linn.*	
1914 p.xxiii	Sambuci Flores	*Sambucus nigra Linn.*	
1914 p.xxiii	Sassafras Radix	*Sassafras officinale Nees, Laurineae*	
1914 p.xxiii	Sinapis Albae Semina	*Sinapis alba Linn.*	
1914 p.xxiii	Sinapis Nigrae Semina	*Sinapis nigra Linn.*	
1914 p.xxiii	Sinapis	*Sinapis nigra Linn. & S. alba Linn.*	
1914 p.xxiii	Extractum Sarsae Liquidum	*Smilax officinalis Humb. & Bonpl.*	
1914 p.xxiii	Liquor Sarsae Compositus Concentratus	*Smilax officinalis Humb. & Bonpl.*	
1914 p.xxiii	Sarsae Radix	*Smilax officinalis Humb. & Bonpl.*	
1914 p.xxiii	Extractum Taraxaci Liquidum	*Taraxacum Dens Leonis DC.*	
1914 p.xxiii	Galbanum	*Umbelliferous plant?*	
1914 p.xxiii	Pilula Galbani Composita	*Umbelliferous plant?*	
1914 p.xxiii	Infusum Tinosporae		
1914 p.xxiii	Infusum Toddaliae		

1914 p.xxiii	Tinctura Tinosporae		
1914 p.xxiii	Tinospora		
1914 p.xxiii	Toddalia		
1914 p.xxiii	Tylophorae Folia		57
1932 p.xxxii	Terebinthina Canadensis	*Abies balsamea Aiton, Hort. Kew*	
1932 p.xxxii	Decoctum Acaciae Corticis	*Acacia arabica Willd.*	
1932 p.xxxii	Catechu Nigrum	*Acacia Catechu Willd. Enum.*	
1932 p.xxxii	Trochiscus Catechu	*Acacia Catechu Willd. Enum.*	
1932 p.xxxii	Acaciae Cortex	*Acacia Linn.*	
1932 p.xxxii	Tinctura Aconiti	*Aconitum napellus Linn.*	
1932 p.xxxii	Unguentum Aconitinae	*Aconitum napellus Linn.*	
1932 p.xxxii	Belae Fructus	*Aegle Marmelos Correa*	
1932 p.xxxii	Extractum Belae Liquidum	*Aegle Marmelos Correa*	
1932 p.xxxii	Agropyrum	*Agropyrum repens Beauvois*	
1932 p.xxxii	Decoctum Agropyri	*Agropyrum repens Beauvois*	
1932 p.xxxii	Extractum Agropyri Liquidum	*Agropyrum repens Beauvois*	
1932 p.xxxii	Pilula Aloes et Myrrhae	*Aloe sp. & Balsamodendron Myrrha Ehren.*	
1932 p.xxxii	Decoctum Aloes Compositum	*Aloe spp.*	
1932 p.xxxii	Extractum Aloes	*Aloe spp.*	
1932 p.xxxii	Alstonia	*Alstonia scholaris R. Br.*	
1932 p.xxxii	Infusum Alstoniae	*Alstonia scholaris R. Br.*	
1932 p.xxxii	Tinctura Alstoniae	*Alstonia scholaris R. Br.*	
1932 p.xxxii	Amygdala Amara	*Amygdala communis var dulcis DC*	
1932 p.xxxii	Amygdala Dulcis	*Amygdala communis var dulcis DC*	
1932 p.xxxii	Mistura Amygdalae	*Amygdala communis var dulcis DC*	

1932 p.xxxii	Pulvis Amygdalae Compositus	*Amygdala communis var dulcis DC*	
1932 p.xxxii	Pyrethri Radix	*Anacyclus Pyrethrum DC.*	
1932 p.xxxii	Tinctura Pyrethri	*Anacyclus Pyrethrum DC.*	
1932 p.xxxii	Mucilago Gummi Indici	*Anogeissus latifolia Wall.*	
1932 p.xxxii	Anthemidis Flores	*Anthemis nobilis Linn.*	
1932 p.xxxii	Oleum Anthemidis	*Anthemis nobilis Linn.*	
1932 p.xxxii	Infusum Uvae Ursi	*Arctostaphylos Uva Ursi Spreng. Syst.*	
1932 p.xxxii	Uvae Ursi Folia	*Arctostaphylos Uva Ursi Spreng. Syst.*	
1932 p.xxxii	Tinctura Serpentariae	*Aristolochia Serpentaria Linn.*	
1932 p.xxxii	Arnicae Flores	*Arnica montana Linn.*	
1932 p.xxxii	Tinctura Arnicae Florum	*Arnica montana Linn.*	
1932 p.xxxii	Trochiscus Santonini	*Artemisia cina Berg*	
1932 p.xxxii	Unguentum Belladonnae	*Atropa Belladonna Linn.*	
1932 p.xxxii	Tinctura Buchu	*Barosma betulina (Thunb.) Bartl. & Wendl.*	
1932 p.xxxii	Berberis	*Berberis vulgare Linn.*	
1932 p.xxxii	Tinctura Berberis	*Berberis vulgare Linn.*	
1932 p.xxxii	Linimentum Sinapis	*Brassica nigra (Linn.) Koch*	
1932 p.xxxii	Oleum Sinapis Volatile	*Brassica nigra (Linn.) Koch*	
1932 p.xxxii	Cusso	*Brayera anthelmintica DC.*	
1932 p.xxxii	Butae Gummi	*Butea frondosa Roxb.*	
1932 p.xxxii	Butae Semina	*Butea frondosa Roxb.*	
1932 p.xxxii	Pulvis Butae Seminum	*Butea frondosa Roxb.*	
1932 p.xxxii	Cannabis Indica	*Cannabis sativa Linn.*	
1932 p.xxxii	Extractum Cannabis Indicae	*Cannabis sativa Linn.*	
1932 p.xxxii	Tinctura Cannabis Indicae	*Cannabis sativa Linn.*	

1932 p.xxxii	Aqua Carui	*Carum Carui Linn.*	
1932 p.xxxii	Tinctura Sennae Composita	*Cassia acutifolia Delile*	
1932 p.xxxii	Cassiae Fructus	*Cassia Fistula Linn.*	
1932 p.xxxii	Trochiscus Ipecacuanhae	*Cephaelis Ipecacuanha DC.*	
1932 p.xxxii	Vinum Ipecacuanhae	*Cephaelis Ipecacuanha DC.*	
1932 p.xxxii	pilula Ipecacuanhae cum Urginea	*Cephaelis Ipecacuanha DC. & Urginea indica Kunth.*	
1932 p.xxxii	Pilula Ipecacuanhae cum Scilla	*Cephaelis Ipecacuanha DC. & urginea Scilla Steinh.*	
1932 p.xxxii	Infusum Cinchonae Acidum	*Chinchona sp.*	
1932 p.xxxii	Tinctura Quininae	*Chinchona sp.*	
1932 p.xxxii	Oliveri Cortex	*Cinnamomum Oliveri Bailey*	
1932 p.xxxii	Tinctura Oliveri Corticis	*Cinnamomum Oliveri Bailey*	
1932 p.xxxii	Pulvis Cinnamomi Compositus	*Cinnamomum zeylandicum Nees, Laurineae*	
1932 p.xxxii	Spiritus Cinnamomi	*Cinnamomum zeylandicum Nees, Laurineae*	
1932 p.xxxii	Tinctura Cinnamomi	*Cinnamomum zeylandicum Nees, Laurineae*	
1932 p.xxxii	Aqua Aurantii Floris	*Citrus Bigaradia Risso*	
1932 p.xxxii	Aurantii Cortex Indicus	*Citrus Bigaradia Risso*	
1932 p.xxxii	Infusum Aurantii Compositum	*Citrus Bigaradia Risso*	
1932 p.xxxii	Syrupus Aurantii Floris	*Citrus Bigaradia Risso*	
1932 p.xxxii	Vinum Aurantii	*Citrus Bigaradia Risso*	
1932 p.xxxii	Succus Limonis	*Citrus Limonum DC.*	
1932 p.xxxii	Infusum Ergotae	*Claviceps purpurea Tulasne*	
1932 p.xxxii	Injectio Ergotae Hypodermica	*Claviceps purpurea Tulasne*	

1932 p.xxxii	Tinctura Ergotae Ammoniata	*Claviceps purpurea Tulasne*	
1932 p.xxxii	Armoraciae Radix	*Cochlearia Armoracia Linn.*	
1932 p.xxxii	Spiritus Armoraciae Compositus	*Cochlearia Armoracia Linn.*	
1932 p.xxxii	Extractum Colchici	*Colchicum autumnale Linn.*	
1932 p.xxxii	Vinum Colchici	*Colchicum autumnale Linn.*	
1932 p.xxxii	Pulvis Scammoniae Compositus	*Convolvulus Scammonia Linn.*	
1932 p.xxxii	Scammoniae Radix	*Convolvulus Scammonia Linn.*	
1932 p.xxxii	Oleum Copaibae	*Copaifera multijuga Hayne*	
1932 p.xxxii	Infusum Cascarillae	*Croton Eluteria Bennett*	
1932 p.xxxii	Tinctura Cascarillae	*Croton Eluteria Bennett*	
1932 p.xxxii	Linimentum Crotonis	*Croton Tiglium Linn.*	
1932 p.xxxii	Oleum Crotonis	*Croton tiglium Linn.*	
1932 p.xxxii	Cubebae Fructus	*Cubeba officinalis Miquel*	
1932 p.xxxii	Oleum Cubebae	*Cubeba officinalis Miquel*	
1932 p.xxxii	Tinctura Cubebae	*Cubeba officinalis Miquel*	
1932 p.xxxii	Cucurbitae Semina Praeparat	*Cucurbita maxima Duchesne*	
1932 p.xxxii	Oleum Graminis Citrati	*Cymbopogon citratus Staph.*	
1932 p.xxxii	Daturae Folia	*Datura Metel Linn.*	
1932 p.xxxii	Daturae Semina	*Datura Metel Linn.*	
1932 p.xxxii	Tinctura Daturae Seminum	*Datura Metel Linn.*	
1932 p.xxxii	Staphagriae Semina	*Delphinium Staphisagria Linn.*	
1932 p.xxxii	Embelia	*Embelia Ribes Burm. F.*	
1932 p.xxxii	Unguentum Eucalypti	*Eucalyptus polybractea R.T. Baker*	
1932 p.xxxii	Euonymi Cortex	*Euonymus atropurpureus Jacq.*	
1932 p.xxxii	Extractum Euonymi	*Euonymus atropurpureus Jacq.*	

1932 p.xxxii	Jalapae resina	*Exogonium Purga Bentham*	
1932 p.xxxii	Tinctura Jalapae	*Exogonium Purga Bentham*	
1932 p.xxxii	Tinctura Jalapae Composita	*Exogonium Purga Bentham*	
1932 p.xxxii	Aqua Foeniculi	*Foeniculum dulce DC.*	
1932 p.xxxii	Galla	*from Quercus infectoria Olivier*	
1932 p.xxxii	Unguentum Gallae	*from Quercus infectoria Olivier*	
1932 p.xxxii	Umguentum Gallae cum Opio	*from Quercus infectoria Olivier & Papaver somniferum Linn.*	
1932 p.xxxii	Oleum Gaultheriae	*Gaultheria procumbens Linn.*	
1932 p.xxxii	Gelsemii Radix	*Gelsemium sempervirens Ait.*	
1932 p.xxxii	Tinctura Gelsemii	*Gelsemium sempervirens Ait.*	
1932 p.xxxii	Decoctum Gossypii Radicis Corticis	*Gossypium herbaceum Linn.*	
1932 p.xxxii	Extractum Gossypii Radicis Corticis Liquidum	*Gossypium herbaceum Linn.*	
1932 p.xxxii	Gossypii Radicis Cortex	*Gossypium herbaceum Linn.*	
1932 p.xxxii	Gossypium	*Gossypium herbaceum Linn.*	
1932 p.xxxii	Extractum Grindeliae Liquidum	*Grindelia camporum Greene*	
1932 p.xxxii	Grindelia	*Grindelia camporum Greene*	
1932 p.xxxii	Guaiaci Lignum	*Guaiacum officinale Linn.*	
1932 p.xxxii	Guaiaci Resina	*Guaiacum officinale Linn.*	
1932 p.xxxii	Mistura Guaiaci	*Guaiacum officinale Linn.*	
1932 p.xxxii	Tinctura Guaiaci Ammoniata	*Guaiacum officinale Linn.*	

1932 p.xxxii	Trochiscus Guaiaci Resinae	*Guaiacum officinale Linn.*	
1932 p.xxxii	Hamamelidis Cortex	*Hamamelis virginiana Linn.*	
1932 p.xxxii	Liquor Hamamelidis	*Hamamelis virginiana Linn.*	
1932 p.xxxii	Tinctura Hamamelidis	*Hamamelis virginiana Linn.*	
1932 p.xxxii	Extractum Hydrastis Liquidum	*Hydrastis canadensis Linn.*	
1932 p.xxxii	Hydrastis Rhizoma	*Hydrastis canadensis Linn.*	
1932 p.xxxii	Tinctura Hydrastis	*Hydrastis canadensis Linn.*	
1932 p.xxxii	Kaladana	*Ipomoea hederacea Jacq.*	
1932 p.xxxii	Kaladanae Resina	*Ipomoea hederacea Jacq.*	
1932 p.xxxii	Tinctura Kaladanae	*Ipomoea hederacea Jacq.*	
1932 p.xxxii	Oleum Juniperi	*Juniperus communis Linn.*	
1932 p.xxxii	Spiritus Juniperi	*Juniperus communis Linn.*	
1932 p.xxxii	Infusum Krameriae	*Krameria triandra Ruiz & Pavon*	
1932 p.xxxii	Spiritus Lavandulae	*Lavandula officinalis Chaix*	
1932 p.xxxii	Tinctura Lavandulae Composita	*Lavandula officinalis Chaix*	
1932 p.xxxii	Aqua Menthae Viridis	*Mentha viridis Linn.*	
1932 p.xxxii	Oleum Menthae Viridis	*Mentha viridis Linn.*	
1932 p.xxxii	Spiritus Myristiciae	*Myristica officinalis Linn.*	
1932 p.xxxii	Infusum Chiratae	*Ophelia Chirata DC.*	
1932 p.xxxii	Tinctura Chiratae	*Ophelia Chirata DC.*	
1932 p.xxxii	Rhoeados Petala	*Papaver Rhoeas Linn.*	
1932 p.xxxii	Syrupus Rhoeados	*Papaver Rhoeas Linn.*	
1932 p.xxxii	Extractum Opii Liquidum	*Papaver somniferum Linn.*	
1932 p.xxxii	Linimentum Opii	*Papaver somniferum Linn.*	
1932 p.xxxii	Pulvis Opii Compositus	*Papaver somniferum Linn.*	

1932 p.xxxii	Tinctura Opii Ammoniata	*Papaver somniferum Linn.*	
1932 p.xxxii	Extractum Picrorhizae Liquidum	*Picrorhiza Kurroa Royle*	
1932 p.xxxii	Tinctura Picrorhizae	*Picrorhiza Kurroa Royle*	
1932 p.xxxii	Anisi Fructus	*Pimpinella Anisum Linn.*	
1932 p.xxxii	Aqua Anisi	*Pimpinella Anisum Linn.*	
1932 p.xxxii	Spiritus Anisi	*Pimpinella Anisum Linn.*	
1932 p.xxxii	Extractum Kavae Liquidum	*Piper methysticum Forst.*	
1932 p.xxxii	Kavae Rhizoma	*Piper methysticum Forst.*	
1932 p.xxxii	Confectio Piperis	*Piper Nigrum Linn.*	
1932 p.xxxii	Decoctum Ispaghulae	*Plantago ovata Forsk.*	
1932 p.xxxii	Ispaghula	*Plantago ovata Forsk.*	
1932 p.xxxii	Tinctura Podophylli	*Podophyllum peltatum Linn.*	
1932 p.xxxii	Tinctura Pruni Virginianae	*Prunus domestica Linn.*	
1932 p.xxxii	Aqua Laurocerasi	*Prunus Laurocerasus Linn.*	
1932 p.xxxii	Laurocerasi Folia	*Prunus Laurocerasus Linn.*	
1932 p.xxxii	Kino	*Pterocarpus Marsupium DC.*	
1932 p.xxxii	Kino Eucalypti	*Pterocarpus Marsupium DC.*	
1932 p.xxxii	Pulvis Kino Compositus	*Pterocarpus Marsupium DC.*	
1932 p.xxxii	Tinctura Kino	*Pterocarpus Marsupium DC.*	
1932 p.xxxii	Trochiscus Kino Eucalypti	*Pterocarpus Marsupium DC.*	
1932 p.xxxii	extractum Rhei	*Rheum spp. Linn.*	
1932 p.xxxii	Infusum Rhei	*Rheum spp. Linn.*	
1932 p.xxxii	Syrupus Rhei	*Rheum spp. Linn.*	
1932 p.xxxii	Mistura Olei Ricini	*Ricinus communis Linn.*	
1932 p.xxxii	Aqua Rosae	*Rosa damascena Mill.*	

1932 p.xxxii	Oleum Rosae	*Rosa damascena Mill.*	
1932 p.xxxii	Unguentum Aquae Rosae	*Rosa damascena Mill.*	
1932 p.xxxii	Confectio Rosae Gallicae	*Rosa gallica Linn.*	
1932 p.xxxii	Infusum Rosae Acidum	*Rosa gallica Linn.*	
1932 p.xxxii	Rosa Gallica Petala	*Rosa gallica Linn.*	
1932 p.xxxii	Syrupus Rosae	*Rosa gallica Linn.*	
1932 p.xxxii	Spiritus Rosmarini	*Rosmarinus officinalis Linn.*	
1932 p.xxxii	Infusum Scoparii	*Sarothamnus Scoparius Wimmer.*	
1932 p.xxxii	Succus Scoparii	*Sarothamnus Scoparius Wimmer.*	
1932 p.xxxii	Extractum Ergotae	*Secale cereale Linn.*	
1932 p.xxxii	Unguentum Staphisagriae	*Staphisagria sp*	
1932 p.xxxii	Extractum Strophanthi	*Strophanthus kombe Oliver*	
1932 p.xxxii	Extractum Taraxaci	*Taraxacum Dens Leonis DC.*	
1932 p.xxxii	Succus Taraxaci	*Taraxacum Dens Leonis DC.*	
1932 p.xxxii	Taraxaci Radix	*Taraxacum Dens Leonis DC.*	
1932 p.xxxii	Pulvis Catechu Compositus	*Uncaria Gambier (Hunter) Roxb.*	
1932 p.xxxii	Tinctura Urgineae	*Urginea indica Kunth.*	
1932 p.xxxii	Syrupus Urgineae	*Urginea indica Kunth.*	
1932 p.xxxii	Pilula Scillae Composita	*Urginea Scilla Steinheil.*	
1932 p.xxxii	Tinctura Valerianae Indicae Ammoniata	*Valeriana officinalis Linn.*	
1932 p.xxxii	Valerianae Indicae Rhizoma	*Valeriana officinalis Linn.*	
1932 p.xxxii	Extractum Viburni Liquidum	*Viburnum prunifolium Linn.*	
1932 p.xxxii	Viburnum	*Viburnum prunifolium Linn.*	
1932 p.xxxii	Unguentum Hamamelidis		101

1948 p.xxix	Pilula Aloes et Ferri	*Aloe sp. & Iron*	
1948 p.xxix	Pilula Aloes et Asafoetidae	*Aloe sp. & Narthex Assafoetida Falconer*	
1948 p.xxix	Aqua Anethi Destillata	*Anethum graveolens Linn.*	
1948 p.xxix	Serpentaria	*Aristolochia Serpentaria Linn.*	
1948 p.xxix	Emplastrum Belladonnae	*Atropa Belladonna Linn.*	
1948 p.xxix	Extractum Belladonnae Herbae	*Atropa Belladonna Linn.*	
1948 p.xxix	Buchu	*Barosma betulina (Thunb.) Bartl. & Wendl.*	
1948 p.xxix	Infusum Buchu Concentratum	*Barosma betulina (Thunb.) Bartl. & Wendl.*	
1948 p.xxix	Infusum Buchu Recens	*Barosma betulina (Thunb.) Bartl. & Wendl.*	
1948 p.xxix	Tinctura Capsici Concentrata	*Capsicum fastigiatum Blume, Bijdr.*	
1948 p.xxix	Infusum Caryophylli Recens	*Caryophyllus aromaticus Linn.*	
1948 p.xxix	Confectio Sennae	*Cassia acutifolia Delile*	
1948 p.xxix	Infusum Sennae Recens	*Cassia acutifolia Delile*	
1948 p.xxix	Cassia	*Cassia Fistula Linn.*	
1948 p.xxix	Cinchona	*Chinchona sp.*	
1948 p.xxix	Extractum Cinchonae	*Chinchona sp.*	
1948 p.xxix	Extractum Cinchonae Liquidum	*Chinchona sp.*	
1948 p.xxix	Quininae Tannas	*Chinchona sp.*	
1948 p.xxix	Tinctura Cinchonae	*Chinchona sp.*	
1948 p.xxix	Tinctura Cinchonae Composita	*Chinchona sp.*	
1948 p.xxix	Tinctura Cinchonae Composita Concentrata	*Chinchona sp.*	
1948 p.xxix	Aqua Cinnamomi Destillata	*Cinnamomum zeylandicum Nees, Laurineae*	

1948 p.xxix	Infusum Aurantii Recens	*Citrus Bigaradia Risso*	
1948 p.xxix	Tinctura Aurantii Concentrata	*Citrus Bigaradia Risso*	
1948 p.xxix	Tinctura Limonis Concentrata	*Citrus Limonum DC.*	
1948 p.xxix	Extractum Colchici Cormi Liquidum	*Colchicum autumnale Linn.*	
1948 p.xxix	Copaiba	*Copaifera multijuga Hayne*	
1948 p.xxix	Infusum Digitalis Recens	*Digitalis purpurea Linn.*	
1948 p.xxix	Tinctura Cardomomi Composita Concentrata	*Elleteria Cardamomum Maton*	
1948 p.xxix	Oleum Santali Australiensis	*Eucarya spicata Sprague & Summerhayes*	
1948 p.xxix	Jalapa	*Exogonium Purga Bentham*	
1948 p.xxix	Jalapa Pulverata	*Exogonium Purga Bentham*	
1948 p.xxix	Pulvis Jalapae Compositus	*Exogonium Purga Bentham*	
1948 p.xxix	Extractum Gentianae	*Gentiana lutea Linn.*	
1948 p.xxix	Infusum Gentianae Compositum Recens	*Gentiana lutea Linn.*	
1948 p.xxix	Tinctura Gentianae Composita Concentrata	*Gentiana lutea Linn.*	
1948 p.xxix	Tinctura Krameriae	*Krameria triandra Ruiz & Pavon*	
1948 p.xxix	Linum	*Linum usitatissumum Linn.*	
1948 p.xxix	Linum Contusum	*Linum usitatissumum Linn.*	
1948 p.xxix	Lobelia	*Lobelia inflata Linn.*	
1948 p.xxix	Tinctura Lobeliae Aetherea	*Lobelia inflata Linn.*	
1948 p.xxix	Tinctura Lobeliae Aetherea Concentrata	*Lobelia inflata Linn.*	
1948 p.xxix	Aqua Menthae Piperitae Destillata	*Mentha piperata Linn.*	

1948 p.xxix	Assafoetida	*Narthex Assafoetida Falconer*	
1948 p.xxix	Tinctura Assafoetidae	*Narthex Assafoetida Falconer*	
1948 p.xxix	Extractum Opii Siccum	*Papaver somniferum Linn.*	
1948 p.xxix	Tinctura Opii Camphorata Concentrata	*Papaver somniferum Linn.*	
1948 p.xxix	Tinctura Quassiae Concentrata	*Picraena excelsa Lindl.*	
1948 p.xxix	Emplastrum Colophonii	*Pinus palustris Mill.*	
1948 p.xxix	Infusum Senegae Recens	*Polygala Senaga Linn.*	
1948 p.xxix	Tinctura Quilliae	*Quillaia Saponaria Molina*	
1948 p.xxix	Salicinum	*Salix spp.*	
1948 p.xxix	Oleum Santali	*Santalum album Linn.*	
1948 p.xxix	Strophanthinum	*Strophanthus kombe Oliver*	
1948 p.xxix	Tamarindus	*Tamarindus indica Linn.*	
1948 p.xxix	Extractum Scillae Liquidum	*Urginea Scilla Steinheil.*	
1948 p.xxix	Urginea	*Urginea Scilla Steinheil.*	
1948 p.xxix	Tinctura Valerianae Ammoniata Concentrata	*Valeriana officinalis Linn.*	
1948 p.xxix	Valeriana Indica	*Valeriana officinalis Linn.*	36
1953 p.xx	Catechu	*Acacia Catechu Willd. Enum.*	
1953 p.xx	Tinctura Catechu	*Acacia Catechu Willd. Enum.*	
1953 p.xx	Aconitum	*Aconitum napellus Linn.*	
1953 p.xx	Linimentum Aconiti	*Aconitum napellus Linn.*	
1953 p.xx	Pilula Aloes	*Aloe sp.*	
1953 p.xx	Anethum	*Anethum graveolens Linn.*	
1953 p.xx	Linimentum Belladonnae	*Atropa Belladonna Linn.*	

1953 p.xx	Myrrha	*Balsamodendron myrrha Ehren.*	
1953 p.xx	Tinctura Myrrhae	*Balsamodendron Myrrha Ehren.*	
1953 p.xx	Spiritus Camphorae	*Camphora officinarum Nees, Laurineae*	
1953 p.xx	Capsicum	*Capsicum fastigiatum Blume, Bijdr.*	
1953 p.xx	Tinctura Capsici	*Capsicum fastigiatum Blume, Bijdr.*	
1953 p.xx	Unguentum Capsici	*Capsicum fastigiatum Blume, Bijdr.*	
1953 p.xx	Oleum Cari	*Carum Carui Linn.*	
1953 p.xx	Infusum Caryophylli	*Caryophyllus aromaticus Linn.*	
1953 p.xx	Infusum Caryophylli Concentratum	*Caryophyllus aromaticus Linn.*	
1953 p.xx	Mistura Sennae Composita	*Cassia sp?*	
1953 p.xx	Infusum Aurantii	*Citrus Bigaradia Risso*	
1953 p.xx	Infusum Aurantii Concentratum	*Citrus Bigaradia Risso*	
1953 p.xx	Calumba	*Cocculus palmatus DC.*	
1953 p.xx	Infusum Calumbae	*Cocculus palmatus DC.*	
1953 p.xx	Infusum Calumbae Concentratum	*Cocculus palmatus DC.*	
1953 p.xx	Infusum Calumbae recens	*Cocculus palmatus DC.*	
1953 p.xx	Tinctura Calumbae	*Cocculus palmatus DC.*	
1953 p.xx	Colchici Semen	*Colchicum autumnale Linn.*	
1953 p.xx	Extractum Colchici Siccum	*Colchicum autumnale Linn.*	
1953 p.xx	Extractum Glycyrhizae	*Glycyrrhiza glabra Linn.*	
1953 p.xx	Ipomoea	*Ipomoea orizabensis (Pelletan) Ledanois*	
1953 p.xx	Ipomoeae Resina	*Ipomoea orizabensis (Pelletan) Ledanois*	
1953 p.xx	Extractum Krameriae Siccum	*Krameria triandra Ruiz & Pavon*	

1953 p.xx	Krameria	*Krameria triandra Ruiz & Pavon*	
1953 p.xx	Trochisci Krameriae	*Krameria triandra Ruiz & Pavon*	
1953 p.xx	Trochisci Krameriae et Cocainae	*Krameria triandra Ruiz & Pavon*	
1953 p.xx	Spiritus Cajuputi	*Melaleuca minor DC.*	
1953 p.xx	Balsumum Peruvianum	*Myrospermum Pereirae Royle, Mat. Med.*	
1953 p.xx	Tinctura Quassiae	*Picraena excelsa Lindl.*	
1953 p.xx	Podophyllum	*Podophyllum peltatum Linn.*	
1953 p.xx	Extractum Senegae Liquidum	*Polygala Senaga Linn.*	
1953 p.xx	Infusum Senegae	*Polygala Senaga Linn.*	
1953 p.xx	Infusum Senegae Concentratum	*Polygala Senaga Linn.*	
1953 p.xx	Senega	*Polygala Senaga Linn.*	
1953 p.xx	Tinctura Senegae	*Polygala Senaga Linn.*	
1953 p.xx	Prunus Serotina	*Prunus serotina Ehrh.*	
1953 p.xx	Syrupus Pruni Serotinae	*Prunus serotina Ehrh.*	
1953 p.xx	Pilula Rhei Composita	*Rheum sp. Linn.*	
1953 p.xx	Ergota	*Secale cereale Linn.*	
1953 p.xx	Ergota Praeparata	*Secale cereale Linn.*	
1953 p.xx	Extractum Ergotae liquidum	*Secale cereale Linn.*	
1953 p.xx	Tabellae Ergotae Praeparatae	*Secale cereale Linn.*	
1953 p.xx	Strophanthus	*Strophanthus kombe Oliver*	
1953 p.xx	Tinctura Strophanthi	*Strophanthus kombe Oliver*	
1953 p.xx	Syrupus Scillae	*Urginea Scilla Steinheil.*	
1953 p.xx	Tinctura Scillae	*Urginea Scilla Steinheil.*	
1953 p.xx	Scilla	*Urginea Scilla Steinheil.*	
1953 p.xx	Tinctura Valerianae Ammoniata	*Valeriana officinalis Linn.*	
1953 p.xx	Valeriana	*Valeriana officinalis Linn.*	28

1958 p.xxiii	Mucilage of Acacia	*Acacia Linn.*	
1958 p.xxiii	Belladonna Root	*Atropa Belladonna Linn.*	
1958 p.xxiii	Liquid Extract of Belladonna	*Atropa Belladonna Linn.*	
1958 p.xxiii	Liquid Extract of Senna	*Cassia acutifolia Delile*	
1958 p.xxiii	Syrup of Senna	*Cassia acutifolia Delile*	
1958 p.xxiii	Chenopodium Oil	*Chenopodium ambrosioides Linn.var. anthelminticum Gray*	
1958 p.xxiii	Lemon Oil	*Citrus Limonum DC.*	
1958 p.xxiii	Tincture of Digitalis	*Digitalis purpurea Linn.*	
1958 p.xxiii	Clove	*Eugenia Caryophyllus (Spreng.) Sprague*	
1958 p.xxiii	Fennel	*Foeniculum dulce DC.*	
1958 p.xxiii	Compound Powder of Liquorice	*Glycyrrhiza glabra Linn.*	
1958 p.xxiii	Dry Extract of Hamamelis	*Hamamelis virginiana Linn.*	
1958 p.xxiii	Lavender Oil	*Lavandula officinalis Chaix.*	
1958 p.xxiii	Emulsion of Peppermint	*Mentha piperata Linn.*	
1958 p.xxiii	Nutmeg	*Myristica fragrans Houtt.*	
1958 p.xxiii	Nutmeg Oil	*Myristica fragrans Houtt.*	
1958 p.xxiii	Concentrated Infusion of Quassia	*Picraena excelsa Lindl.*	
1958 p.xxiii	Infusion of Quassia	*Picraena excelsa Lindl.*	
1958 p.xxiii	Quassia	*Picraena excelsa Lindl.*	
1958 p.xxiii	Volatile Bitter Almond Oil	*Prunus amygdalus Batsch. Var. amara (D.C.) Focke*	
1958 p.xxiii	Liquid Extract of Quillaia	*Quillaia Saponaria Molina*	
1958 p.xxiii	Compound Powder of Rhubarb	*Rheum sp. Linn.*	
1958 p.xxiii	Dry Extract of Nux Vomica	*Strychnos Nux Vomica Linn.*	
1958 p.xxiii	Prepared Nux Vomica	*Strychnos Nux Vomica Linn.*	18

1963 p.xxvi	Concentrated Dill Water	*Anethum graveolens Linn.*	
1963 p.xxvi	Dill Oil	*Anethum graveolens Linn.*	
1963 p.xxvi	Male Fern Extract Capsules	*Aspidium Filix mas Swartz*	
1963 p.xxvi	Camphor Water	*Camphora officinarum Nees, Laurineae*	
1963 p.xxvi	Cinnamon Oil	*Cinnamomum zeylandicum Nees, Laurineae*	
1963 p.xxvi	Concentrated Cinnamon Water	*Cinnamomum zeylandicum Nees, Laurineae*	
1963 p.xxvi	Fresh Lemon Peel	*Citrus Limonum DC.*	
1963 p.xxvi	Lemon Syrup	*Citrus Limonum DC.*	
1963 p.xxvi	Lemon Tincture	*Citrus Limonum DC.*	
1963 p.xxvi	Stramonium Dry Extract	*Datura Stramonium Linn.*	
1963 p.xxvi	Hamamelis	*Hamamelis virginiana Linn.*	
1963 p.xxvi	Hamamelis Liquid Extract	*Hamamelis virginiana Linn.*	
1963 p.xxvi	Hamamelis Ointment	*Hamamelis virginiana Linn.*	
1963 p.xxvi	Cade Oil	*Juniperus Oxycedrus Linn.*	
1963 p.xxvi	Peppermint Spirit	*Mentha piperata Linn.*	
1963 p.xxvi	Rosemary Oil	*Rosmarinus officinalis Linn.*	
1963 p.xxvi	Benzoin	*Styrax Benzoin Dryand.*	
1963 p.xxvi	Compound Benzoin Tincture	*Styrax Benzoin Dryand.*	11
1968 p.xxix	Tragacanth Mucilage	*Astragalus verus Olivier, Voy., DC.*	
1968 p.xxix	Senna Leaf	*Cassia acutifolia Delile*	
1968 p.xxix	Fresh Bitter Orange peel	*Citrus Aurantium Linn.*	
1968 p.xxix	Orange Syrup	*Citrus Aurantium Linn.*	
1968 p.xxix	Orange Tincture	*Citrus Aurantium Linn.*	

1968 p.xxix	Linseed Oil	*Linum usitatissumum Linn.*	
1968 p.xxix	Ginger Syrup	*Zingiber officinale Roscoe*	5
1973 p.xx	Stramonium Liquid Extract	*Datura Stramonium Linn.*	
1973 p.xx	Compound Gentian Tincture	*Gentiana lutea Linn.*	
1973 p.xx	Cottonseed Oil	*Gossypium spp.*	
1973 p.xx	Hyoscyamus Dry Extract	*Hyoscyamus niger Linn.*	
1973 p.xx	Hyoscyamus Liquid Extract	*Hyoscyamus niger Linn.*	
1973 p.xx	Tolu Balsam	*Myroxylon balsamum (Linn.) Harms*	
1973 p.xx	Tolu Syrup	*Myroxylon balsamum (Linn.) Harms*	
1973 p.xx	Cascara Elixir	*Rhamnus Purshianus DC.*	
1973 p.xx	Sesame Oil	*Sesamum indicum Linn.*	7
1980 p.xxvii	Male Fern	*Aspidium Filix mas Swartz*	
1980 p.xxvii	Male Fern Extract	*Aspidium Filix mas Swartz*	
1980 p.xxvii	Camphor Liniment	*Camphora officinarum Nees, Laurineae*	
1980 p.xxvii	Colchicum Corm	*Colchicum autumnale Linn.*	
1980 p.xxvii	Colchicum Liquid extract	*Colchicum autumnale Linn.*	
1980 p.xxvii	Colchicum Tincture	*Colchicum autumnale Linn.*	
1980 p.xxvii	Concentrated Peppermint Water	*Mentha piperata Linn.*	
1980 p.xxvii	Olive Oil	*Olea europaea Linn.*	5
1988 p.xxxi	Compound Tragacanth Powder	*Astragalus verus Olivier, Voy., DC.*	
1988 p.xxxi	Belladonna Adhesive Plaster	*Atropa Belladonna Linn.*	
1988 p.xxxi	Stramonium Tincture	*Datura Stramonium Linn.*	
1988 p.xxxi	Hyoscine Eye Ointment	*Hyoscyamus niger Linn.*	

1988 p.xxxi	Hyoscyamus Tincture	*Hyoscyamus niger Linn.*	
1988 p.xxxi	Lavender Oil	*Lavandula officinalis Chaix.*	
1988 p.xxxi	Tolu Balsam	*Myroxylon balsamum (Linn.) Harms*	
1988 p.xxxi	Pumilio Pine Oil	*Pinus mugo Turra var. pumilio zenari*	
1988 p.xxxi	Concentrated Senega Infusion	*Polygala Senaga Linn.*	
1988 p.xxxi	Senega Liquid Extract	*Polygala Senaga Linn.*	
1988 p.xxxi	Wild Cherry Bark	*Prunus serotina Ehrh.*	
1988 p.xxxi	Wild Cherry Syrup	*Prunus serotina Ehrh.*	
1988 p.xxxi	Cascara Liquid Extract	*Rhamnus Purshianus DC.*	
1988 p.xxxi	Compound Rhubarb Oral Powder	*Rheum sp. Linn.*	
1988 p.xxxi	Nux Vomica	*Strychnos Nux Vomica Linn.*	
1988 p.xxxi	Nux Vomica Liquid Extract	*Strychnos Nux Vomica Linn.*	
1988 p.xxxi	Nux Vomica Tincture	*Strychnos Nux Vomica Linn.*	
1988 p.xxxi	Siam Benzoin	*Styrax tonkinensis Craib.*	
1988 p.xxxi	Squill Elixir	*Urginea Scilla Steinheil.*	
1988 p.xxxi	Squill Tincture	*Urginea Scilla Steinheil.*	
1988 p.xxxi	Squill Vinegar	*Urginea Scilla Steinheil.*	14
1993 p.xxxiv	Catechu	*Acacia Catechu Willd. Enum.*	
1993 p.xxxiv	Catechu Tincture	*Acacia Catechu Willd. Enum.*	
1993 p.xxxiv	Powdered Catechu	*Acacia Catechu Willd. Enum.*	
1993 p.xxxiv	Powdered Aloes	*Aloe sp.*	
1993 p.xxxiv	Natural Camphor	*Camphora officinarum Nees, Laurineae*	
1993 p.xxxiv	Digitalis Tablets	*Digitalis purpurea Linn.*	
1993 p.xxxiv	Prepared Digitalis	*Digitalis purpurea Linn.*	
1993 p.xxxiv	Lobelia	*Lobelia inflata Linn.*	
1993 p.xxxiv	Powdered Lobelia	*Lobelia inflata Linn.*	

1993 p.xxxiv	Prepared Opium	*Papaver somniferum Linn.*	
1993 p.xxxiv	Cascara Elixir	*Rhamnus Purshianus DC.*	
1993 p.xxxiv	Compound Rhubarb Mixture	*Rheum sp. Linn.*	
1993 p.xxxiv	Concentrated Raspberry Jiuce	*Rubus idaeus Linn.*	
1993 p.xxxiv	Raspberry Syrup	*Rubus idaeus Linn.*	9

Table VI: Deletions of plant species from British Pharmacopoeias 1885–1993

Year	Number of deleted entries
1867	3
1885	11
1914	104
1932	187
1948	59
1953	56
1958	24
1963	18
1968	7
1973	9
1980	8
1988	21
1993	134

Total 521 entries

There were occasional additions as well, but these were insignificant compared with the systematic deletions of plant formulations. *E.g. In the 1948 BP there is a long list of additions since 1932, which contains some plant preparations: Infusions (Senna, Quassia, Gentian), Suppositories, Tablets (Digitalis, Ergot, Ipecacuanha), Extracts (Colchicus, Scilla, Stramonium), Oils (Amygdala, Hippoglossum), Tablets (Ephedrine, Quinine) and Tinctures (Capsicum*, Cardamom*, Cinchona*, Gentian*, Lemon*, Lobelia*, Opium*, Quassia*, Valerian*). But in some cases, these replaced concentrated tinctures of the same plant that had been deleted from the 1948 BP.*

Table VII: List of plants/extracts in index of BP 1993
(Volume II, 15th and New Edition Dec 1993)

Index name	Species name	Properties/use
Acacia*	Acacia Senegal L	laxative
Agar*	Gelidium spp.	pharmaceutical aid
Alexandrian Senna fruit	Cassia senna L.	stimulant laxative
Almond Oil*	Prunus dulcis Miller	-
Anise & Oil*	Pimpinella anisum L.	carminative & flavour
Arachis Oil*	Arachis hypogaea L.	-
Barbados Aloes*	Aloe barbadensis Miller	laxative
Belladonna herb*	Atropa belladonna L	antispasmodic
Black Currant	Ribes nigrum L.	flavour, vitamin C source
Cape Aloes*	Aloe ferox Miller	laxative
Caraway	Carum carvi L.	flavour
Cardamom & oil*	Elettaria cardamomum Maton	carminative & flavour
Carnauba wax	Copernicia cerifera Mart.	pharmaceutical aid
Cascara	Rhamnus purshianus DC	stimulant laxative
Castor oil	Ricinus communis L.	emollient & stimulant laxative
Chamomile flowers	Anthemis nobilis L.	Eur. Ph. -
Chinchona bark*	Chinchona pubescens Vahl.	bitter
Cinnamon*	Cinnamonum zeylandicum Nees	flavour & carminative
Clove	Syzygium aromaticum (L.) Merrill	carminative & flavour
Coconut oil	Cocus nucifera L.	-
Coriander	Coriander sativum L.	flavour
Digitalis leaf*	Digitalis purpurea L.	anti-inflammatory & analgesic
Dill oil*	Anethum graveolens L.	carminative
Eucalyptus oil	Eucalyptus globulus Labill.	-
Fig*	Ficus carica L.	demulcent
Frangula bark	Rhamnus frangula L.	stimulant laxative
Gentian*	Gentiana lutea L.	bitter
Ginger*	Zingiber officinale Roscoe	flavour
Hyoscyamus* Leaf	Hyoscyamus niger L	antispasmodic
Inulin	Helianthus tuberosus	monitor of glomular filtration rate
Ipecacuanha	Cephaelis ipecacuanha (Brot.) A. Rich	expectorant, emetic
Ispaghula husk	Plantago ovata Forssk.	antidiarrhoeal; bulk-forming laxative

Lemon oil*	Citrus limon (L.) Burm.	flavour
Linseed*	Linum usitatissimum L.	demulcent
Liquorice*	Glycyrrhiza glabra L.	flavour
Matricaria flowers	Matricaria recutita L.	- (European pharmacopoeia)
Nutmeg oil*	Myristica fragrans Houtt.	flavour
Olive oil*	Olea europaea L.	-
Opium*	Papaver somniferum L.	narcotic analgesic
Orange oil	Citrus aurantium L.	flavour
Peppermint leaf*	Mentha x piperita L.	carminative
Quillaia	Quillaja saponaria Molina	emulsifying agent
Rhatany root*	Krameria triandra Ruiz & Pavon	astringent
Rhubarb*	Rheum officinale Baillon	laxative
Senega root*	Polygala senega L.	expectorant
Soya oil	Glycine max (L.) Merr.	-
Spearmint Oil*	Mentha spicata L.	flavour
Squill*	Drimia maritima (L.) Stearn	expectorant
Stramonium Leaf*	Datura stramonium L.	antispasmodic
Theobroma oil	Theobroma cacao L.	suppository basis
Turpentine oil	Pinus spp	rubifacient
Valerian*	Valeriana officinalis L.	sedative

52 entries
* denotes presence in 1864 BP 1864 – 31 entries

Notes: of the 52 entries:

+ eight are used solely for flavouring
+ eight are laxatives
+ other uses are as anti-inflammatory, analgesic, antispasmodic, astringent, expectorant, carminative, emollient, demulcent, rubifacient and sedative agents
+ no action has been given for the oils: olive, almond, coconut, palm kernel, soya
+ the starches are used for pharmaceutical preparations: corn, wheat
+ chamomile flowers included but no action given (part of European Pharmacopoeia)
+ synthetic caffeine and ephedrine included are in BP

Table VIII: Plant entries in Pharmacopée Française between the years 1881 and 1937 (23 different plant species in various formulations)

Entry name	Species Name	1818	1837	1866	1888	1908	1937
Camomille tisane	*Anthemis nobilis L.*	+	-	+	+	+	+
Bluets	*Centaurea cyanus*	+	+	+	+	-	-
Muguet	*Convallaria majalis L.*	+	+	+	+	+	+
Staphisagria	*Delphinium Staphisagria L.*	+	-	+	+	+	+
Milpertuis commun	*Hypericum perforatum L.*	+	+	+	+	+	+
Milpertuis huile	*Hypericum perforatum L.*	-	-	+	+	-	-
Hysope eau distillée (E.D.)	*Hyssopus officinalis L.*	-	-	+	+	-	-
Hysope herbe	*Hyssopus officinalis L.*	+	+	+	+	+	+
Hysope tisane	*Hyssopus officinalis L.*	-	-	+	-	-	+
Noyer commun	*Juglans regia*	+	+	-	-	+	+
Genèvrier commune baies	*Juniperus communis L.*	+	+	+	+	+	+
Genèvrier commune essence	*Juniperus communis L.*	-	-	+	+	+	+
Lavandre vraie eau distillée	*Lavandula vera D.C.*	+	-	+	+	+	+
Lavandre vraie essence	*Lavandula vera D.C.*	+	+	+	+	+	+
Lavandre vraie herbe	*Lavandula vera D.C.*	+	+	+	+	+	+
Mélisse alcoolat composée	*Melissa officinalis L.*	-	-	+	+	+	+
Mélisse eau distillée	*Melissa officinalis L.*	-	-	+	+	-	-
Mélisse herbe	*Melissa officinalis L.*	+	+	+	+	+	+
Mélisse tisane	*Melissa officinalis L.*	-	-	+	-	-	+
Marjolaine	*Origanum marjorana L.*	+	+	+	+	+	+
Rose à cent feuilles E.D	*Rosa centifolia L.*	+	+	-	+	+	+
Rose à cent feuilles herbe	*Rosa centifolia L.*	+	+	+	+	+	+
Rose à cent feuilles H.V.	*Rosa centifolia L.*	+	+	-	+	+	+
Rose pâle herbe	*Rosa centifolia L.*	+	+	+	+	+	+
Rose huile volatile	*Rosa damascena Mill.*	+	+	+	+	+	+
Rose rouge de Provins herbe	*Rosa gallica L.*	+	+	+	+	+	+
Rose rouge de Provins mellite	*Rosa gallica L.*	+	+	+	+	+	+

Romarin huile volatile	Rosmarinus offinalis L.	+	+	+	+	+	+
Sauge des Prés	Salvia pratensis	+	+	+	+	+	+
Sauge sclarée	Salvia sclarea	+	+	+	-	-	-
Sureau commun	Sambucus nigra L.	+	+	+	+	+	+
Reine des Prés	Spiraea sp?	+	-	+	+	-	-
Thym	Thymus vulgaris L.	+	+	+	+	+	+
Tilleul eau distillée	Tilia chordata Mill.	+	+	+	+	+	+
Tilleul herbe	Tilia chordata Mill.	+	+	+	+	+	+
Tilleul tisane	Tilia chordata Mill.	+	+	+	+	+	+
Valériane eau distillée	Valeriana officinalis L.	-	+	+	+	+	+
Valériane officinale herbe	Valeriana officinalis L.	+	+	+	+	+	+
Framboise sirop de	Rubus idaeus Linn.	+	+	+	+	+	+
Framboise suc de	Rubus idaeus Linn.	-	-	+	+	+	+

Appendix II

Note I: Plant Provenances

Name	Latin Name	Provenance
St John's Wort	*Hypericum perforatum*	Chevenoz meadow
Lemon Balm	*Melissa officinalis*	School of Phytotherapy
Lavender	*Lavandula officinalis – Hidcote* *L. officinalis – Number 9* *L. officinalis – Maillette* *L.officinalis – Les Courmettes*	Suffolk Seeds Downderry Nursery, Kent Downderry Nursery, Kent Wildcrafted from hills above Cannes
Hyssop	*Hyssopus officinalis*	Suffolk Seeds
Echinacea	*Echinacea purpurea*	Thompson & Morgan
Marigold	*Calendula officinalis*	Chelsea Physic Garden
Yarrow	*Achillea millefolium*	Chevenoz meadow
Skullcap	*Scutellaria lateriflora*	School of Phytotherapy
White Hoarhound	*Marrubium vulgare*	School of Phytotherapy
Wormwood	*Artemesia absinthium*	Chelsea Physic Garden
German Camomile	*Matricaria recutita*	Chelsea Physic Garden
Clary Sage	*Salvia sclarea*	Suffolk Seeds
Agrimony	*Agrimonia eupatoria*	Chevenoz meadow
Staphisagria	*Delphinium staphisagria*	Chelsea Physic Garden
Betony	*Stachys officinalis*	Chevenoz meadow
Lovage	*Levisticum officinale*	Future Foods
Marian Thistle	*Silybum marianum*	Future Foods
Arnica	*Arnica montana*	School of Phytotherapy
Holy Basil	*Ocimum sanctum*	Peter Wilde
Love in a Mist	*Nigella damascena*	School of Phytotherapy

Rosemary	*Rosmarinus officinalis* *Varieties: Marenca, Boule,* *Sudbury Blue*	National Rosemary Collection. Pandora Thorsby
Rose Geranium	*Pelargonium graveolens*	Seeds from Kirstenbosch Botanic Garden, Cape Town, South Africa.

Note II: Chevenoz Roses: from Peter Beales 2004+ plantings

Madame Hardy
Marie-Louise
Quatre Saisons
St Nicholas
Amelia
Blush Damask
Botzaris
Celsiana
Ispahan
Kazanlik
Gloire de Dijon
Agatha
R. centifolia

Also:
L'Abondance
Comte de Chambord
Falstaff
Parfum de L'Hay
Gipsy Boy
William Lobb
Gloire de Guilan
Tuscany Superb
Mme Isaac Perière
R. alba semi-plena
R. gallica officinalis
Zéphirine Drouhin
Rose de Mai (R. gallica x R. centifolia)

Appendix III

Synopsis of Maria Thun: Thun, Maria and Thun, Matthias: The Biodynamic Sowing and Planting Calendar. 2006 (ongoing). Floris Books. ISBN 0-86315-493-X

This little booklet explains in some detail one of the most difficult to comprehend of the moon's rhythms: the influences of the constellations on plant growth.

The size of these constellations varies so the moon passes through a new constellation every two to four days, bringing with it a new character of cosmic influence. Historically, by observing the effects that a particular part of the heavens contains stars brought to Earth, the constellation was said to have a certain 'influence'. Thus, instinct, observation and direct experience formulated the nature of the constellations (i.e. those influences perceived/observed on Earth when the moon was in a particular part of the sky). It did not relate to the properties of those stars in the constellation at all. Human imagination gave the groups of stars symbols that best represented the qualities of the influences brought about.

Continuing with the mediaeval astrological model, the twelve constellations are grouped according to their influences and form four trigons. Each constellation in a trigon has a similar influence on the Earth. And to each is assigned a classical Element – Water/Air/Earth/Fire – which is influenced by it. Thus, a series of correspondences or connections has been created since ancient times, relating the rhythms of the cosmos to the constellations, to the Elements, to climate and its effects on plants. These basic rhythms are also interrupted by the influence of the planets and their positions relative to the Sun, the Earth and other planets.

Based on the results of years of her meticulous plant trials, Maria Thun described the follow relationships as 'regularities which become apparent from plant trials and weather observations'.

Zodiac Sign	Element	Microclimate	Plant organ influenced
Pisces	Water	Moist	Leaf
Aries	Fire	Warmth	Fruit/Seed
Taurus	Earth	Cool/Cold	Root
Gemini	Air	Airy/Light	Flower
Cancer	Water	Moist	Leaf
Leo	Fire	Warmth	Fruit/Seed
Virgo	Earth	Cool/Cold	Root
Libra	Air	Airy/Light	Flower
Scorpio	Water	Moist	Leaf
Sagittarius	Fire	Warmth	Fruit/Seed
Capricorn	Earth	Cool/Cold	Root
Aquarius	Air	Airy/Light	Flower

And later in the text, she states that through their work they have ascertained the following relationships:

Correspondences between the planets, the Elements and the constellations

Planets	Element	Constellation
Saturn, Mercury, Pluto	Fire	Capricorn, Leo, Sagittarius
Sun	Earth	Taurus, Virgo, Aries
Jupiter, Venus, Uranus	Air	Gemini, Libra, Aquarius
Moon, Mars, Neptune	Water	Cancer, Scorpio, Pisces

Her explanation is that the planets influence the weather via the Elements. When a planet passes in front of a zodiacal constellation of the same Element, its effect is intensified (e.g. Mercury in Aries), and when in front of a constellation of a different Element, the effect is weakened or is non-existent. This gives rise to weather patterns.

And then there are the planets – those huge and bright 'wanderers' with seemingly irregular paths across the sky. Sometimes they appear to move from east to west and then zigzag back in their retrograde motion. Since ancient times, observers and stargazers have known them to be different from the fixed stars in the firmament that make up their backcloth. These enormous bodies all have their gravitational pull on Earth, to a greater or lesser extent according to their distance, and also they work in conjunction with each other, exerting positive or negative effects on living things. Millennia of observations have brought about an understanding that when a certain planet is in a certain position in the sky (against the background of the fixed stars), there are specific influences on growth and behaviour. And when there are combinations of more than one planet's position relative to the sun in the sky, things are more complicated, but nevertheless sometimes predictable. All this gave rise to astrology – the sometime art and sometime science of prediction of events, and even human behaviour, according to cosmic influences.

Permission to reproduce tables from Floris Books, Edinburgh.

Appendix IV

Essential Oils and Hydrolats

1. Record Sheet

(Parameters recorded were as below.)

DISTILLATION RECORDS

Date				Record Number
Still Number	I	II	III	Batch Number
Plant				
Parts				
Source				Mass (kg)
Fresh/wilted/dry				Height of Charge (cm)

Distillation: Warm-up Time

	Heater on	Start	1st Distillate through	Warm-up time
Heater I				
Heater II				

Distillation: Run

	Sample I	Sample II	Sample III
Time start			
Time finish			
Volume of distillate (ml)			
Temp of reservoir (°C)			
Temp of cooling tank (°C)			
Temp of distillate (°C)			
Volume of E.O. (ml)			

Observations:

Weather conditions:

Calendrier lunaire:

2. Gas chromatography analyses

(As in Price, Len and Shirley: Understanding Hydrolats: the specific Hydrosols for Aromatherapy. 2004. Churchill Livingstone, an imprint of Elsevier Ltd. ISBN 0443 07316 3. Appendix D: Analyses of distilled plant waters, Source A Herbes de Chevenoz p 231+; Appendix E: Hydrolat Gas Chromatograms performed by Dr Bill Morden p 257+ (4).)

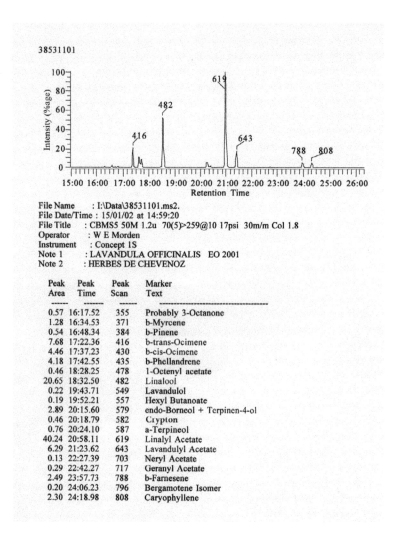

38531101

File Name   : I:\Data\38531101.ms2.
File Date/Time : 15/01/02 at 14:59:20
File Title   : CBMS5 50M 1.2u 70(5)>259@10 17psi 30m/m Col 1.8
Operator   : W E Morden
Instrument   : Concept 1S
Note 1   : LAVANDULA OFFICINALIS   EO 2001
Note 2   : HERBES DE CHEVENOZ

Peak Area	Peak Time	Peak Scan	Marker Text
0.57	16:17.52	355	Probably 3-Octanone
1.28	16:34.53	371	b-Myrcene
0.54	16:48.34	384	b-Pinene
7.68	17:22.36	416	b-trans-Ocimene
4.46	17:37.23	430	b-cis-Ocimene
4.18	17:42.55	435	b-Phellandrene
0.46	18:28.25	478	1-Octenyl acetate
20.65	18:32.50	482	Linalool
0.22	19:43.71	549	Lavandulol
0.19	19:52.21	557	Hexyl Butanoate
2.89	20:15.60	579	endo-Borneol + Terpinen-4-ol
0.46	20:18.79	582	Crypton
0.76	20:24.10	587	a-Terpineol
40.24	20:58.11	619	Linalyl Acetate
6.29	21:23.62	643	Lavandulyl Acetate
0.13	22:27.39	703	Neryl Acetate
0.29	22:42.27	717	Geranyl Acetate
2.49	23:57.73	788	b-Farnesene
0.20	24:06.23	796	Bergamotene Isomer
2.30	24:18.98	808	Caryophyllene

Herbes de Chevenoz lavender essential oil (see Chapter XIII – Lavender)

Appendix V

Tincture preparation methods

1. Harvesting of plants

Plants were harvested according to the parts required and the stage of development stated in the British Herbal Pharmacopoeia (1984 edition). They were then weighed out and cut into 1cm lengths.

2. Tincture preparation

The recipe chosen was usually the Herbal Apothecary fresh plant tincture recipe, i.e. one part fresh plant material to three parts of 25% alcohol. The alcohol concentration was calculated to take account of 60% water content and the alcohol was diluted with spring water according to the calculations shown below. Dry weight (DW) determinations were also set up with 100g fresh weight (FW) material for later use. The plant material and diluted alcohol were put in a glass bottling jar, sealed and shaken. The jars were shaken daily and left for between two and three weeks. The plant material was then pressed using a Vigo plant press and the expressed liquid decanted and stored in polypropylene tincture bottles.

3. Alcohol concentration calculations

e.g. 100g fresh weight in a 1:3 25% recipe

Assumption for this calculation: 100g FW plant material contains 60g water, therefore 100g FW will produce 360ml diluted alcohol (which needs to be equivalent to 25% alcohol). In later years, this was amended to 70% water content.

360ml 25% alcohol = 300ml y% alcohol

therefore y = 360 × 25/100 × 100/300 = 30% alcohol

Diluting 40% alcohol to 30% alcohol:

x ml 40% alcohol = 300ml 30% alcohol

x = 300 × 30/100 × 100/40 = 225ml 40% alcohol + 75ml water

to give a volume of 300ml 30% alcohol, which will be diluted by the water in the fresh plant material to give a final concentration of 25% alcohol.

NB: This calculation does not take into account the fact that 100g FW plant material only contains 40g dry matter. As with the Herbal Apothecary recipe, it is assumed that this is accounted by the recipe 1:3 25% instead of the dry weight recipe of 1:5 25%.

e.g. for *Achillea millefolium* using 40% *eau de vie* and 300g FW plant material

Assume 60% water content

300g FW contains 180g water. Recipe 1:3 25%

i.e. 300g FW + 900ml 25% alcohol (at end of extraction)

which is equivalent to 120g DW 1180g x% alcohol at beginning of extraction

To make up tincture:

x ml 40% alcohol = 900ml 30% alcohol therefore x = 675

675ml 40% alcohol diluted to 900ml (i.e. with 225ml water)

The alcohol used in tincture preparations was either vodka (45% or 50%), *eau de vie* (40%) or 95% alcohol from sugar beet (food grade).

4. Dry weight determinations

100g FW material samples were weighed out and left at room temperature until they had reached constant weight. Averages given below:

Plant	Date	Original weight	Final weight	% water
Viscum album	15.7.97	100g	25g	75%
Urtica dioica	15.7.97	50g	15g	70%
Agrimonia eupatoria	17.7.97	50g	16g	68%

Therefore 60% water content in the fresh weights of these plants was an underestimation. Since most plant samples were leafy (unlike *Viscum*, which also contained fruits), later tinctures were prepared using 32% alcohol to compensate for the higher water content.

5. Ethanol dilutions

For the three different alcohols used to make 1000ml liquid according to British Herbal Pharmacopoeia recipes.

95% ethanol to 40% x ml × 95/100 = 1000ml × 40/100 x = 1000 × 40/100 × 100/95 = 421 421ml 95% ethanol + 579ml water	40% ethanol to 25% x ml × 40/100 = 1000ml × 25/100 x = 1000 × 25/100 × 100/40 = 625 625ml ethanol + 375ml water
38% ethanol to 25% x ml × 38/100 = 1000ml × 25/100 x = 1000 × 25/100 × 100/38 = 658 658ml ethanol + 342ml water	95% ethanol to 25% x ml × 95/100 = 1000ml × 25/100 x = 1000 × 25/100 × 100/95 = 263 263ml ethanol + 737ml water
95% ethanol to 45% x ml × 95/100 = 1000ml × 25/100 x = 474 474ml ethanol + 526ml water	95% ethanol to 32% x ml × 95/100 = 1000ml × 32/100 x = 337 337ml ethanol + 663ml water
45% ethanol to 32% x ml × 45/100 = 1000ml × 32/100 x = 711 711ml ethanol + 289ml water	

6. Tincture making records
(key: V = vodka, E = *eau de vie*)

Date started	Plant	Source	Parts	FW (g)	Alcohol dilution	Date pressed	Volume (ml)
25.6.97	*Viscum Album*	Chevenoz Orchard	Leafy shoots + berries	200	2:5 25%	15.7.97	590
25.6.97	*Agrimonia eupatoria*	Chevenoz	Flowering leafy shoots	100	1:5 25%	15.7.97	510
28.6.97	*Equisetum arvense*	Chevenoz	Aerial shoots	200	1:3 25%	17.7.97	700
29.6.97	*Achillea millefolium I*	Chevenoz	Flowering shoots	100	1:3 25%	18.7.97	320

8.7.97	*Achillea millefolium II*	Chevenoz	Flowering shoots	200	1:3 25%	2.8.97	740
17.7.97	*Achillea millefolium III*	Chevenoz	Flowering shoots	300	1:3 25%	8.8.97	1080
26.6.97	*Filipendula ulmaria I*	Chevenoz wild collected	Flowering shoots	200	1:3 25%	16.7.97	700
30.6.97	*Filipendula ulmaria II*	Chevenoz wild	Flowering shoots	300	1:3 25%	16.7.97	1010
30.6.97	*Alchemilla vulgaris I*	Chevenoz	Aerial parts with flowers	100	1:3 25%	18.7.97	335
8.7.97	*Hypericum perforatum I*	Chevênoz	Flowering shoots	200	1:3 25%	2.8.97	-
8.7.97	*Hypericum perforatum II*	Chevenoz	Flowering shoots	100	1:3 25%	2.8.97	1150 combined I&II
8.7.97	*Melissa officinalis I*	Chevenoz	Leafy shoots	110	1:4 45% (V)	2.8.97	480
13.7.97	*Melissa officinalis II*	Ditto	Ditto	110	1:4 50% (V)	3.8.97	500
9.7.97	*Lavendula officinalis I*	Chevenoz	Flowers	200	1:3 45% (V)	2.8.97	860
12.7.97	*Lavendula officinalis II*	Chevenoz	Flowers	200	1:3 50% (V)	2.8.97	825
20.7.97	*Calendula officinalis I*	Chevenoz	Flower heads	100	1:5 25% (E)	11.8.97	520
2.8.97	*C.officinalis II*	Chevenoz	Flower heads	200	1:5 25% (E)	21.8.97	-
2.8.97	*C.officinalis III*	Chevenoz	Flower heads	200	1:5 25% (E)	21.8.97	II + III 1960

7. Infused oil records: 2003

Date started	Plant name	Plant source	Plant parts	Quantity plant (g) : oil (ml)	Oil source & Sell By Date	Date pressed	Oil quality
24.06.03	*Hypericum perforatum I*	H de C	Flowering tops	1000:3200	Almond oil EOL	14.07.03	Lovely colour
07.07.03	*Hypericum perforatum II*	H de C	Flowering tops	675:3200	Almond oil EOL	29.07.03	
07.07.03	*Hypericum perforatum III*	H de C	Flowering tops	675:3200	Almond oil EOL	29.07.03	
09.07.03	*Hypericum perforatum IV*	Les Chatelards	Flowering tops	675:3200	Almond oil EOL	29.07.03	
09.07.03	*Ditto*	Ditto	Ditto	675:3200	Grapeseed oil EN 1/04	29.07.03	
16.07.03	*Hypericum VI*	H de C	Flowering tops	650:3200	Grapeseed oil EN 1/04	06.08.03	
16.07.03	*Hypericum VII*	H de C	Ditto	650:3200	Grapeseed oil EN 1/04	06.08.03	
24.07.03	*Hypericum VIII*	H de C	Ditto	610:3000	Grapeseed oil EN 1/05	14.08.03	
24.07.03	*Hypericum IX*	H de C	Ditto	610:3000	Grapeseed oil EN1/05	14.08.03	Excellent coloured oils
25.07.03	*Hypericum X*	H de C / Vinzier*	Ditto	620:3000	Grapeseed oil EN 1/05	14.08.03	* plants mixture of late flowering from Vinzier 2/3 and v. young from H de C 1/3

29.07.03	Hypericum XI	H de C	Ditto	740:3200	Grapeseed oil EN 1/05	19.08.03	Higher proportion of young leaves to flowers (side shoots). Beautiful oil
05.08.03	Hypericum XII	H de C	Ditto	400:2000	Grapeseed oil EN 1/05	27.08.03	Beautiful coloured oil
05.08.03	Hypericum XIII	H de C	Ditto	400:2000	Grapeseed oil EN 1/05	27.08.03	Beautiful coloured oil
05.08.03	Calendula I	H de C	Dried flowers	200:2000	Almond oil EOL	27.08.03	Beautiful coloured oil
08.08.03	Calendula II	H de C	Dried flowers	170:2000	Grapeseed oil EN 1/05		
11.08.03	Hypericum XIV	H de C	Ditto	610:<3000	Grapeseed oil EN1/05		

(SBD is 'sell-by date')

8. Infused oil records: 2002

Date started	Plant name	Plant source	Plant parts	Quantity plant (g) : oil (ml)	Oil source & Sell By Date	Date pressed	Oil quality
17.07.02	Hypericum perforatum I	H de C	flowering shoots 15cm		Almond oil EOL	07.08.02	>3l good colour
19.07.02	Hypericum II	H de C		1000g FW in 3200ml oil	Grapeseed EN 11.03	09.08.02	
19.07.02	Hypericum III	H de C		1000g FW in 3200ml oil	ditto	09.08.02	

19.07.02	*Hypericum IV*			800g in 3200ml		08.08.02	
19.07.02	*Hypericum V*			800g in 3200ml		08.02.02	
19.07.02	*Hypericum VI*			800g in 3200ml		08.08.02	
19.07.02	*Hypericum VII*			800g in 3200ml		08.08.02	`
19.07.02	*Hypericum VIII*			800g in 3200ml		08.08.02	
19.07.02	*Hypericum IX*			800g in 3200ml		09.08.02	
19.07.02	*Hypericum X*			800g in 3200ml		09.08.02	
19.07.02	*Hypericum XI*			800g in 3200ml		09.08.02	
19.07.02	*Hypericum XII*			800g in 3200ml		09.08.02	

Bibliography

The references cited below are in no way a comprehensive literature search on the many topics covered in the text. They represent those books that have served the purpose of a collective vade mecum *to guide me on this journey. Many of my copies are 'well thumbed' and annotated...*

Anderson, Carol A., Phillipson, Linda. A. and David, J. : Herbal Medicines: A Guide for Health-care professionals. 1996. London Pharmaceutical Press. ISBN 0 85369 289 0

Anderson, William and Hicks, Clive: Green Man – the Archetype of our Oneness with the Earth. 1990. Harper Collins. ISBN 0-00-599255

Bach, E: Heal Thyself. 1931. C.W. Daniel Co Ltd. Saffron Walden. ISBN 0 85207 040. Reprinted 1993

Bach, E: The Twelve Healers. 1933. C.W. Daniel Co Ltd. Saffron Walden. ISBN 0 85207 041 1. Reprinted 1993

Barfield, Owen: Saving the Appearances. Second edition. 1988. Wesleyan University Press. ISBN 0-8195-6205-x (paperback)

Bonnelle, Claire: *Des hommes et des plantes*. 1993. CPIE Vercors, F-38250

Breverton, Terry: Physicians of Myddfai Cures and remedies of the Mediaeval World. 2012. ISBN 978-0-9574894-1-7

Breuss, R: The Breuss Cancer Cure. (Translation from German.) 1995. Alive Books, Canada. ISBN 0-920470-56-4

British Herbal Pharmacopoeia 1983. Published by British Herbal Medicine Association. ISBN 0 903032 07 4

British Herbal Compendium Volume I. Edited by Peter R. Bradley. 1992. Copyright British Herbal Medicine Association. ISBN 0 903032 09 0

British Pharmacopoeia 1864. Spottiswoode & Co for the General Medical Council

British Pharmaceutical Codex 1949. Spottiswoode & Co for the General Medical Council

Burne-Jones, Edward: The Flower Book. 1994. Taschen Verlag GmbH. ISBN 3-8228-9043-X

Caddy, John: A Return to Subjectivity. 2006. Trafford Publishing. ISBN 1-4120-8366-4

Chatelaine, Claude and Baud, George: *Habundantia: La vie au Val d'Abondance à travers le temps.* Sopizet. 1983. ASIN: B0014MWQE6

Cowan, Eliot: Plant Spirit Medicine. 1995. Swan Raven & Co, USA. ISBN 0-926524-09-7

Culpeper, Nicholas: Culpeper's Complete Herbal. 1992. Bloomsbury Books under licence from Omega Books. ISBN 1 85471 140 7

Cunningham, Scott: Encyclopedia of Magical Herbs. 1997. Llewellyn Publications, Minnesota, USA. ISBN 0-87542-122-9

Cunningham, Scott: Magical Aromatherapy. 1996. Llewellyn Publications, Minnesota, USA

Cunningham, Scott: The Complete Book of Incense, Oils & Brews. 2003. Llewellyn Publications. ISBN 0-87542-128-8

Damian, Peter and Kate: Scent & Psyche. 1995. Healing Arts Press.Vermont. ISBN 0-89281-530-2

Davis, Patricia: Subtle Aromatherapy. 1991. C.W. Daniel Co Ltd. ISBN 0 85207 227 9 7-9

Denny, E.F.K.: Field Distillation for Herbaceous Oils. Second edition. 1991. From British Library Document Supply Centre, 2006

'Findhorn Garden' written by the Findhorn Community with foreword by Sir George Trevelyan. 3rd edition, 2003 (1st edition 1976). Findhorn Press. ISBN 1-84409-018-3

Gagliano, Monica: Thus Spoke the Plant. 2018. North Atlantic Books, CA. ISBN 978 1 623172 43 5

Gattefossé, Réne-Maurice: Gattefossé's Aromatherapy. 1993. (First published in French 1937 as 'Aromathérapie: Les Huiles essentielles, hormones végétales'.) C.W. Daniel Co Ltd. ISBN 0 85207 236 8

Gerard's Herbal: The History of Plants. Edited by Marcus Woodward. 1994. Published by Senate, an imprint of Studio Editions Ltd. London. ISBN 1 85958 051 3

Gray, Patience: Honey from a Weed. 2009. Paperback edition. Prospect Books. ISBN 978-1-903018-20-0

Grieve, Mrs M. FRHS: A Modern Herbal. Edited by Mrs C.F. Leyel. First published in 1931 by Jonathan Cape. Current edition published in 1994 by Cresset Books. ISBN 1-85501-249-9

Günther, Ernest: The Essential Oils. 1948. NY Volumes I to VI Van Nostrand Co: Vol III p440 Lavandula officinalis.

Halifax, Joan: Shamanic Voices – the Shaman as Seer, Poet and Healer. 1979. Penguin Books ISBN 0 14 02.22.73

Hallé, Francis: Eloge de la Plante, pour une nouvelle Biologie. 1999, Edition du Seuil, Paris. Translated by David Lee in 2002: In Praise of Plants. Timber Press, USA. ISBN 0-88192-550-0

Harding, Stephan: Animate Earth: Science, Intuition and Gaia: Second edition. 2009. Green Books Ltd. ISBN 978 1 900322 54 6

Harner, Michael: The Way of the Shaman. 3rd edition. 1990. Harper & Row. ISBN 0-06-250373-1

Heron, John: Sacred Science. 1998. PCCS Books. ISBN 1 898059 21 7

Hillman, James: The Soul's Code. 1997. Bantam Books. ISBN 0-553-50634-X

Ingermann, Sandra: Soul Retrieval. 1991. Harper, San Francisco. ISBN 006250406

Jung, C.G: Memories, Dreams, Reflections. 1963, Fontana Press. ISBN 0-00-654027-9

Jung, C.G: Collected Works (22 volumes). 1970. Routledge. ISBN 10: 0-710016336

Kaptchuk, Ted: The Web that has no Weaver – Understanding Chinese Medicine. 2000. Contemporary Books/McGraw-Hill. ISBN 0-8092-2840-8

Keller, Evelyn Fox: A Feeling for the Organism. The life and work of Barbara McClintock. 1983. W.H. Freeman & Co, New York. ISBN 0-7167-1504-X (paperback)

Kimmerer, Robin Wall: Braiding Sweetgrass: Indigenous Wisdom, Scientific Knowledge and the Teachings of Plants. 2013. Milkweed Editions. ISBN 978-1-57131-335-5

Kuhn, Thomas: The Structure of Scientific Revolutions. 2012. (50th anniversary edition.) University of Chicago Press. ISBN 978-0-226-45811-3

Lawless, Julia: Aromatherapy and the Mind: the psychological and emotional effects of Essential Oils. 1998. Thorsons. An Imprint of HarperCollins.

ISBN 0 7225 2927 9. Her beautiful chapter on Scent, Soul and Psyche speaks of the Garden of the Soul and the role that scent plays in inspiring the imagination.

Loori, John Daido: The Zen of Creativity. 2005. Ballantire Books. Trade Paperback Edition. Copyright 2004 Dharma Communication.

Lovelock, James: Gaia – a New Look at Life on Earth 1982. Oxford University Press. ISBN 0-19-286218-9

Maendl, Andrew: Rudolf Steiner Medicine. 2003 Sophia Books. An imprint of Rudolf Steiner Books. ISBN 1-85584-133-9

Maury, Marguerite: Guide to Aromatherapy. The Secret of Life & Youth. 1989. C.W. Daniel Company Ltd. ISBN 0 85207 163 9

Mailhebiau, Philippe: Portrait in Oils. 1995. C.W. Daniel Co Ltd. ISBN 0 85207 237 6

Minter, Susan: The Apothecaries' Garden – A History of the Chelsea Physic Garden. 2000. Sutton Publishing Ltd. ISBN 0 7509 2449 7

Mojay, Gabriel: Aromatherapy for Healing the Spirit. 1997. Gaia Books Ltd. London. ISBN 978 0 89281 887 8

Moss, Nan and Corbin, David: Weather Shamanism: Harmonising our connection with the Elements. 2008. Bear & Co publishers. ISBN 978 1591439219

Nature Scientific Correspondence: Vol 392/16 April 1998. Tree stem diameters fluctuate with tides. Ernst Zuercher, Swiss Federal Institute of Technology, Zurich & Maria- Giulia Cantiani, University of Trento, Italy.

Naydler, Jeremy: (excerpts selected by) Goethe on Science. 1996. Floris Books English edition ISBN 0-86315-237-6

Newall, I. and Wren, R.W: Potter's New Cyclopaedia of Botanical Drugs and Preparations. First published in 1907. Completely revised edition by Williamson and Evans. 1988. C.W. Daniel Company Ltd. ISBN 0 85207 197 3

Ody, Penelope: The Complete Medicinal Herbal: A Practical Guide to the Healing Properties of Herbs, with More Than 250 Remedies for Common Ailments. 1993. Dorling Kindersley Ltd. ISBN 0 7513 0025 X

Paungger, Johanna and Poppe, Thomas: The Art of Timing. 2000. C.W. Daniel Co Ltd. ISBN 0-85207-334-8

Pert, Candice: Molecules of Emotion: why you feel the way you feel. 1998. Simon & Schuster UK Ltd. ISBN 0-671-03397-2

Pietak, Alexis Mari: Life as Energy – Opening the Mind to a New Science of Life. 2011. Floris Books. ISBN 9780863157974

Price, Len and Shirley: Understanding Hydrolats: the specific Hydrosols for Aromatherapy. 2004. Churchill Livingstone, an imprint of Elsevier Ltd. ISBN 0443 07316 3. This volume has detailed analyses of my hydrolats (Appendices D and E).

Price, Shirley: Aromatherapy and your emotions. How to use essential oils to balance body & Mind. 2000. Thorsons. An Imprint of HarperCollins. ISBN 0 7225 3862 6

Reichel-Dolmatoff, Gerardo: Rainforest Shamans. 1997. Green Books Ltd, Totnes, Devon. ISBN 0 9527302 4 3

Robertson, Pamela: Charles Rennie Mackintosh – Art is the Flower. 1997. Pavilion Books. ISBN 10 1857939123

Roe, Evelyn: Dissertation submitted for the M.Sc. Holistic Science, Schumacher College and Plymouth University. August 2013

Segaller, Stephen and Berger, Merrill: The Wisdom of the Dream. The World of C.G. Jung. 1989. Shambhala Publications. ISBN 978-0877735120

Shapiro, Rose: The Suckers: how Alternative Medicine makes fools of us all. 2008. Vintage Publishing. ISBN 1846550289

Sheldrake, Rupert: The Science Delusion. 2012. Coronet. An imprint of Hodder & Stoughton. ISBN 978 1 444 72790 01

Small Wright, Machaelle: Co-creative Science.1997 Published by Perelandra Ltd. VA 20188 USA. ISBN 0-927978-25-3

Squire, Sir John: Grass of Parnassus – an Anthology of Poetry for Schools. 1947. Hardback edition. London Edward Arnold publisher

Thun, Maria: Gardening for Life. The Biodynamic Way. English edition. 1999. Hawthorn Press. ISBN 1 869 890 32 9

Thun, Maria and Thun, Matthias: The Biodynamic Sowing and Planting Calendar. 2006 (ongoing). Floris Books. ISBN 0-86315-493-X

Tisserand, Robert: The Art of Aromatherapy. 1997. C.W. Daniel Co Ltd. ISBN 0 85207 140 X

Tobyn, Graeme: Culpeper's Medicine. A practice of Western Holistic Medicine. 1997. Element Books Ltd. ISBN 1-85230-943-1

Valnet, Jean: The Practice of Aromatherapy. 1982. C.W. Daniel Co Ltd. ISBN 085207 143

Watson, Lyall: Lifetide. Hodder & Stoughton. 1979. ISBN 0-340248-56-4

Weeks, Nora: The Medical Discoveries of Edward Bach. 1940. C.W. Daniel Co Ltd, Saffron Walden. Copyright The Dr Edward Bach Healing Centre 1973. ISBN 85207 001 2

Wulf, Andrea: The Invention of Nature: the Adventures of Alexander von Humboldt, the lost Hero of Science 2016 John Murray publishers ISBN 978-1-84854-900-5

Wellcome Library research. So many references here:

Charobot and Hébert. Bull.soc.chim. [3] 31 (1904) 402

Charobot and Laloue. *Compte rendu.* 147 (1908) 144

Fölsch, Max. Hartlebens Verlag, Wein und Leipzig. *'Die Fabrikation und Verarbeitung von ätherischen Ölen.'* 1930

Gaponenkov and Aleshin J. Applied Chem. USSR 8 (1935) 1049

Günther, Ernest. The Essential Oils. 1948. NY. Volumes I to VI. Van Nostrand Co: Vol IV p675

ibid. Vol III. p440

ibid. Vol III. p724

von Rechenberg, C. *'Theorie der Gewinnung und Trennung der ätherischen Öle.'* Schimmel und Co. Miltitz bei Leipsig. 1910

Worwood, Valerie Ann: The Fragrant Pharmacy: a complete guide to Aromatherapy and Essential Oils. 1991. Bantam Books. ISBN 0 553 40397 4

Worwood, Valerie Ann: The Fragrant Mind: Aromatherapy for Personality, Mind, Mood and Emotion. 1995. Bantam Books. ISBN 0 553 40799 6

Worwood, Valerie Ann: The Fragrant Heavens, The Spiritual dimension of Fragrance and Aromatherapy. 1999. Bantam Books. ISBN 0-553-50579-3

Contacts and websites

Biochemical Pathways. https://www.roche.com/sustainability/philanthropy/science_education/pathways.htm

British Medical Herbalists Association. https://bhma.info/

Chelsea Physic Garden, 66 Royal Hospital Road, Chelsea, London SW3 4HS. https://www.chelseaphysicgarden.co.uk

Cherfas, Jeremy. Formerly founder of Future Foods, now a science communicator. www.jeremycherfas.net

Colorado School of Clinical Herbalism. www.clinicalherbalism.com

Findhorn Foundation. www.findhorn.org

Harner, Michael and Sandra. 'The Way of the Shaman: The Work of Michael and Sandra Harner'. https://www.youtube.com/watch?v=JNloOTQoRzA, also https://www.youtube.com/watch?v=fbGbp-QEjCk

Institute of Traditional Herbal Medicine & Aromatherapy (ITHMA). 2018. www.aromatherapy-studies.com

L'Almanach savoyard. www.almanach-savoyard.fr/

Le Calendrier lunaire. www.calendrier-lunaire.fr

Marciano, Marisa, Naturopathic Herbalist. Vancouver, Canada. https://thenaturopathicherbalist.com/about-3/dr-marisa-marciano/

Nasr, Joe. Founder of Avicenna Herbs. http://www.avicennaherbs.co.uk/

National Institute of Medical Herbalists. https://www.nimh.org.uk/

Purce, Jill. http://www.jillpurce.com/ The Healing Voice https://www.youtube.com/watch?v=yoj6FAarThQ

Scandinavian Center for Shamanic Studies. www.shamanism.dk and http://www.shamanism.dk/who.htm. Jonathan Horwitz, Annette Høst and Zara Waldebäck.

Schumacher College. www.schumachercollege.org.uk

Scientific & Medical Network. https://explore.scimednet.org

Simonton, O. Carl. www.simontoncenter.com

Society of the Apothecaries. http://www.apothecaries.org/charity/history/our-history

Wellcome Library, 183 Euston Road, London, NW1 2BE. https://wellcomelibrary.org/

Wells, Charles and Jan. Founders of Essentially Oils. Chipping Norton, Oxon. No longer operational.

Zhang, Charlie. 1997. Article Electromagnetic Body versus Chemical Body. www.datadiwan.de/SciMedNet/library/articlesN81+/N81Zhang_electrochem.htm

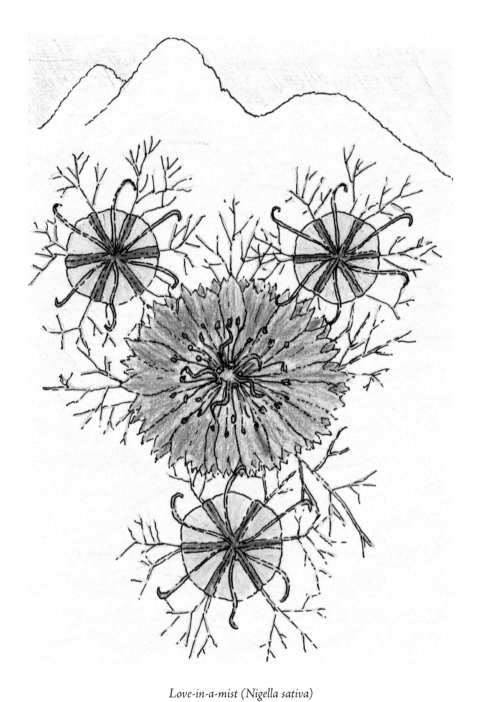

Love-in-a-mist (Nigella sativa)
A widely used medicinal herb, spice and food. Native to Southern Europe, India and Asia.
It is sometimes called a miracle herb because of its many uses.